SO-BBN-080

Introduction

Addressing Capabilities

Instruction Set Summary

Integer Instructions

Floating Point Instructions

Supervisor (Privileged) Instructions

CPU32 Instructions

Instruction Format Summary

Processor Instruction Summary

Exception Processing Reference

S-Record Output Format

68K FAX-IT

FAX 512-891-8593

The Motorola High-End Technical Publication Department provides a FAX number for you to submit any questions and comments about this document. We welcome your suggestions for improving our documentation or any questions concerning our products.

Please provide the part number and revision number (located in upper right hand corner on the front page), and the title of the document when submitting. When referring to items in the manual please reference by the page number, paragraph number, figure number, table number, and line number if needed. Reference the line number from the top of the page.

When we receive a FAX between the hours of 7:30 AM and 5:00 PM EST, Monday through Friday, we will provide you a response within two hours. If the FAX is received after 5:00 PM or on the weekend, we will provide you a response within two hours on the first working day following receipt of the FAX.

When sending a FAX, please provide your name, company, FAX number, voice number including area code (so we can talk to a real person if needed).

M68000

Family Programmer's Reference Manual

Motorola reserves the right to make changes without further notice to any products herein to improve reliability, function or design. Motorola does not assume any liability arising out of the application or use of any product or circuit described herein; neither does it convey any license under its patent rights nor the rights of others. Motorola products are not designed, intended, or authorized for use as components in systems intended for surgical implant into the body, or other applications intended to support or sustain life, or for any other application in which the failure of the Motorola product could create a situation where personal injury or death may occur. Should Buyer purchase or use Motorola products for any such unintended or unauthorized application, Buyer shall indemnify and hold Motorola and its officers, employees, subsidiaries, affiliates, and distributors harmless against all claims, costs, damages, and expenses, and reasonable attorney fees arising out of, directly or indirectly, any claim of personal injury or death associated with such unintended or unauthorized use, even if such claim alleges that Motorola was negligent regarding the design or manufacture of the part. Motorola and the Ⓜ are registered trademarks of Motorola, Inc. Motorola, Inc. is an Equal Opportunity/Affirmative Action Employer.

©MOTOROLA INC., 1992

PREFACE

This manual contains detailed information about the software instructions used by the microprocessors and coprocessors in the M68000 family. The manual is organized as follows:

Section 1 Introduction—This section contains information on the M68000 family programming model, register description, integer and floating-point data formats and data types as well as information on format organization in registers and memory. Also included is a table of notational conventions used throughout this manual.

Section 2 Addressing Capabilities—This section presents detailed information on the format of instructions and their various bit field definitions and possible encodings. Also included are descriptions of addressing modes and other data structures used by the M68000 family.

Section 3 Instruction Set Summary—This section includes extensive information on the instruction set (grouped by operational category), descriptions of the operands used by instructions, and guidelines on how to use the instructions.

Section 4 Integer Instructions—This section provides all integer instruction (nonprivileged) operations described in detail and organized alphabetically.

Section 5 Floating-Point Instructions—This section provides all nonprivileged floating-point instruction operations described in detailed and organized alphabetically.

Section 6 Supervisor (Privileged) Instructions—This section provides all privileged instruction operations described in detail and organized alphabetically.

Section 7 CPU32 Instructions—This section provides all CPU32 instruction operations described in detail and organized alphabetically.

Section 8 Instruction Format Summary—This section contains all the M68000 instruction formats (binary), arranged by opcode.

Appendix A Processor Instruction Summary—This section contains a table listing of all the M68000 family instructions arranged alphabetically and cross-referenced to show which instructions are applicable to which processors. Each processor is also listed with a table of the instructions and the addressing modes that apply to that processor.

Appendix B Exception Processing Reference—This section presents information on exception vector assignments for the M68000 family and illustrations of exception stack frames and floating-point stack frames.

Appendix C S-Record Format—This section provides detailed information on the S-record format.

TABLE OF CONTENTS

TABLE OF CONTENTS (Continued)

Section 2
Addressing Capabilities

TABLE OF CONTENTS (Continued)

Section 3
Instruction Set Summary

TABLE OF CONTENTS (Continued)

TABLE OF CONTENTS (Concluded)

LIST OF ILLUSTRATIONS

LIST OF ILLUSTRATIONS (Continued)

LIST OF TABLES

LIST OF TABLES (Continued)

Alphabetized List of Instruction Set

Alphabetized List of Instruction Set (Continued)

Alphabetized List of Instruction Set (Concluded)

SECTION 1
INTRODUCTION

This manual contains detailed information about software instructions used by the microprocessors and coprocessors in the M68000 family, including:

MC68000	— 16-/32-Bit Microprocessor
MC68EC000	— 16-/32-Bit Embedded Controller
MC68HC000	— Low Power 16-/32-Bit Microprocessor
MC68008	— 16-Bit Microprocessor with 8-Bit Data Bus
MC68010	— 16-/32-Bit Virtual Memory Microprocessor
MC68020	— 32-Bit Virtual Memory Microprocessor
MC68EC020	— 32-Bit Embedded Controller
MC68030	— Second-Generation 32-Bit Enhanced Microprocessor
MC68EC030	— 32-Bit Embedded Controller
MC68040	— Third-Generation 32-Bit Microprocessor
MC68LC040	— Third-Generation 32-Bit Microprocessor
MC68EC040	— 32-Bit Embedded Controller
MC68330	— Integrated CPU32 Processor
MC68340	— Integrated Processor with DMA
MC68851	— Paged Memory Management Unit
MC68881	— Floating-Point Coprocessor
MC68882	— Enhanced Floating-Point Coprocessor

NOTE

All references to the MC68000, MC68020, and MC68030 include the corresponding embedded controllers, MC68EC000, MC68EC020, and MC68EC030. All references to the MC68040 include the MC68LC040 and MC68EC040. This referencing method applies throughout the manual unless otherwise specified.

The M68000 family programming model consists of two register groups: user and supervisor. User programs executing in the user mode only use the registers in the user group. System software executing in the supervisor mode can access all registers and uses the control registers in the supervisor group to perform supervisor functions. The following paragraphs provide a brief description of the registers in the user and supervisor models as well as the data organization in the registers.

1.1 INTEGER UNIT USER PROGRAMMING MODEL

Figure 1-1 illustrates the integer portion of the user programming model. It consists of the following registers:

- 16 General-Purpose 32-Bit Registers (D7–D0, A7–A0)
- 32-Bit Program Counter (PC)
- 8-Bit Condition Code Register (CCR)

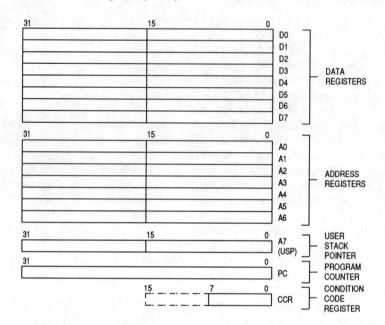

Figure 1-1. M68000 Family User Programming Model

1.1.1 Data Registers (D7–D0)

These registers are for bit and bit field (1–32 bits), byte (8 bits), word (16 bits), long-word (32 bits), and quad-word (64 bits) operations. They also can be used as index registers.

1.1.2 Address Registers (A7–A0)

These registers can be used as software stack pointers, index registers, or base address registers. The base address registers can be used for word and long-word operations. Register A7 is used as a hardware stack pointer during stacking for subroutine calls and exception handling. In the user programming model, A7 refers to the user stack pointer (USP).

1.1.3 Program Counter

The PC contains the address of the instruction currently executing. During instruction execution and exception processing, the processor automatically increments the contents or places a new value in the PC. For some addressing modes, the PC can be used as a pointer for PC relative addressing.

1.1.4 Condition Code Register

Consisting of five bits, the CCR, the status register's lower byte, is the only portion of the status register (SR) available in the user mode. Many integer instructions affect the CCR, indicating the instruction's result. Program and system control instructions also use certain combinations of these bits to control program and system flow. The condition codes meet two criteria: consistency across instructions, uses, and instances and meaningful results with no change unless it provides useful information.

Consistency across instructions means that all instructions that are special cases of more general instructions affect the condition codes in the same way. Consistency across uses means that conditional instructions test the condition codes similarly and provide the same results whether a compare, test, or move instruction sets the condition codes. Consistency across instances means that all instances of an instruction affect the condition codes in the same way.

The first four bits represent a condition of the result generated by an operation. The fifth bit or the extend bit (X-bit) is an operand for multiprecision computations. The carry bit (C-bit) and the X-bit are separate in the M68000 family to simplify programming techniques that use them (refer to Table 3-18 as an example). In the instruction set definitions, the CCR is illustrated as follows:

X	N	Z	V	C

X—Extend
  Set to the value of the C-bit for arithmetic operations; otherwise not affected or set to a specified result.

N—Negative
  Set if the most significant bit of the result is set; otherwise clear.

Z—Zero
  Set if the result equals zero; otherwise clear.

V—Overflow
  Set if an arithmetic overflow occurs implying that the result cannot be represented in the operand size; otherwise clear.

C—Carry

Set if a carry out of the most significant bit of the operand occurs for an addition, or if a borrow occurs in a subtraction; otherwise clear.

1.2 FLOATING-POINT UNIT USER PROGRAMMING MODEL

The following paragraphs describe the registers for the floating-point unit user programming model. Figure 1-2 illustrates the M68000 family user programming model's floating-point portion for the MC68040 and the MC68881/MC68882 floating-point coprocessors. It contains the following registers:

- 8 Floating-Point Data Registers (FP7–FP0)
- 16-Bit Floating-Point Control Register (FPCR)
- 32-Bit Floating-Point Status Register (FPSR)
- 32-Bit Floating-Point Instruction Address Register (FPIAR)

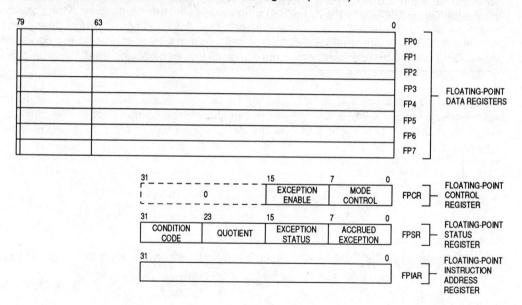

Figure 1-2. M68000 Family Floating-Point Unit User Programming Model

1.2.1 Floating-Point Data Registers (FP7–FP0)

These floating-point data registers are analogous to the integer data registers for the M68000 family. They always contain extended-precision numbers. All external operands, despite the data format, are converted to extended-precision values before being used in any calculation or being stored in a floating-point data register. A reset or a null-restore operation sets FP7–FP0 positive, nonsignaling not-a-numbers (NANs).

1.2.2 Floating-Point Control Register (FPCR)

The FPCR (see Figure 1-3) contains an exception enable (ENABLE) byte and a mode control (MODE) byte. The user can read or write to the FPCR. Motorola reserves bits 31–16 for future definition; these bits are always read as zero and are ignored during write operations. The reset function or a restore operation of the null state clears the FPCR. When cleared, this register provides the IEEE *754 Standard for Binary Floating-Point Arithmetic* defaults.

1.2.2.1 EXCEPTION ENABLE BYTE. Each bit of the ENABLE byte (see Figure 1-3) corresponds to a floating-point exception class. The user can separately enable traps for each class of floating-point exceptions.

1.2.2.2 MODE CONTROL BYTE. MODE (see Figure 1-3) controls the user-selectable rounding modes and precisions. Zeros in this byte select the IEEE 754 standard defaults. The rounding mode (RND) field specifies how inexact results are rounded, and the rounding precision (PREC) field selects the boundary for rounding the mantissa. Refer to Table 3-21 for encoding information.

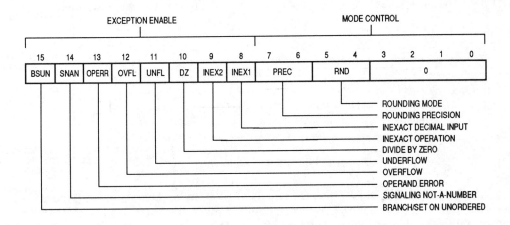

Figure 1-3. Floating-Point Control Register

1.2.3 Floating-Point Status Register (FPSR)

The FPSR (see Figure 1-2) contains a floating-point condition code (FPCC) byte, a floating-point exception status (EXC) byte, a quotient byte, and a floating-point accrued exception (AEXC) byte. The user can read or write to all the bits in the FPSR. Execution of most floating-point instructions modifies this register. The reset function or a restore operation of the null state clears the FPSR.

1.2.3.1 FLOATING-POINT CONDITION CODE BYTE. The FPCC byte, illustrated in Figure 1-4, contains four condition code bits that set after completion of all arithmetic instructions involving the floating-point data registers. The move floating-point data register to effective address, move multiple floating-point data register, and move system control register instructions do not affect the FPCC.

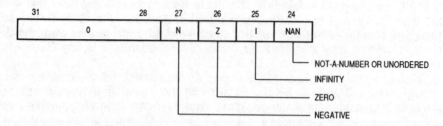

Figure 1-4. FPSR Condition Code Byte

1.2.3.2 QUOTIENT BYTE. The quotient byte contains the seven least significant bits of the unsigned quotient as well as the sign of the entire quotient (see Figure 1-5). The quotient bits can be used in argument reduction for transcendentals and other functions. For example, seven bits are more than enough to figure out the quadrant of a circle in which an operand resides. The quotient bits remain set until the user clears them.

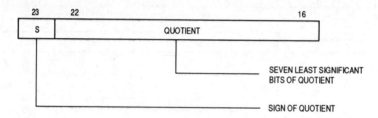

Figure 1-5. FPSR Quotient Byte

1.2.3.3 EXCEPTION STATUS BYTE. The EXC byte, illustrated in Figure 1-6, contains a bit for each floating-point exception that might have occurred during the most recent arithmetic instruction or move operation. This byte is cleared at the start of all operations that generate floating-point exceptions. Operations that do not generate floating-point exceptions do not clear this byte. An exception handler can use this byte to determine which floating-point exception(s) caused a trap.

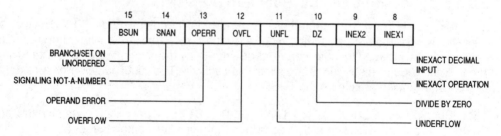

Figure 1-6. FPSR Exception Status Byte

M68000 FAMILY PROGRAMMER'S REFERENCE MANUAL   MOTOROLA

1.2.3.4 ACCRUED EXCEPTION BYTE. The AEXC byte contains five exception bits (see Figure 1-7) required by the IEEE 754 standard for trap disabled operations. These exceptions are logical combinations of the bits in the EXC byte. The AEXC byte contains a history of all floating-point exceptions that have occurred since the user last cleared the AEXC byte. In normal operations, only the user clears this byte by writing to the FPSR; however, a reset or a restore operation of the null state can also clear the AEXC byte.

Many users elect to disable traps for all or part of the floating-point exception classes. The AEXC byte makes it unnecessary to poll the EXC byte after each floating-point instruction. At the end of most operations (FMOVEM and FMOVE excluded), the bits in the EXC byte are logically combined to form an AEXC value that is logically ORed into the existing AEXC byte. This operation creates "sticky" floating-point exception bits in the AEXC byte that the user needs to poll only once—i.e., at the end of a series of floating-point operations.

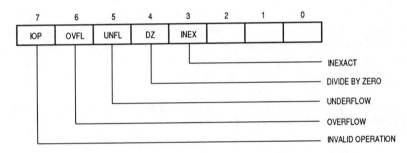

Figure 1-7. FPSR Accrued Exception Byte

Setting or clearing the AEXC bits neither causes nor prevents an exception. The following equations show the comparative relationship between the EXC byte and AEXC byte. Comparing the current value in the AEXC bit with a combination of bits in the EXC byte derives a new value in the corresponding AEXC bit. These equations apply to setting the AEXC bits at the end of each operation affecting the AEXC byte:

New AEXC Bit	= Old AEXC Bit	V	EXC Bits
IOP	= IOP	V	(SNAN V OPERR)
OVFL	= OVFL	V	(OVFL)
UNFL	= UNFL	V	(UNFL ∧ INEX2)
DZ	= DZ	V	(DZ)
INEX	= INEX	V	(INEX1 V INEX2 V OVFL)

1.2.4 Floating-Point Instruction Address Register (FPIAR)

The integer unit can be executing instructions while the FPU is simultaneously executing a floating-point instruction. Additionally, the FPU can concurrently execute two floating-point instructions. Because of this nonsequential instruction execution, the PC value stacked by the FPU, in response to a floating-point exception trap, may not point to the offending instruction.

For the subset of the FPU instructions that generate exception traps, the 32-bit FPIAR is loaded with the logical address of the instruction before the processor executes it. The floating-point exception handler can use this address to locate the floating-point instruction that caused an exception. Since the FPU FMOVE to/from the FPCR, FPSR, or FPIAR and FMOVEM instructions cannot generate floating-point exceptions, these instructions do not modify the FPIAR. A reset or a null-restore operation clears the FPIAR.

1.3 SUPERVISOR PROGRAMMING MODEL

System programers use the supervisor programming model to implement sensitive operating system functions—e.g., I/O control and memory management unit (MMU) subsystems. The following paragraphs briefly describe the registers in the supervisor programming model. They can only be accessed via privileged instructions. Table 1-1 lists the supervisor registers and the processors not related to paged memory management. For information concerning page memory management programming, refer to the device-specific user's manual. Table 1-2 lists the supervisor registers and the processors related to paged memory management.

Table 1-1. Supervisor Registers Not Related To Paged Memory Management

Registers	68000 68008 68HC000 68HC001 68EC000	68010	68020 68EC020	CPU32	68030	68EC030	68040	68EC040	68LC040
AC1, AC0						x			
ACUSR						x			
CAAR			x		x	x			
CACR			x		x	x	x	x	x
DACR1, DACR0								x	
DFC		x	x	x	x	x	x	x	x
DTT1, DTT0							x		x
IACR1, IACR0								x	
ITT1, ITT0							x		x
MSP			x		x	x	x	x	x
SFC		x	x	x	x	x	x	x	x
SR	x	x	x	x	x	x	x	x	x
SSP/ISP	x	x	x	x	x	x	x	x	x
TT1, TT0					x				
VBR		x	x	x	x	x	x	x	x

AC1, AC0 = Access Control Registers
ACUSR = Access Control Unit Status Register
CAAR = Cache Address Register
CACR = Cache Control Register
DACR1, DACR0 = Data Access Control Registers
DFC = Destination Function Code Register
DTT1, DTT0 = Data Transparent Translation Registers
IACR1, IACR0 = Instruction Access Control Registers

ITT1, ITT0 = Instruction Transparent Translation Registers
MSP = Master Stack Pointer Register
SFC = Source Function Code Register
SR = Status Register
SSP/ISP = Supervisor and Interrupt Stack Pointer
TT1, TT0 = Transparent Translation Registers
VBR = Vector Base Register

**Table 1-2. Supervisor Registers
Related To Paged Memory Management**

Registers	Devices			
	68851	68030	68040	68LC040
AC	x			
CAL	x			
CRP	x	x		
DRP	x			
PCSR	x			
PMMUSR, MMUSR	x	x	x	x
SCC	x			
SRP	x	x	x	x
TC	x	x	x	x
URP			x	x
VAL	x			

AC	=	Access Control Register
CAL	=	Current Access Level Register
CRP	=	CPU Root Pointer
DRP	=	DMA Root Pointer
PCSR	=	PMMU Control Register
PMMUSR	=	Paged Memory Management Unit Status Register
MMUSR	=	Memory Management Unit Status Register
SCC	=	Stack Change Control Register
SRP	=	Supervisor Root Pointer Register
TC	=	Translation Control Register
URP	=	User Root Pointer
VAL	=	Valid Access Level Register

1.3.1 Address Register 7 (A7)

In the supervisor programming model register, A7 refers to the interrupt stack pointer, A7' (ISP) and the master stack pointer, A7" (MSP). The supervisor stack pointer is the active stack pointer (ISP or MSP). For processors that do not support ISP or MSP, the system stack is the system stack pointer (SSP). The ISP and MSP are general-purpose address registers for the supervisor mode. They can be used as software stack pointers, index registers, or base address registers. The ISP and MSP can be used for word and long-word operations.

1.3.2 Status Register

Figure 1-8 illustrates the SR, which stores the processor status and contains the condition codes that reflect the results of a previous operation. In the supervisor mode, software can access the full SR, including the interrupt priority mask and additional control bits. These bits indicate the following states for the processor: one of two trace modes (T1, T0), supervisor or user mode (S), and master or interrupt mode (M). For the MC68000, MC68EC000, MC68008, MC68010, MC68HC000, MC68HC001, and

CPU32, only one trace mode supported, where T0 is always zero, and only one system stack where the M-bit is always zero. I2, I1, and I0 define the interrupt mask level.

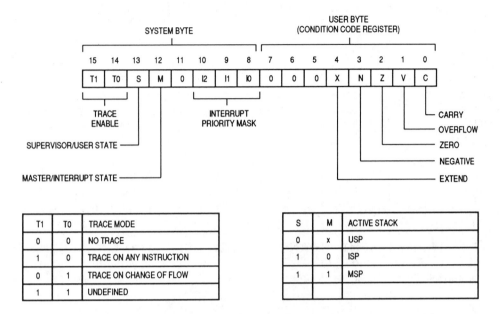

Figure 1-8. Status Register

1.3.3 Vector Base Register (VBR)

The VBR contains the base address of the exception vector table in memory. The displacement of an exception vector adds to the value in this register, which accesses the vector table.

1.3.4 Alternate Function Code Registers (SFC and DFC)

The alternate function code registers contain 3-bit function codes. Function codes can be considered extensions of the 32-bit logical address that optionally provides as many as eight 4-Gbyte address spaces. The processor automatically generates function codes to select address spaces for data and programs at the user and supervisor modes. Certain instructions use SFC and DFC to specify the function codes for operations.

1.3.5 ACU Status Register (MC68EC030 only)

The access control unit status register (ACUSR) is a 16-bit register containing the status information returned by execution of the PTEST instruction. The PTEST instruction searches the access control (AC) registers to determine a match for a specified address. A match in either or both of the AC registers sets bit 6 in the ACUSR. All other bits in the ACUSR are undefined and must not be used.

1.3.6 Transparent Translation/Access Control Registers

Transparent translation is actually a misnomer since the whole address space transparently translates in an embedded control environment with no on-chip MMU present as well as in processors that have built-in MMUs. For processors that have built-in MMUs, such as the MC68030, MC68040, and MC68LC040, the transparent translation (TT) registers define blocks of logical addresses that are transparently translated to corresponding physical addresses. These registers are independent of the on-chip MMU. For embedded controllers, such as the MC68EC030 and MC68EC040, the access control registers (AC) are similar in function to the TT registers but just named differently. The AC registers' main function are to define blocks of address space that control address space properties such as cachability. The following paragraphs describe these registers.

NOTE

For the paged MMU related supervisor registers, please refer to the appropriate user's manual for specific programming detail.

1.3.6.1 TRANSPARENT TRANSLATION/ACCESS CONTROL REGISTER FIELDS FOR THE M68030. Figure 1-9 illustrates the MC68030 transparent translation/MC68EC030 access control register format.

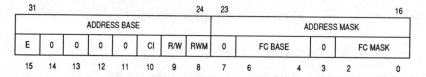

Figure 1-9. MC68030 Transparent Translation/ MC68EC030 Access Control Register Format

Address Base

This 8-bit field is compared with address bits A31–A24. Addresses that match in this comparison (and are otherwise eligible) are transparently translated/access controlled.

Address Mask

This 8-bit field contains a mask for the address base field. Setting a bit in this field causes the corresponding bit of the address base field to be ignored. Blocks of memory larger than 16 Mbytes can be transparently translated/accessed controlled by setting some logical address mask bits to ones. The low-order bits of this field normally are set to define contiguous blocks larger than 16 Mbytes, although this is not required.

E—Enable

    0 = Transparent translation/access control disabled
    1 = Transparent translation/access control enabled

CI—Cache Inhibit

    0 = Caching allowed
    1 = Caching inhibited

R/W—Read/Write

    0 = Only write accesses permitted
    1 = Only read accesses permitted

R/WM—Read/Write Mask

    0 = R/W field used
    1 = R/W field ignored

FC BASE—Function Code Base

    This 3-bit field defines the base function code for accesses to be transparently translated with this register. Addresses with function codes that match the FC BASE field (and are otherwise eligible) are transparently translated.

FC MASK—Function Code Mask

    This 3-bit field contains a mask for the FC BASE field. Setting a bit in this field causes the corresponding bit of the FC BASE field to be ignored.

1.3.6.2 TRANSPARENT TRANSLATION/ACCESS CONTROL REGISTER FIELDS FOR THE M68040. Figure 1-10 illustrates the MC68040 and MC68LC040 transparent translation/ MC68EC040 access control register format.

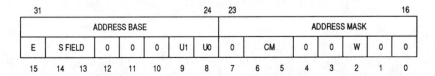

Figure 1-10. MC68040 and MC68LC040 Transparent Translation/ MC68EC040 Access Control Register Format

Address Base

    This 8-bit field is compared with address bits A31–A24. Addresses that match in this comparison (and are otherwise eligible) are transparently translated/access controlled.

Address Mask

This 8-bit field contains a mask for the address base field. Setting a bit in this field causes the corresponding bit in the address base field to be ignored. Blocks of memory larger than 16 Mbytes can be transparently translated/access controlled by setting some logical address mask bits to ones. The low-order bits of this field normally are set to define contiguous blocks larger than 16 Mbytes, although this not required.

E—Enable

This bit enables and disables transparent translation/access control of the block defined by this register.

    0 = Transparent translation/access control disabled
    1 = Transparent translation/access control enabled

S—Supervisor/User Mode

This field specifies the use of the FC2 in matching an address.

    00 = Match only if FC2 is 0 (user mode access)
    01 = Match only if FC2 is 1 (supervisor mode access)
    1X = Ignore FC2 when matching

U1, U2—User Page Attributes

The MC68040, MC68E040, MC68LC040 do not interpret these user-defined bits. If an external bus transfer results from the access, U0 and U1 are echoed to the UPA0 and UPA1 signals, respectively.

CM—Cache Mode

This field selects the cache mode and access serialization for a page as follows:

    00 = Cachable, Writethrough
    01 = Cachable, Copyback
    10 = Noncachable, Serialized
    11 = Noncachable

W—Write Protect

This bit indicates if the block is write protected. If set, write and read-modify-write accesses are aborted as if the resident bit in a table descriptor were clear.

    0 = Read and write accesses permitted
    1 = Write accesses not permitted

1.4 INTEGER DATA FORMATS

The operand data formats supported by the integer unit, as listed in Table 1-3, include those supported by the MC68030 plus a new data format (16-byte block) for the MOVE16 instruction. Integer unit operands can reside in registers, memory, or instructions themselves. The operand size for each instruction is either explicitly encoded in the instruction or implicitly defined by the instruction operation.

Table 1-3. Integer Data Formats

Operand Data Format	Size	Notes
Bit	1 Bit	—
Bit Field	1–32 Bits	Field of Consecutive Bit
Binary-Coded Decimal (BCD)	8 Bits	Packed: 2 Digits/Byte; Unpacked: 1 Digit/Byte
Byte Integer	8 Bits	—
Word Integer	16 Bits	—
Long-Word Integer	32 Bits	—
Quad-Word Integer	64 Bits	Any Two Data Registers
16-Byte	128 Bits	Memory Only, Aligned to 16-Byte Boundary

1.5 FLOATING-POINT DATA FORMATS

The following paragraphs describe the FPU's operand data formats. The FPU supports seven data formats. There are three signed binary integer formats (byte, word, and long word) that are identical to those supported by the integer unit. The FPU supports the use of the packed decimal real format. The MC68881 and MC68882 support this format in hardware and the processors starting with the MC68040 support it in software. The FPU also supports three binary floating-point formats (single, double, and extended precision) that fully comply with the IEEE 754 standard. All references in this manual to extended-precision format imply the double-extended-precision format defined by the IEEE 754 standard.

1.5.1 Packed Decimal Real Format

Figure 1-11 illustrates the packed decimal real format which is three long words consisting of a 3-digit base 10 exponent and a 17-digit base 10 mantissa. The first two long words, digits 15–0, are 64 bits and map directly to bit positions 63–0 of the extended-precision real format. There are two separate sign bits, one for the exponent, the other for the mantissa. An extra exponent (EXP3) is defined for overflows that can occur when converting from the extended-precision real format to the packed decimal real format.

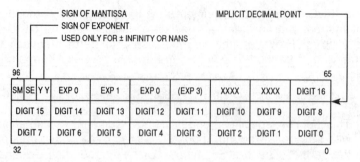

NOTE: XXXX indicates "don't care", which is zero when written and ignored when read.

Figure 1-11. Packed Decimal Real Format

1.5.2 Binary Floating-Point Formats

Figure 1-12 illustrates the three binary floating-point data formats. The exponent in the three binary floating-point formats is an unsigned binary integer with an implied bias added to it. When subtracting the bias from the exponent's value, the result represents a signed twos complement power of two. This yields the magnitude of a normalized floating-point number when multiplied by the mantissa. A program can execute a CMP instruction that compares floating-point numbers in memory using biased exponents, despite the absolute magnitude of the exponents.

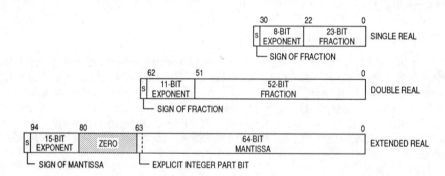

Figure 1-12. Binary Floating-Point Data Formats

Data formats for single- and double-precision numbers differ slightly from those for extended-precision numbers in the representation of the mantissa. For all three precisions, a normalized mantissa is always in the range (1.0...2.0). The extended-precision data format represents the entire mantissa, including the explicit integer part bit. Single- and double-precision data formats represent only a fractional portion of the mantissa (the fraction) and always imply the integer part as one.

The IEEE 754 standard has created the term significand to bridge the difference between mantissa and fraction and to avoid the historical implications of the term mantissa. The IEEE 754 standard defines a significand as the component of a binary floating-point number that includes an explicit or implicit leading bit to the left of the implied binary point. However, this manual uses the term mantissa for extended-precision formats and fraction for single- and double-precision formats instead of the IEEE term significand.

NOTE

This section specifies ranges using traditional set notation with the format "bound...bound" specifying the boundaries of the range. The bracket types enclosing the range define whether the endpoint is inclusive or exclusive. A square bracket indicates inclusive, and a parenthesis indicates exclusive. For example, the range specification "[1.0...2.0]" defines the range of numbers greater than or equal to 1.0 and less than or equal to 2.0. The range specification "(0.0...+inf)" defines the range of numbers greater than 0.0 and less than positive infinity, but not equal to.

1.6 FLOATING-POINT DATA TYPES

Each floating-point data format supports five, unique, floating-point data types: 1) normalized numbers, 2) denormalized numbers, 3) zeros, 4) infinities, and 5) NANs. Exponent values in each format represent these special data types. The normalized data type never uses the maximum or minimum exponent value for a given format, except the extended-precision format. The packed decimal real data format does not support denormalized numbers.

There is a subtle difference between the definition of an extended-precision number with an exponent equal to zero and a single- or double-precision number with an exponent equal to zero. The zero exponent of a single- or double-precision number denormalizes the number's definition, and the implied integer bit is zero. An extended-precision number with an exponent of zero may have an explicit integer bit equal to one. This results in a normalized number, though the exponent is equal to the minimum value. For simplicity, the following discussion treats all three floating-point formats in the same manner, where an exponent value of zero identifies a denormalized number. However, remember the extended-precision format can deviate from this rule.

1.6.1 Normalized Numbers

Normalized numbers encompass all numbers with exponents laying between the maximum and minimum values. Normalized numbers can be positive or negative. For normalized numbers in single and double precision the implied integer bit is one. In extended precision, the mantissa's MSB, the explicit integer bit, can only be a one (see Figure 1-13); and the exponent can be zero.

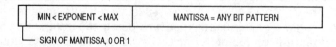

Figure 1-13. Normalized Number Format

1.6.2 Denormalized Numbers

Denormalized numbers represent real values near the underflow threshold. The detection of the underflow for a given data format and operation occurs when the result's exponent is less than or equal to the minimum exponent value. Denormalized numbers can be positive or negative. For denormalized numbers in single and double precision the implied integer bit is a zero. In extended precision, the mantissa's MSB, the explicit integer bit, can only be a zero (see Figure 1-14).

Figure 1-14. Denormalized Number Format

Traditionally, the detection of underflow causes floating-point number systems to perform a "flush-to-zero". This leaves a large gap in the number line between the smallest magnitude normalized number and zero. The IEEE 754 standard implements gradual underflows: the result mantissa is shifted right (denormalized) while the result exponent is incremented until reaching the minimum value. If all the mantissa bits cf the result are shifted off to the right during this denormalization, the result becomes zero. Usually a gradual underflow limits the potential underflow damage to no more than a round-off error. This underflow and denormalization description ignores the effects of rounding and the user-selectable rounding modes. Thus, the large gap in the number line created by "flush-to-zero" number systems is filled with representable (denormalized) numbers in the IEEE "gradual underflow" floating-point number system.

Since the extended-precision data format has an explicit integer bit, a number can be formatted with a nonzero exponent, less than the maximum value, and a zero integer bit. The IEEE 754 standard does not define a zero integer bit. Such a number is an unnormalized number. Hardware does not directly support denormalized and unnormalized numbers, but implicitly supports them by trapping them as unimplemented data types, allowing efficient conversion in software.

1.6.3 Zeros

Zeros can be positive or negative and represent the real values +0.0 and −0.0 (see Figure 1-15).

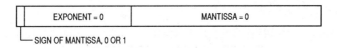

Figure 1-15. Zero Format

1.6.4 Infinities

Infinities can be positive or negative and represent real values that exceed the overflow threshold. A result's exponent greater than or equal to the maximum exponent value indicates the overflow for a given data format and operation. This overflow description ignores the effects of rounding and the user-selectable rounding models. For single- and double-precision infinities the fraction is a zero. For extended-precision infinities, the mantissa's MSB, the explicit integer bit, can be either one or zero (see Figure 1-16).

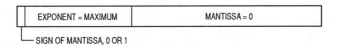

Figure 1-16. Infinity Format

1.6.5 Not-A-Numbers

When created by the FPU, NANs represent the results of operations having no mathematical interpretation, such as infinity divided by infinity. All operations involving a NAN operand as an input return a NAN result. When created by the user, NANs can protect against unitialized variables and arrays or represent user-defined data types. For extended-precision NANs, the mantissa's MSB, the explicit integer bit, can be either one or zero (see Figure 1-17).

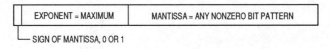

Figure 1-17. Not-A-Number Format

The FPU implements two different types of NANs identified by the value of the MSB of the mantissa for single- and double-precision, and the MSB of the mantissa minus one for extended-precision. If the bit is set, it is a nonsignaling NAN, otherwise, it is an SNAN. An SNAN can be used as an escape mechanism for a user-defined, non-IEEE data type. The FPU never creates an SNAN resulting from an operation.

The IEEE specification defines NAN processing used as an input to an operation. A nonsignaling NAN must be returned when using an SNAN as an input and there is a disabled SNAN trap. The FPU does this by using the source SNAN, setting the MSB of the mantissa, and storing the resulting nonsignaling NAN in the destination. Because of the IEEE formats for NANs, the result of setting an SNAN MSB is always a nonsignaling NAN.

When the FPU creates a NAN, the NAN always contains the same bit pattern in the mantissa. All bits of the mantissa are ones for any precision. When the user creates a NAN, any nonzero bit pattern can be stored in the mantissa.

1.6.6 Data Format and Type Summary

Tables 1-4 through 1-6 summarize the data type specifications for single-, double-, and extended-precision data formats. Packed decimal real formats support all data types except denormalized numbers. Table 1-7 summarizes the data types for the packed decimal real format.

Table 1-4. Single-Precision Real Format Summary

Data Format	
31 30 23 22 0	
s e f	

Field Size In Bits	
Sign (s)	1
Biased Exponent (e)	8
Fraction (f)	23
Total	32

Interpretation of Sign	
Positive Fraction	s = 0
Negative Fraction	s = 1

Normalized Numbers	
Bias of Biased Exponent	+127 ($7F)
Range of Biased Exponent	$0 < e < 255$ ($FF)
Range of Fraction	Zero or Nonzero
Fraction	1.f
Relation to Representation of Real Numbers	$(-1)^s \times 2^{e-127} \times 1.f$

Denormalized Numbers	
Biased Exponent Format Minimum	0 ($00)
Bias of Biased Exponent	+126 ($7E)
Range of Fraction	Nonzero
Fraction	0.f
Relation to Representation of Real Numbers	$(-1)^s \times 2^{-126} \times 0.f$

Signed Zeros	
Biased Exponent Format Minimum	0 ($00)
Fraction	0.f = 0.0

Signed Infinities	
Biased Exponent Format Maximum	255 ($FF)
Fraction	0.f = 0.0

NANs	
Sign	Don't Care
Biased Exponent Format Maximum	255 ($FF)
Fraction	Nonzero

Representation of Fraction
  Nonsignaling
  Signaling
  Nonzero Bit Pattern Created by User
  Fraction When Created by FPCP
	
	0.1xxxx...xxxx
	0.0xxxx...xxxx
	xxxx...xxxx
	11111...1111

Approximate Ranges	
Maximum Positive Normalized	3.4×10^{38}
Minimum Positive Normalized	$1.2 \times 10^{s-38}$
Minimum Positive Denormalized	1.4×10^{-45}

Table 1-5. Double-Precision Real Format Summary

Data Format	
63 62 52 51 0	
| s | e | f |	

Field Size (in Bits)	
Sign (s)	1
Biased Exponent (e)	11
Fraction (f)	52
Total	64

Interpretation of Sign	
Positive Fraction	$s = 0$
Negative Fraction	$s = 1$

Normalized Numbers	
Bias of Biased Exponent	+1023 ($3FF)
Range of Biased Exponent	$0 < e < 2047$ ($7FF)
Range of Fraction	Zero or Nonzero
Fraction	1.f
Relation to Representation of Real Numbers	$(-1)^s \times 2^{e-1023} \times 1.f$

Denormalized Numbers	
Biased Exponent Format Minimum	0 ($000)
Bias of Biased Exponent	+1022 ($3FE)
Range of Fraction	Nonzero
Fraction	0.f
Relation to Representation of Real Numbers	$(-1)^s \times 2^{-1022} \times 0.f$

Signed Zeros	
Biased Exponent Format Minimum	0 ($00)
Fraction (Mantissa/Significand)	$0.f = 0.0$

Signed Infinities	
Biased Exponent Format Maximum	2047 ($7FF)
Fraction	$0.f = 0.0$

NANs	
Sign	0 or 1
Biased Exponent Format Maximum	255 ($7FF)
Fraction	Nonzero

Representation of Fraction
  Nonsignaling
  Signaling
  Nonzero Bit Pattern Created by User
  Fraction When Created by FPCP
	1xxxx...xxxx
	0xxxx...xxxx
	xxxxx...xxxx
	11111...1111

Approximate Ranges	
Maximum Positive Normalized	18×10^{308}
Minimum Positive Normalized	2.2×10^{-308}
Minimum Positive Denormalized	4.9×10^{-324}

Table 1-6. Extended-Precision Real Format Summary

Data Format		
95 94 80 79 64 63 62 0		
s | e | z | j | f		

Field Size (in Bits)	
Sign (s)	1
Biased Exponent (e)	15
Zero, Reserved (u)	16
Explicit Integer Bit (j)	1
Mantissa (f)	63
Total	96

Interpretation of Unused Bits	
Input	Don't Care
Output	All Zeros

Interpretation of Sign	
Positive Mantissa	s = 0
Negative Mantissa	s = 1

Normalized Numbers	
Bias of Biased Exponent	+16383 ($3FFF)
Range of Biased Exponent	$0 <= e < 32767$ ($7FFF)
Explicit Integer Bit	1
Range of Mantissa	Zero or Nonzero
Mantissa (Explicit Integer Bit and Fraction)	1.f
Relation to Representation of Real Numbers	$(-1)^s \times 2^{e-16383} \times 1.f$

Denormalized Numbers	
Biased Exponent Format Minimum	0 ($0000)
Bias of Biased Exponent	+16383 ($3FFF)
Explicit Integer Bit	0
Range of Mantissa	Nonzero
Mantissa (Explicit Integer Bit and Fraction)	0.f
Relation to Representation of Real Numbers	$(-1)^s \times 2^{-16383} \times 0.f$

Signed Zeros	
Biased Exponent Format Minimum	0 ($0000)
Mantissa (Explicit Integer Bit and Fraction)	0.0

Signed Infinities	
Biased Exponent Format Maximum	32767 ($7FFF)
Explicit Integer Bit	Don't Care
Mantissa (Explicit Integer Bit and Fraction)	x.000...0000

Table 1-6. Extended-Precision Real Format Summary (Continued)

NANs	
Sign	Don't Care
Explicit Integer Bit	Don't Care
Biased Exponent Format Maximum	32767 ($7FFF)
Mantissa	Nonzero

Representation of Mantissa
  Nonsignaling
  Signaling
  Nonzero Bit Pattern Created by User
  Mantissa When Created by FPCP
	
	x.1xxxx...xxxx
	x.0xxxx...xxxx
	x.xxxxx...xxxx
	1.11111...1111

Approximate Ranges	
Maximum Positive Normalized	1.2×10^{4932}
Minimum Positive Normalized	1.7×10^{-4932}
Minimum Positive Denormalized	3.7×10^{4951}

Table 1-7. Packed Decimal Real Format Summary

Data Type	SM	SE	Y	Y	3-Digit Exponent	1-Digit Integer	16-Digit Fraction
±Infinity	0/1	1	1	1	$FFF	$XXXX	$00...00
±NAN	0/1	1	1	1	$FFF	$XXXX	Nonzero
±SNAN	0/1	1	1	1	$FFF	$XXXX	Nonzero
+Zero	0	0/1	X	X	$000–$999	$XXX0	$00...00
–Zero	1	0/1	X	X	$000–$999	$XXX0	$00...00
+In-Range	0	0/1	X	X	$000–$999	$XXX0–$XXX9	$00...01–$99...99
–In-Range	1	0/1	X	X	$000–$999	$XXX0–$XXX9	$00...01–$99...99

A packed decimal real data format with the SE and both Y bits set, an exponent of $FFF, and a nonzero 16-bit decimal fraction is a NAN. When the FPU uses this format, the fraction of the NAN is moved bit-by-bit into the extended-precision mantissa of a floating-point data register. The exponent of the register is set to signify a NAN, and no conversion occurs. The MSB of the most significant digit in the decimal fraction (the MSB of digit 15) is a don't care, as in extended-precision NANs, and the MSB of minus one of digit 15 is the SNAN bit. If the NAN bit is a zero, then it is an SNAN.

If a non-decimal digit ($A–$F) appears in the exponent of a zero, the number is a true zero. The FPU does not detect non-decimal digits in the exponent, integer, or fraction digits of an in-range packed decimal real data format. These non-decimal digits are converted to binary in the same manner as decimal digits; however, the result is probably useless although it is repeatable. Since an in-range number cannot overflow or underflow when converted to extended precision, conversion from the packed decimal real data format always produces normalized extended-precision numbers.

1.7 ORGANIZATION OF DATA IN REGISTERS

The following paragraphs describe data organization within the data, address, and control registers.

1.7.1 Organization of Integer Data Formats in Registers

Each integer data register is 32 bits wide. Byte and word operands occupy the lower 8- and 16-bit portions of integer data registers, respectively. Long-word operands occupy the entire 32 bits of integer data registers. A data register that is either a source or destination operand only uses or changes the appropriate lower 8 or 16 bits (in byte or word operations, respectively). The remaining high-order portion does not change and goes unused. The address of the least significant bit (LSB) of a long-word integer is zero, and the MSB is 31. For bit fields, the address of the MSB is zero, and the LSB is the width of the register minus one (the offset). If the width of the register plus the offset is greater than 32, the bit field wraps around within the register. Figure 1-18 illustrates the organization of various data formats in the data registers.

An example of a quad word is the product of a 32-bit multiply or the quotient of a 32-bit divide operation (signed and unsigned). Quad words may be organized in any two integer data registers without restrictions on order or pairing. There are no explicit instructions for the management of this data format, although the MOVEM instruction can be used to move a quad word into or out of registers.

Binary-coded decimal (BCD) data represents decimal numbers in binary form. Although there are many BCD codes, the BCD instructions of the M68000 family support two formats, packed and unpacked. In these formats, the LSBs consist of a binary number having the numeric value of the corresponding decimal number. In the unpacked BCD format, a byte defines one decimal number that has four LSBs containing the binary value and four undefined MSBs. Each byte of the packed BCD format contains two decimal numbers; the least significant four bits contain the least significant decimal number and the most significant four bits contain the most significant decimal number.

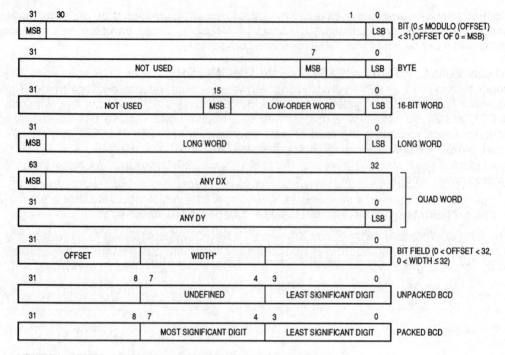

Figure 1-18. Organization of Integer Data Formats in Data Registers

Because address registers and stack pointers are 32 bits wide, address registers cannot be used for byte-size operands. When an address register is a source operand, either the low-order word or the entire long-word operand is used, depending upon the operation size. When an address register is the destination operand, the entire register becomes affected, despite the operation size. If the source operand is a word size, it is sign-extended to 32 bits and then used in the operation to an address register destination. Address registers are primarily for addresses and address computation support. The instruction set includes instructions that add to, compare, and move the contents of address registers. Figure 1-19 illustrates the organization of addresses in address registers.

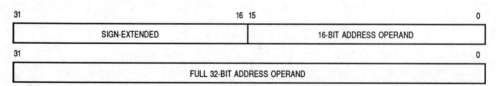

Figure 1-19. Organization of Integer Data Formats in Address Registers

Control registers vary in size according to function. Some control registers have undefined bits reserved for future definition by Motorola. Those particular bits read as zeros and must be written as zeros for future compatibility.

All operations to the SR and CCR are word-size operations. For all CCR operations, the upper byte is read as all zeros and is ignored when written, despite privilege mode. The alternate function code registers, supervisor function code (SFC) and data function code (DFC), are 32-bit registers with only bits 0–2 implemented. These bits contain the address space values for the read or write operands of MOVES, PFLUSH, and PTEST instructions. Values transfer to and from the SFC and DFC by using the MOVEC instruction. These are long-word transfers; the upper 29 bits are read as zeros and are ignored when written.

1.7.2 Organization of Integer Data Formats in Memory

The byte-addressable organization of memory allows lower addresses to correspond to higher order bytes. The address N of a long-word data item corresponds to the address of the highest order word's MSB. The lower order word is located at address N + 2, leaving the LSB at address N + 3 (see Figure 1-20). Organization of data formats in memory is consistent with the M68000 family data organization. The lowest address (nearest $00000000) is the location of the MSB, with each successive LSB located at the next address (N + 1, N + 2, etc.). The highest address (nearest $FFFFFFFF) is the location of the LSB.

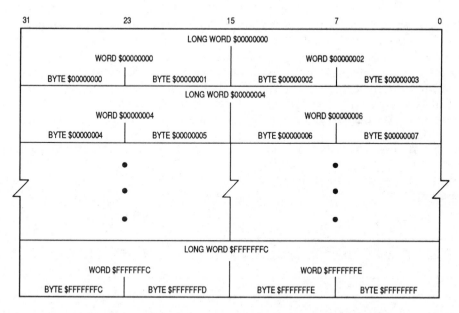

Figure 1-20. Memory Operand Addressing

Figure 1-21 illustrates the organization of IU data formats in memory. A base address that selects one byte in memory, the base byte, specifies a bit number that selects one bit, the bit operand, in the base byte. The MSB of the byte is seven.

The following conditions specify a bit field operand:

1. A base address that selects one byte in memory.
2. A bit field offset that shows the leftmost (base) bit of the bit field in relation to the MSB of the base byte.
3. A bit field width that determines how many bits to the right of the base bit are in the bit field.

The MSB of the base byte is bit field offset 0; the LSB of the base byte is bit field offset 7; and the LSB of the previous byte in memory is bit field offset -1. Bit field offsets may have values between 2^{-31} to $2^{31}-1$, and bit field widths may range from 1 to 32 bits.

A 16-byte block operand, supported by the MOVE16 instruction, has a block of 16 bytes, aligned to a 16-byte boundary. An address that can point to any byte in the block specifies this operand.

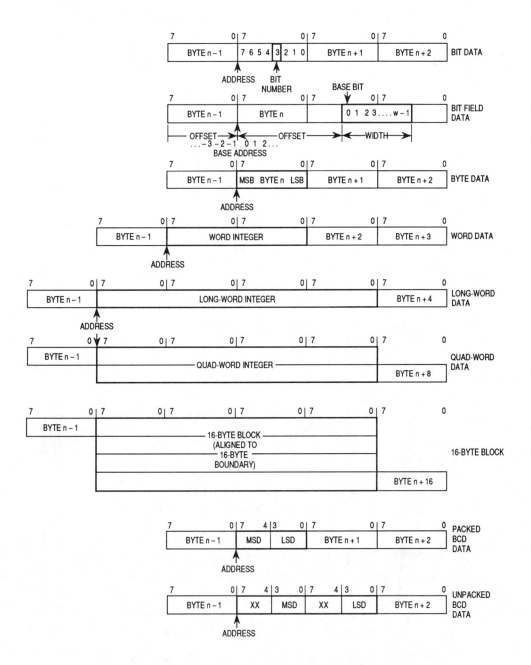

Figure 1-21. Memory Organization for Integer Operands

1.7.3 Organization of FPU Data Formats in Registers and Memory

The eight, 80-bit floating-point data registers are analogous to the integer data registers and are completely general purpose (i.e., any instruction may use any register). The MC68040 supports only some data formats and types in hardware. Table 1-8 lists the data formats supported by the MC68040.

Table 1-8. MC68040 FPU Data Formats and Data Types

Number Types	Data Formats						
	Single-Precision Real	Double-Precision Real	Extended-Precision Real	Packed-Decimal Real	Byte Integer	Word Integer	Long-Word Integer
Normalized	*	*	*	†	*	*	*
Zero	*	*	*	†	*	*	*
Infinity	*	*	*	†			
NAN	*	*	*	†			
Denormalized	†	†	†	†			
Unnormalized			†	†			

NOTES:
* = Data Format/Type Supported by On-Chip MC68040 FPU Hardware
† = Data Format/Type Supported by Software (MC68040FPSP)

Figure 1-22 illustrates the floating-point data format for the single-, double-, and extended-precision binary real data organization in memory.

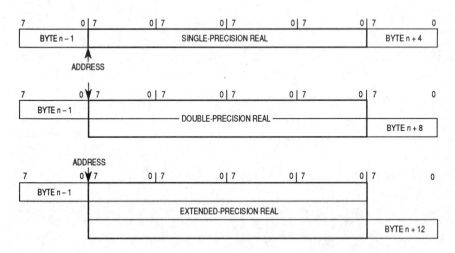

Figure 1-22. Organization of FPU Data Formats in Memory

SECTION 2
ADDRESSING CAPABILITIES

Most operations take a source operand and a destination operand, compute them, and store the result in the destination location. Single-operand operations take a destination operand, compute it, and store the result in the destination location. External microprocessor references to memory are either program references that refer to program space or data references that refer to data space. They access either instruction words or operands (data items) for an instruction. Program space is the section of memory that contains the program instructions and any immediate data operands residing in the instruction stream. Data space is the section of memory that contains the program data. Data items in the instruction stream can be accessed with the program counter relative addressing modes; these accesses classify as program references.

2.1 INSTRUCTION FORMAT

M68000 family instructions consist of at least one word; some have as many as 11 words. Figure 2-1 illustrates the general composition of an instruction. The first word of the instruction, called the simple effective address operation word, specifies the length of the instruction, the effective addressing mode, and the operation to be performed. The remaining words, called brief and full extension words, further specify the instruction and operands. These words can be floating-point command words, conditional predicates, immediate operands, extensions to the effective addressing mode specified in the simple effective address operation word, branch displacements, bit number or bit field specifications, special register specifications, trap operands, pack/unpack constants, or argument counts.

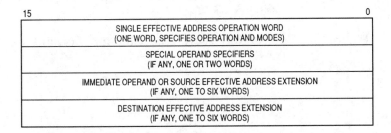

15   0

| SINGLE EFFECTIVE ADDRESS OPERATION WORD (ONE WORD, SPECIFIES OPERATION AND MODES) |
| SPECIAL OPERAND SPECIFIERS (IF ANY, ONE OR TWO WORDS) |
| IMMEDIATE OPERAND OR SOURCE EFFECTIVE ADDRESS EXTENSION (IF ANY, ONE TO SIX WORDS) |
| DESTINATION EFFECTIVE ADDRESS EXTENSION (IF ANY, ONE TO SIX WORDS) |

Figure 2-1. Instruction Word General Format

An instruction specifies the function to be performed with an operation code and defines the location of every operand. Instructions specify an operand location by register specification, the instruction's register field holds the register's number; by effective address, the instruction's effective address field contains addressing mode information; or by implicit reference, the definition of the instruction implies the use of specific registers.

The single effective address operation word format is the basic instruction word (see Figure 2-2). The encoding of the mode field selects the addressing mode. The register field contains the general register number or a value that selects the addressing mode when the mode field contains opcode 111. Some indexed or indirect addressing modes use a combination of the simple effective address operation word followed by a brief extension word. Other indexed or indirect addressing modes consist of the simple effective address operation word and a full extension word. The longest instruction is a MOVE instruction with a full extension word for both the source and destination effective addresses and eight other extension words. It also contains 32-bit base displacements and 32-bit outer displacements for both source and destination addresses. Figure 2-2 illustrates the three formats used in an instruction word; Table 2-1 lists the field definitions for these three formats.

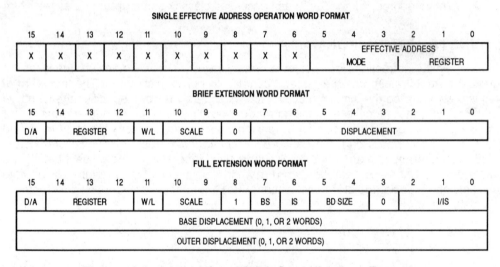

Figure 2-2. Instruction Word Specification Formats

Table 2-1. Instruction Word Format Field Definitions

Field	Definition
Instruction	
Mode	Addressing Mode
Register	General Register Number
Extensions	
Register	Index Register Number
D/A	Index Register Type 0 = Dn 1 = An
W/L	Word/Long-Word Index Size 0 = Sign-Extended Word 1 = Long Word
Scale	Scale Factor 00 = 1 01 = 2 10 = 4 11 = 8
BS	Base Register Suppress 0 = Base Register Added 1 = Base Register Suppressed
IS	Index Suppress 0 = Evaluate and Add Index Operand 1 = Suppress Index Operand
BD SIZE	Base Displacement Size 00 = Reserved 01 = Null Displacement 10 = Word Displacement 11 = Long Displacement
I/IS	Index/Indirect Selection Indirect and Indexing Operand Determined in Conjunction with Bit 6, Index Suppress

For effective addresses that use a full extension word format, the index suppress (IS) bit and the index/indirect selection (I/IS) field determine the type of indexing and indirect action. Table 2-2 lists the index and indirect operations corresponding to all combinations of IS and I/IS values.

Table 2-2. IS-I/IS Memory Indirect Action Encodings

IS	Index/Indirect	Operation
0	000	No Memory Indirect Action
0	001	Indirect Preindexed with Null Outer Displacement
0	010	Indirect Preindexed with Word Outer Displacement
0	011	Indirect Preindexed with Long Outer Displacement
0	100	Reserved
0	101	Indirect Postindexed with Null Outer Displacement
0	110	Indirect Postindexed with Word Outer Displacement
0	111	Indirect Postindexed with Long Outer Displacement
1	000	No Memory Indirect Action
1	001	Memory Indirect with Null Outer Displacement
1	010	Memory Indirect with Word Outer Displacement
1	011	Memory Indirect with Long Outer Displacement
1	100–111	Reserved

2.2 EFFECTIVE ADDRESSING MODES

Besides the operation code, which specifies the function to be performed, an instruction defines the location of every operand for the function. Instructions specify an operand location in one of three ways. A register field within an instruction can specify the register to be used; an instruction's effective address field can contain addressing mode information; or the instruction's definition can imply the use of a specific register. Other fields within the instruction specify whether the register selected is an address or data register and how the register is to be used. **Section 1 Introduction** contains detailed register descriptions.

An instruction's addressing mode specifies the value of an operand, a register that contains the operand, or how to derive the effective address of an operand in memory. Each addressing mode has an assembler syntax. Some instructions imply the addressing mode for an operand. These instructions include the appropriate fields for operands that use only one addressing mode.

2.2.1 Data Register Direct Mode

In the data register direct mode, the effective address field specifies the data register containing the operand.

```
GENERATION:                    EA = Dn
ASSEMBLER SYNTAX:              Dn
EA MODE FIELD:                 000
EA REGISTER FIELD:             REG. NO.
NUMBER OF EXTENSION WORDS:     0
```

DATA REGISTER ————————————————————| OPERAND |

2.2.2 Address Register Direct Mode

In the address register direct mode, the effective address field specifies the address register containing the operand.

```
GENERATION:                    EA = An
ASSEMBLER SYNTAX:              An
EA MODE FIELD:                 001
EA REGISTER FIELD:             REG. NO.
NUMBER OF EXTENSION WORDS:     0
```

ADDRESS REGISTER ————————————————————| OPERAND |

2.2.3 Address Register Indirect Mode

In the address register indirect mode, the operand is in memory. The effective address field specifies the address register containing the address of the operand in memory.

```
GENERATION:                    EA = (An)
ASSEMBLER SYNTAX:              (An)
EA MODE FIELD:                 010
EA REGISTER FIELD:             REG. NO.
NUMBER OF EXTENSION WORDS:     0
```

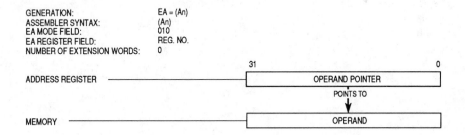

2.2.4 Address Register Indirect with Postincrement Mode

In the address register indirect with postincrement mode, the operand is in memory. The effective address field specifies the address register containing the address of the operand in memory. After the operand address is used, it is incremented by one, two, or four depending on the size of the operand: byte, word, or long word, respectively. Coprocessors may support incrementing for any operand size, up to 255 bytes. If the address register is the stack pointer and the operand size is byte, the address is incremented by two to keep the stack pointer aligned to a word boundary.

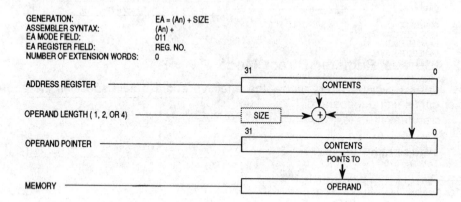

```
GENERATION:                  EA = (An) + SIZE
ASSEMBLER SYNTAX:            (An) +
EA MODE FIELD:               011
EA REGISTER FIELD:           REG. NO.
NUMBER OF EXTENSION WORDS:   0
```

2.2.5 Address Register Indirect with Predecrement Mode

In the address register indirect with predecrement mode, the operand is in memory. The effective address field specifies the address register containing the address of the operand in memory. Before the operand address is used, it is decremented by one, two, or four depending on the operand size: byte, word, or long word, respectively. Coprocessors may support decrementing for any operand size up to 255 bytes. If the address register is the stack pointer and the operand size is byte, the address is decremented by two to keep the stack pointer aligned to a word boundary.

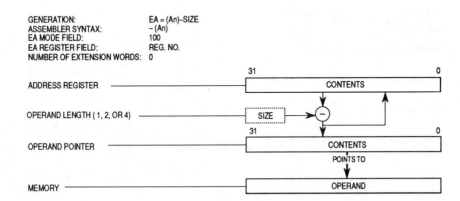

```
GENERATION:                 EA = (An)–SIZE
ASSEMBLER SYNTAX:           – (An)
EA MODE FIELD:              100
EA REGISTER FIELD:          REG. NO.
NUMBER OF EXTENSION WORDS:  0
```

2.2.6 Address Register Indirect with Displacement Mode

In the address register indirect with displacement mode, the operand is in memory. The sum of the address in the address register, which the effective address specifies, plus the sign-extended 16-bit displacement integer in the extension word is the operand's address in memory. Displacements are always sign-extended to 32 bits prior to being used in effective address calculations.

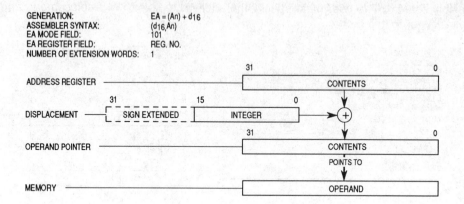

GENERATION: $EA = (An) + d_{16}$
ASSEMBLER SYNTAX: (d_{16}, An)
EA MODE FIELD: 101
EA REGISTER FIELD: REG. NO.
NUMBER OF EXTENSION WORDS: 1

2.2.7 Address Register Indirect with Index (8-Bit Displacement) Mode

This addressing mode requires one extension word that contains an index register indicator and an 8-bit displacement. The index register indicator includes size and scale information. In this mode, the operand is in memory. The operand's address is the sum of the address register's contents; the sign-extended displacement value in the extension word's low-order eight bits; and the index register's sign-extended contents (possibly scaled). The user must specify the address register, the displacement, and the index register in this mode.

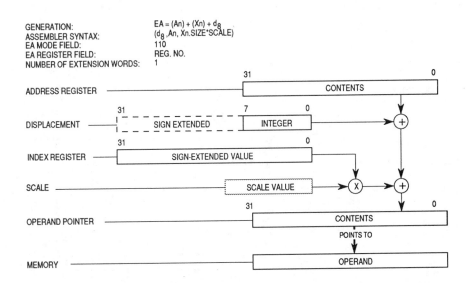

GENERATION: EA = (An) + (Xn) + d$_8$
ASSEMBLER SYNTAX: (d$_8$,An, Xn.SIZE*SCALE)
EA MODE FIELD: 110
EA REGISTER FIELD: REG. NO.
NUMBER OF EXTENSION WORDS: 1

2.2.8 Address Register Indirect with Index (Base Displacement) Mode

This addressing mode requires an index register indicator and an optional 16- or 32-bit sign-extended base displacement. The index register indicator includes size and scaling information. The operand is in memory. The operand's address is the sum of the contents of the address register, the base displacement, and the scaled contents of the sign-extended index register.

In this mode, the address register, the index register, and the displacement are all optional. The effective address is zero if there is no specification. This mode provides a data register indirect address when there is no specific address register and the index register is a data register.

```
GENERATION:                    EA = (An) + (Xn) + bd
ASSEMBLER SYNTAX:              (bd,An,Xn.SIZE*SCALE)
EA MODE FIELD:                 110
EA REGISTER FIELD:             REG. NO.
NUMBER OF EXTENSION WORDS:     1,2, OR 3
```

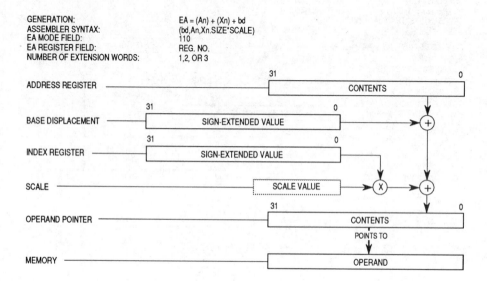

2.2.9 Memory Indirect Postindexed Mode

In this mode, both the operand and its address are in memory. The processor calculates an intermediate indirect memory address using a base address register and base displacement. The processor accesses a long word at this address and adds the index operand (Xn.SIZE*SCALE) and the outer displacement to yield the effective address. Both displacements and the index register contents are sign-extended to 32 bits.

In the syntax for this mode, brackets enclose the values used to calculate the intermediate memory address. All four user-specified values are optional. Both the base and outer displacements may be null, word, or long word. When omitting a displacement or suppressing an element, its value is zero in the effective address calculation.

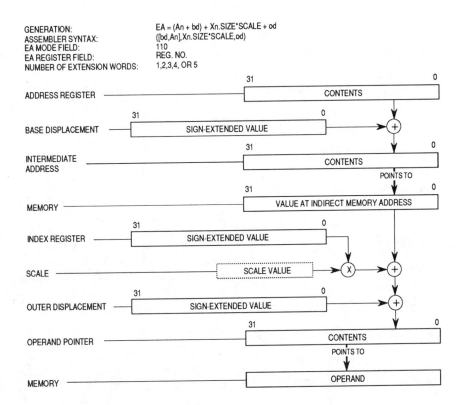

```
GENERATION:                  EA = (An + bd) + Xn.SIZE*SCALE + od
ASSEMBLER SYNTAX:            ([bd,An],Xn.SIZE*SCALE,od)
EA MODE FIELD:               110
EA REGISTER FIELD:           REG. NO.
NUMBER OF EXTENSION WORDS:   1,2,3,4, OR 5
```

2.2.10 Memory Indirect Preindexed Mode

In this mode, both the operand and its address are in memory. The processor calculates an intermediate indirect memory address using a base address register, a base displacement, and the index operand (Xn.SIZE*SCALE). The processor accesses a long word at this address and adds the outer displacement to yield the effective address. Both displacements and the index register contents are sign-extended to 32 bits.

In the syntax for this mode, brackets enclose the values used to calculate the intermediate memory address. All four user-specified values are optional. Both the base and outer displacements may be null, word, or long word. When omitting a displacement or suppressing an element, its value is zero in the effective address calculation.

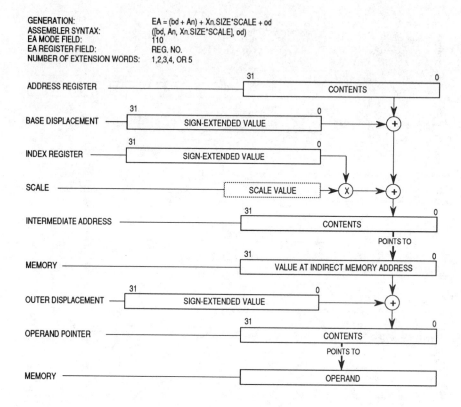

GENERATION: EA = (bd + An) + Xn.SIZE*SCALE + od
ASSEMBLER SYNTAX: ([bd, An, Xn.SIZE*SCALE], od)
EA MODE FIELD: 110
EA REGISTER FIELD: REG. NO.
NUMBER OF EXTENSION WORDS: 1,2,3,4, OR 5

2.2.11 Program Counter Indirect with Displacement Mode

In this mode, the operand is in memory. The address of the operand is the sum of the address in the program counter (PC) and the sign-extended 16-bit displacement integer in the extension word. The value in the PC is the address of the extension word. This is a program reference allowed only for reads.

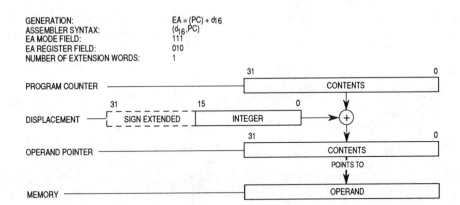

```
GENERATION:                  EA = (PC) + d16
ASSEMBLER SYNTAX:            (d16,PC)
EA MODE FIELD:               111
EA REGISTER FIELD:           010
NUMBER OF EXTENSION WORDS:   1
```

2.2.12 Program Counter Indirect with Index (8-Bit Displacement) Mode

This mode is similar to the mode described in **2.2.7 Address Register Indirect with Index (8-Bit Displacement) Mode**, except the PC is the base register. The operand is in memory. The operand's address is the sum of the address in the PC, the sign-extended displacement integer in the extension word's lower eight bits, and the sized, scaled, and sign-extended index operand. The value in the PC is the address of the extension word. This is a program reference allowed only for reads. The user must include the displacement, the PC, and the index register when specifying this addressing mode.

```
GENERATION:                EA = (PC) + (Xn) + d8
ASSEMBLER SYNTAX:          (d8,PC,Xn.SIZE*SCALE)
EA MODE FIELD:             111
EA REGISTER FIELD:         011
NUMBER OF EXTENSION WORDS: 1
```

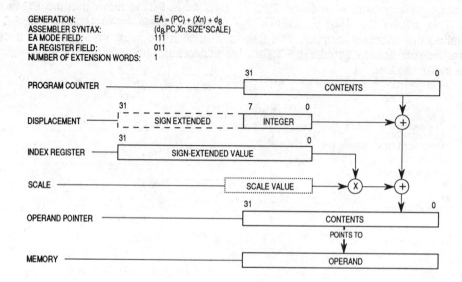

2.2.13 Program Counter Indirect with Index (Base Displacement) Mode

This mode is similar to the mode described in **2.2.8 Address Register Indirect with Index (Base Displacement) Mode**, except the PC is the base register. It requires an index register indicator and an optional 16- or 32-bit sign-extended base displacement. The operand is in memory. The operand's address is the sum of the contents of the PC, the base displacement, and the scaled contents of the sign-extended index register. The value of the PC is the address of the first extension word. This is a program reference allowed only for reads.

In this mode, the PC, the displacement, and the index register are optional. The user must supply the assembler notation ZPC (a zero value PC) to show that the PC is not used. This allows the user to access the program space without using the PC in calculating the effective address. The user can access the program space with a data register indirect access by placing ZPC in the instruction and specifying a data register as the index register.

GENERATION: EA = (PC) + (Xn) + bd
ASSEMBLER SYNTAX: (bd, PC, Xn. SIZE*SCALE)
EA MODE FIELD: 111
EA REGISTER FIELD: 011
NUMBER OF EXTENSION WORDS: 1,2, OR 3

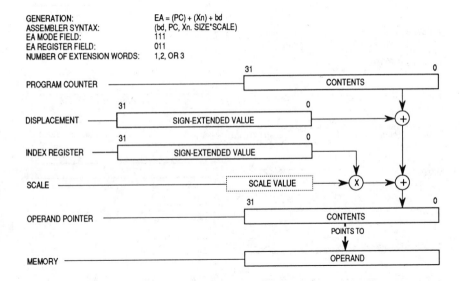

2.2.14 Program Counter Memory Indirect Postindexed Mode

This mode is similar to the mode described in **2.2.9 Memory Indirect Postindexed Mode**, but the PC is the base register. Both the operand and operand address are in memory. The processor calculates an intermediate indirect memory address by adding a base displacement to the PC contents. The processor accesses a long word at that address and adds the scaled contents of the index register and the optional outer displacement to yield the effective address. The value of the PC used in the calculation is the address of the first extension word. This is a program reference allowed only for reads.

In the syntax for this mode, brackets enclose the values used to calculate the intermediate memory address. All four user-specified values are optional. The user must supply the assembler notation ZPC (a zero value PC) to show the PC is not used. This allows the user to access the program space without using the PC in calculating the effective address. Both the base and outer displacements may be null, word, or long word. When omitting a displacement or suppressing an element, its value is zero in the effective address calculation.

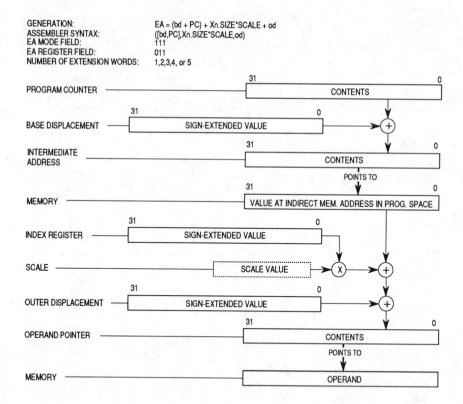

```
GENERATION:                   EA = (bd + PC) + Xn.SIZE*SCALE + od
ASSEMBLER SYNTAX:             ([bd,PC],Xn.SIZE*SCALE,od)
EA MODE FIELD:                111
EA REGISTER FIELD:            011
NUMBER OF EXTENSION WORDS:    1,2,3,4, or 5
```

2.2.15 Program Counter Memory Indirect Preindexed Mode

This mode is similar to the mode described in **2.2.10 Memory Indirect Preindexed Mode**, but the PC is the base register. Both the operand and operand address are in memory. The processor calculates an intermediate indirect memory address by adding the PC contents, a base displacement, and the scaled contents of an index register. The processor accesses a long word at immediate indirect memory address and adds the optional outer displacement to yield the effective address. The value of the PC is the address of the first extension word. This is a program reference allowed only for reads.

In the syntax for this mode, brackets enclose the values used to calculate the intermediate memory address. All four user-specified values are optional. The user must supply the assembler notation ZPC showing that the PC is not used. This allows the user to access the program space without using the PC in calculating the effective address. Both the base and outer displacements may be null, word, or long word. When omitting a displacement or suppressing an element, its value is zero in the effective address calculation.

GENERATION: EA = (bd + PC) + Xn.SIZE*SCALE + od
ASSEMBLER SYNTAX: ([bd,PC],Xn.SIZE*SCALE,od)
EA MODE FIELD: 111
EA REGISTER FIELD: 011
NUMBER OF EXTENSION WORDS: 1,2,3,4, or 5

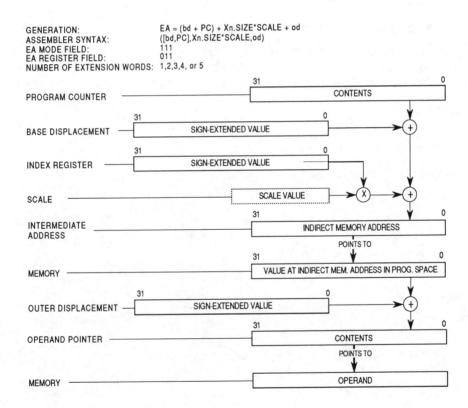

2.2.16 Absolute Short Addressing Mode

In this addressing mode, the operand is in memory, and the address of the operand is in the extension word. The 16-bit address is sign-extended to 32 bits before it is used.

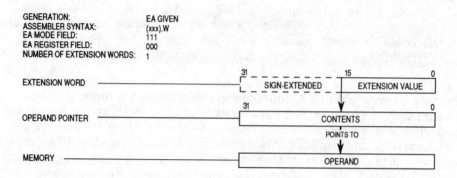

```
GENERATION:                 EA GIVEN
ASSEMBLER SYNTAX:           (xxx).W
EA MODE FIELD:              111
EA REGISTER FIELD:          000
NUMBER OF EXTENSION WORDS:  1
```

2.2.17 Absolute Long Addressing Mode

In this addressing mode, the operand is in memory, and the operand's address occupies the two extension words following the instruction word in memory. The first extension word contains the high-order part of the address; the second contains the low-order part of the address.

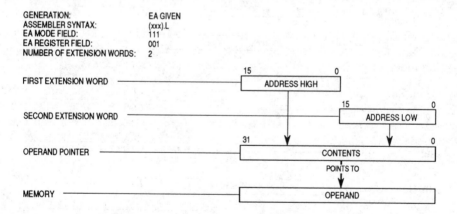

```
GENERATION:                 EA GIVEN
ASSEMBLER SYNTAX:           (xxx).L
EA MODE FIELD:              111
EA REGISTER FIELD:          001
NUMBER OF EXTENSION WORDS:  2
```

2.2.18 Immediate Data

In this addressing mode, the operand is in one or two extension words. Table 2-3 lists the location of the operand within the instruction word format. The immediate data format is as follows:

```
GENERATION:                OPERAND GIVEN
ASSEMBLER SYNTAX:          #<xxx>
EA MODE FIELD:             111
EA REGISTER FIELD:         100
NUMBER OF EXTENSION WORDS: 1,2,4, OR 6, EXCEPT FOR PACKED DECIMAL REAL OPERANDS
```

Table 2-3. Immediate Operand Location

Operation Length	Location
Byte	Low-order byte of the extension word.
Word	The entire extension word.
Long Word	High-order word of the operand is in the first extension word; the low-order word is in the second extension word.
Single-Precision	In two extension words.
Double-Precision	In four extension words.
Extended-Precision	In six extension words.
Packed-Decimal Real	In six extension words.

2.3 EFFECTIVE ADDRESSING MODE SUMMARY

Effective addressing modes are grouped according to the use of the mode. Data addressing modes refer to data operands. Memory addressing modes refer to memory operands. Alterable addressing modes refer to alterable (writable) operands. Control addressing modes refer to memory operands without an associated size.

These categories sometimes combine to form new categories that are more restrictive. Two combined classifications are alterable memory (addressing modes that are both alterable and memory addresses) and data alterable (addressing modes that are both alterable and data). Table 2-4 lists a summary of effective addressing modes and their categories.

Table 2-4. Effective Addressing Modes and Categories

Addressing Modes	Syntax	Mode Field	Reg. Field	Data	Memory	Control	Alterable
Register Direct							
Data	Dn	000	reg. no.	X	—	—	X
Address	An	001	reg. no.	—	—	—	X
Register Indirect							
Address	(An)	010	reg. no.	X	X	X	X
Address with Postincrement	(An)+	011	reg. no.	X	X	—	X
Address with Predecrement	−(An)	100	reg. no.	X	X	—	X
Address with Displacement	(d_{16},An)	101	reg. no.	X	X	X	X
Address Register Indirect with Index							
8-Bit Displacement	(d_8,An,Xn)	110	reg. no.	X	X	X	X
Base Displacement	(bd,An,Xn)	110	reg. no.	X	X	X	X
Memory Indirect							
Postindexed	([bd,An],Xn,od)	110	reg. no.	X	X	X	X
Preindexed	([bd,An,Xn],od)	110	reg. no.	X	X	X	X
Program Counter Indirect							
with Displacement	(d_{16},PC)	111	010	X	X	X	—
Program Counter Indirect with Index							
8-Bit Displacement	(d_8,PC,Xn)	111	011	X	X	X	—
Base Displacement	(bd,PC,Xn)	111	011	X	X	X	—
Program Counter Memory Indirect							
Postindexed	([bd,PC],Xn,od)	111	011	X	X	X	X
Preindexed	([bd,PC,Xn],od)	111	011	X	X	X	X
Absolute Data Addressing							
Short	(xxx).W	111	000	X	X	X	—
Long	(xxx).L	111	000	X	X	X	—
Immediate	#<xxx>	111	100	X	X	—	—

2.4 BRIEF EXTENSION WORD FORMAT COMPATIBILITY

Programs can be easily transported from one member of the M68000 family to another in an upward-compatible fashion. The user object code of each early member of the family, which is upward compatible with newer members, can be executed on the newer microprocessor without change. Brief extension word formats are encoded with information that allows the CPU32, MC68020, MC68030, and MC68040 to distinguish the basic M68000 family architecture's new address extensions. Figure 2-3 illustrates these brief extension word formats. The encoding for SCALE used by the CPU32, MC68020, MC68030, and MC68040 is a compatible extension of the M68000 family architecture. A value of zero for SCALE is the same encoding for both extension words. Software that uses this encoding is compatible with all processors in the M68000 family. Both brief extension word formats do not contain the other values of SCALE. Software can be easily migrated in an upward-compatible direction, with downward support only for nonscaled addressing. If the MC68000 were to execute an instruction that encoded a scaling factor, the scaling factor would be ignored and would not access the desired memory address. The earlier microprocessors do not recognize the brief extension word formats implemented by newer processors. Although they can detect illegal instructions, they do not decode invalid encodings of the brief extension word formats as exceptions.

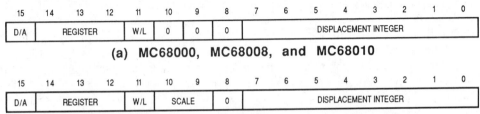

Figure 2-3. M68000 Family Brief Extension Word Formats

2.5 FULL EXTENSION ADDRESSING MODES

The full extension word format provides additional addressing modes for the MC68020, MC68030, and MC68040. There are four elements common to these full extension addressing modes: a base register (BR), an index register (Xn), a base displacement (bd), and an outer displacement (od). Each of these four elements can be suppressed independently of each other. However, at least one element must be active and not suppressed. When an element is suppressed, it has an effective value of zero.

BR can be suppressed through the BS field of the full extension word format. The encoding of bits 0–5 in the single effective address word format (see Figure 2-2) selects BR as either the PC when using program relative addressing modes, or An when using non-program relative addressing modes. The value of the PC is the address of the extension word. For the non-program relative addressing modes, BR is the contents of a selected An.

SIZE and SCALE can be used to modify Xn. The W/L field in the full extension format selects the size of Xn as a word or long word. The SCALE field selects the scaling factor, shifts the value of the Xn left multiplying the value by 1, 2, 4, or 8, respectively, without actually changing the value. Scaling can be used to calculate the address of arrayed structures. Figure 2-4 illustrates the scaling of an Xn.

The bd and od can be either word or long word. The size of od is selected through the encoding of the I/IS field in the full extension word format (refer to Table 2-2). There are two main modes of operation that use these four elements in different ways: no memory indirect action and memory indirect. The od is provided only for using memory indirect addressing modes of which there are three types: with preindex, with postindex, and with index suppressed.

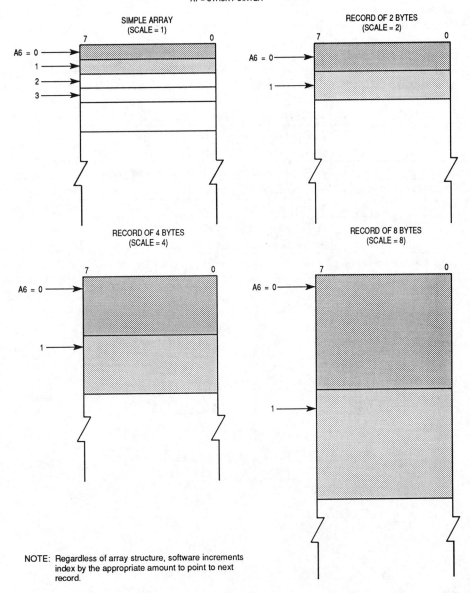

SYNTAX: MOVE.B (A5, A6.L*SCALE),(A7)
WHERE
 A5 = ADDRESS OF ARRAY STRUCTURE
 A6 = INDEX NUMBER OF ARRAY ITEM
 A7 = STACK POINTER

SIMPLE ARRAY
(SCALE = 1)

RECORD OF 2 BYTES
(SCALE = 2)

RECORD OF 4 BYTES
(SCALE = 4)

RECORD OF 8 BYTES
(SCALE = 8)

NOTE: Regardless of array structure, software increments index by the appropriate amount to point to next record.

Figure 2-4. Addressing Array Items

2.5.1 No Memory Indirect Action Mode

No memory indirect action mode uses BR, Xn with its modifiers, and bd to calculate the address of the required operand. Data register indirect (Dn) and absolute address with index (bd,Xn.SIZE*SCALE) are examples of the no memory indirect action mode. Figure 2-5 illustrates the no memory indirect action mode.

BR	Xn	bd	Addressing Mode
S	S	S	Not Applicable
S	S	A	Absolute Addressing Mode
S	A	S	Register Indirect
S	A	A	Register Indirect with Constant Index
An	S	S	Address Register Indirect
An	S	A	Address Register Indirect with Constant Index
An	A	S	Address Register Indirect with Variable Index
An	A	A	Address Register Indirect with Constant and Variable Index
PC	S	S	PC Relative
PC	S	A	PC Relative with Constant Index
PC	A	S	PC Relative with Variable Index
PC	A	A	PC Relative with Constant and Variable Index

NOTE: S indicates suppressed and A indicates active.

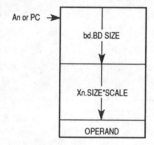

Figure 2-5. No Memory Indirect Action

2.5.2 Memory Indirect Modes

Memory indirect modes fetch two operands from memory. The BR and bd evaluate the address of the first operand, intermediate memory pointer (IMP). The value of IMP and the od evaluates the address of the second operand.

There are three types of memory indirect modes: pre-index, post-index, and index register suppressed. Xn and its modifiers can be allocated to determine either the address of the IMP (pre-index) or to the address of the second operand (post-index).

2.5.2.1 Memory Indirect with Preindex. The Xn is allocated to determine the address of the IMP. Figure 2-6 illustrates the memory indirect with pre-indexing mode.

BR	Xn	bd	od	IMP Addressing Mode	Operand Addressing Mode
S	A	S	S	Register Indirect	Memory Pointer Directly to Data Operand
S	A	S	A	Register Indirect	Memory Pointer as Base with Displacement to Data Operand
S	A	A	S	Register Indirect with Constant Index	Memory Pointer Directly to Data Operand
S	A	A	A	Register Indirect with Constant Index	Memory Pointer as Base with Displacement to Data Operand
An	A	S	S	Address Register Indirect with Variable Index	Memory Pointer Directly to Data Operand
An	A	S	A	Address Register Indirect with Variable Index	Memory Pointer as Base with Displacement to Data Operand
An	A	A	S	Address Register Indirect with Constant and Variable Index	Memory Pointer Directly to Data Operand
An	A	A	A	Address Register Indirect with Constant and Variable Index	Memory Pointer as Base with Displacement to Data Operand
PC	A	S	S	PC Relative with Variable Index	Memory Pointer Directly to Data Operand
PC	A	S	A	PC Relative with Variable Index	Memory Pointer as Base with Displacement to Data Operand
PC	A	A	S	PC Relative with Constant and Variable Index	Memory Pointer Directly to Data Operand
PC	A	A	A	PC Relative with Constant and Variable Index	Memory Pointer as Base with Displacement to Data Operand

NOTE: S indicates suppressed and A indicates active.

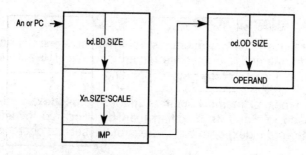

Figure 2-6. Memory Indirect with Preindex

2.5.2.2 Memory Indirect with Postindex. The Xn is allocated to evaluate the address of the second operand. Figure 2-7 illustrates the memory indirect with post-indexing mode.

BR	Xn	bd	od	IMP Addressing Mode	Operand Addressing Mode
S	A	S	S	—	—
S	A	S	A	—	—
S	A	A	S	Absolute Addressing Mode	Memory Pointer with Variable Index to Data Operand
S	A	A	A	Absolute Addressing Mode	Memory Pointer with Constant and Variable Index to Data Operand
An	A	S	S	Address Register Indirect	Memory Pointer with Variable Index to Data Operand
An	A	S	A	Address Register Indirect	Memory Pointer with Constant and Variable Index to Data Operand
An	A	A	S	Address Register Indirect with Constant Index	Memory Pointer with Variable Index to Data Operand
An	A	A	A	Address Register Indirect with Constant Index	Memory Pointer with Constant and Variable Index to Data Operand
PC	A	S	S	PC Relative	Memory Pointer with Variable Index to Data Operand
PC	A	S	A	PC Relative	Memory Pointer with Constant and Variable Index to Data Operand
PC	A	A	S	PC Relative with Constant Index	Memory Pointer with Variable Index to Data Operand
PC	A	A	A	PC Relative with Constant Index	Memory Pointer with Constant and Variable Index to Data Operand

NOTE: S indicates suppressed and A indicates active.

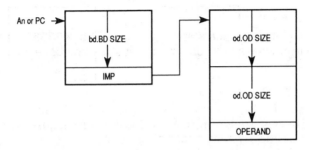

Figure 2-7. Memory Indirect with Postindex

2.5.2.3 Memory Indirect with Index Suppressed.
The Xn is suppressed. Figure 2-8 illustrates the memory indirect with index suppressed mode.

BR	Xn	bd	od	IMP Addressing Mode	Operand Addressing Mode
S	S	S	S	—	—
S	S	S	A	—	—
S	S	A	S	Absolute Addressing Mode	Memory Pointer Directly to Data Operand
S	S	A	A	Absolute Addressing Mode	Memory Pointer as Base with Displacement to Data Operand
An	S	S	S	Address Register Indirect	Memory Pointer Directly to Data Operand
An	S	S	A	Address Register Indirect	Memory Pointer as Base with Displacement to Data Operand
An	S	A	S	Address Register Indirect with Constant Index	Memory Pointer Directly to Data Operand
An	S	A	A	Address Register Indirect with Constant Index	Memory Pointer as Base with Displacement to Data Operand
PC	S	S	S	PC Relative	Memory Pointer Directly to Data Operand
PC	S	S	A	PC Relative	Memory Pointer as Base with Displacement to Data Operand
PC	S	A	S	PC Relative with Constant Index	Memory Pointer Directly to Data Operand
PC	S	A	A	PC Relative with Constant Index	Memory Pointer as Base with Displacement to Data Operand

NOTE: S indicates suppressed and A indicates active.

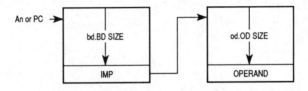

Figure 2-8. Memory Indirect with Index Suppress

2.6 OTHER DATA STRUCTURES

Stacks and queues are common data structures. The M68000 family implements a system stack and instructions that support user stacks and queues.

2.6.1 System Stack

Address register seven (A7) is the system stack pointer. Either the user stack pointer (USP), the interrupt stack pointer (ISP), or the master stack pointer (MSP) is active at any one time. Refer to **Section 1 Introduction** for details on these stack pointers. To keep data on the system stack aligned for maximum efficiency, the active stack pointer is automatically decremented or incremented by two for all byte-size operands moved to or from the stack. In long-word-organized memory, aligning the stack pointer on a long-word address significantly increases the efficiency of stacking exception frames, subroutine calls and returns, and other stacking operations.

The user can implement stacks with the address register indirect with postincrement and predecrement addressing modes. With an address register the user can implement a stack that fills either from high memory to low memory or from low memory to high memory. Important consideration are:

- Use the predecrement mode to decrement the register before using its contents as the pointer to the stack.

- Use the postincrement mode to increment the register after using its contents as the pointer to the stack.

- Maintain the stack pointer correctly when byte, word, and long-word items mix in these stacks.

To implement stack growth from high memory to low memory, use −(An) to push data on the stack and (An)+ to pull data from the stack. For this type of stack, after either a push or a pull operation, the address register points to the top item on the stack.

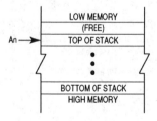

To implement stack growth from low memory to high memory, use (An)+ to push data on the stack and –(An) to pull data from the stack. After either a push or pull operation, the address register points to the next available space on the stack.

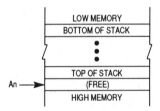

2.6.2 Queues

The user can implement queues, groups of information waiting to be processed, with the address register indirect with postincrement or predecrement addressing modes. Using a pair of address registers, the user implements a queue that fills either from high memory to low memory or from low memory to high memory. Two registers are used because the queues get pushed from one end and pulled from the other. One address register contains the put pointer; the other register the get pointer. To implement growth of the queue from low memory to high memory, use the put address register to put data into the queue and the get address register to get data from the queue.

After a put operation, the put address register points to the next available space in the queue; the unchanged get address register points to the next item to be removed from the queue. After a get operation, the get address register points to the next item to be removed from the queue; the unchanged put address register points to the next available space in the queue.

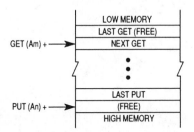

To implement the queue as a circular buffer, the relevant address register should be checked and adjusted. If necessary, do this before performing the put or get operation. Subtracting the buffer length (in bytes) from the register adjusts the address register. To implement growth of the queue from high memory to low memory, use the put address register indirect to put data into the queue and get address register indirect to get data from the queue.

After a put operation, the put address register points to the last item placed in the queue; the unchanged get address register points to the last item removed from the queue. After a get operation, the get address register points to the last item placed in the queue.

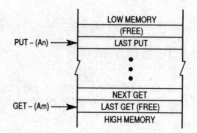

To implement the queue as a circular buffer, the get or put operation should be performed first. Then the relevant address register should be checked and adjusted, if necessary. Adding the buffer length (in bytes) to the address register contents adjusts the address register.

SECTION 3
INSTRUCTION SET SUMMARY

This section briefly describes the M68000 family instruction set, using Motorola's assembly language syntax and notation. It includes instruction set details such as notation and format, selected instruction examples, and an integer condition code discussion. The section concludes with a discussion of floating-point details such as computational accuracy, conditional test definitions, an explanation of the operation table, and a discussion of not-a-numbers (NANs) and postprocessing.

3.1 INSTRUCTION SUMMARY

Instructions form a set of tools that perform the following types of operations:

Data Movement	Program Control
Integer Arithmetic	System Control
Logical Operations	Cache Maintenance
Shift and Rotate Operations	Multiprocessor Communications
Bit Manipulation	Memory Management
Bit Field Manipulation	Floating-Point Arithmetic
Binary-Coded Decimal Arithmetic	

The following paragraphs describe in detail the instruction for each type of operation. Table 3-1 lists the notations used throughout this manual. In the operand syntax statements of the instruction definitions, the operand on the right is the destination operand.

Table 3-1. Notational Conventions

Single- And Double-Operand Operations	
+	Arithmetic addition or postincrement indicator.
−	Arithmetic subtraction or predecrement indicator.
×	Arithmetic multiplication.
÷	Arithmetic division or conjunction symbol.
~	Invert; operand is logically complemented.
Λ	Logical AND
V	Logical OR
⊕	Logical exclusive OR
♦	Source operand is moved to destination operand.
♦♦	Two operands are exchanged.
<op>	Any double-operand operation.
<operand>tested	Operand is compared to zero and the condition codes are set appropriately.
sign-extended	All bits of the upper portion are made equal to the high-order bit of the lower portion.
Other Operations	
TRAP	Equivalent to Format + Offset Word ♦ (SSP); SSP − 2 ♦ SSP; PC ♦ (SSP); SSP − 4 ♦ SSP; SR ♦ (SSP); SSP − 2 ♦ SSP; (Vector) ♦ PC
STOP	Enter the stopped state, waiting for interrupts.
<operand>10	The operand is BCD; operations are performed in decimal.
If <condition> then <operations> else <operations>	Test the condition. If true, the operations after "then" are performed. If the condition is false and the optional "else" clause is present, the operations after "else" are performed. If the condition is false and else is omitted, the instruction performs no operation. Refer to the Bcc instruction description as an example.
Register Specification	
An	Any Address Register n (example: A3 is address register 3)
Ax, Ay	Source and destination address registers, respectively.
Dc	Data register D7–D0, used during compare.
Dh, Dl	Data register's high- or low-order 32 bits of product.
Dn	Any Data Register n (example: D5 is data register 5)
Dr, Dq	Data register's remainder or quotient of divide.
Du	Data register D7–D0, used during update.
Dx, Dy	Source and destination data registers, respectively.
MRn	Any Memory Register n.
Rn	Any Address or Data Register
Rx, Ry	Any source and destination registers, respectively.
Xn	Index Register

Table 3-1. Notational Conventions (Continued)

Data Format And Type	
+ inf	Positive Infinity
<fmt>	Operand Data Format: Byte (B), Word (W), Long (L), Single (S), Double (D), Extended (X), or Packed (P).
B, W, L	Specifies a signed integer data type (twos complement) of byte, word, or long word.
D	Double-precision real data format (64 bits).
k	A twos complement signed integer (−64 to +17) specifying a number's format to be stored in the packed decimal format.
P	Packed BCD real data format (96 bits, 12 bytes).
S	Single-precision real data format (32 bits).
X	Extended-precision real data format (96 bits, 16 bits unused).
− inf	Negative Infinity
Subfields and Qualifiers	
#<xxx> or #<data>	Immediate data following the instruction word(s).
( )	Identifies an indirect address in a register.
[ ]	Identifies an indirect address in memory.
bd	Base Displacement
ccc	Index into the MC68881/MC68882 Constant ROM
d_n	Displacement Value, n Bits Wide (example: d_{16} is a 16-bit displacement).
LSB	Least Significant Bit
LSW	Least Significant Word
MSB	Most Significant Bit
MSW	Most Significant Word
od	Outer Displacement
SCALE	A scale factor (1, 2, 4, or 8 for no-word, word, long-word, or quad-word scaling, respectively).
SIZE	The index register's size (W for word, L for long word).
{offset:width}	Bit field selection.
Register Names	
CCR	Condition Code Register (lower byte of status register)
DFC	Destination Function Code Register
FPcr	Any Floating-Point System Control Register (FPCR, FPSR, or FPIAR)
FPm, FPn	Any Floating-Point Data Register specified as the source or destination, respectively.
IC, DC, IC/DC	Instruction, Data, or Both Caches
MMUSR	MMU Status Register
PC	Program Counter
Rc	Any Non Floating-Point Control Register
SFC	Source Function Code Register
SR	Status Register

3

Table 3-1. Notational Conventions (Concluded)

Register Codes	
*	General Case
C	Carry Bit in CCR
cc	Condition Codes from CCR
FC	Function Code
N	Negative Bit in CCR
U	Undefined, Reserved for Motorola Use.
V	Overflow Bit in CCR
X	Extend Bit in CCR
Z	Zero Bit in CCR
—	Not Affected or Applicable.
Stack Pointers	
ISP	Supervisor/Interrupt Stack Pointer
MSP	Supervisor/Master Stack Pointer
SP	Active Stack Pointer
SSP	Supervisor (Master or Interrupt) Stack Pointer
USP	User Stack Pointer
Miscellaneous	
<ea>	Effective Address
<label>	Assemble Program Label
<list>	List of registers, for example D3–D0.
LB	Lower Bound
m	Bit m of an Operand
m–n	Bits m through n of Operand
UB	Upper Bound

3.1.1 Data Movement Instructions

The MOVE and FMOVE instructions with their associated addressing modes are the basic means of transferring and storing addresses and data. MOVE instructions transfer byte, word, and long-word operands from memory to memory, memory to register, register to memory, and register to register. MOVE instructions transfer word and long-word operands and ensure that only valid address manipulations are executed. In addition to the general MOVE instructions, there are several special data movement instructions: MOVE16, MOVEM, MOVEP, MOVEQ, EXG, LEA, PEA, LINK, and UNLK. The MOVE16 instruction is an MC68040 extension to the M68000 instruction set.

The FMOVE instructions move operands into, out of, and between floating-point data registers. FMOVE also moves operands to and from the floating-point control register (FPCR), floating-point status register (FPSR), and floating-point instruction address register (FPIAR). For operands moved into a floating-point data register, FSMOVE and FDMOVE explicitly select single- and double-precision rounding of the result, respectively. FMOVEM moves any combination of either floating-point data registers or floating-point control registers. Table 3-2 lists the general format of these integer and floating-point data movement instructions.

Table 3-2. Data Movement Operation Format

Instruction	Operand Syntax	Operand Size	Operation
EXG	Rn, Rn	32	Rn ◆◆ Rn
FMOVE	FPm,FPn	X	Source ◆ Destination
	<ea>,FPn	B, W, L, S, D, X, P	
	FPm,<ea>	B, W, L, S, D, X, P	
	<ea>,FPcr	32	
	FPcr,<ea>	32	
FSMOVE, FDMOVE	FPm,FPn	X	Source ◆ Destination; round destination to single or double precision.
	<ea>,FPn	B, W, L, S, D, X	
FMOVEM	<ea>,<list>[1]	32, X	Listed Registers ◆ Destination
	<ea>,Dn	X	
	<list>[1],<ea>	32, X	Source ◆ Listed Registers
	Dn,<ea>	X	
LEA	<ea>,An	32	<ea> ◆ An
LINK	An,#<d>	16, 32	SP − 4 ◆ SP; An ◆ (SP); SP ◆ An, SP + D ◆ SP
MOVE	<ea>,<ea>	8, 16, 32	Source ◆ Destination
MOVE16	<ea>,<ea>	16 bytes	Aligned 16-Byte Block ◆ Destination
MOVEA	<ea>,An	16, 32 ◆ 32	
MOVEM	list,<ea>	16, 32	Listed Registers ◆ Destination
	<ea>,list	16, 32 ◆ 32	Source ◆ Listed Registers
MOVEP	Dn, (d_{16},An)	16, 32	Dn 31–24 ◆ (An + d_n); Dn 23–16 ◆ (An + d_n + 2); Dn 15–8 ◆ (An + d_n + 4); Dn 7–0 ◆ (An + d_n + 6)
	(d_{16},An),Dn		(An + d_n) ◆ Dn 31–24; (An + d_n + 2) ◆ Dn 23–16; (An + d_n + 4) ◆ Dn 15–8; (An + d_n + 6) ◆ Dn 7–0
MOVEQ	#<data>,Dn	8 ◆ 32	Immediate Data ◆ Destination
PEA	<ea>	32	SP − 4 ◆ SP; <ea> ◆ (SP)
UNLK	An	32	An ◆ SP; (SP) ◆ An; SP + 4 ◆ SP

NOTE1: A register list includes any combination of the eight floating-point data registers or any combination of three control registers (FPCR, FPSR, and FPIAR). If a register list mask resides in a data register, only floating-point data registers may be specified.

3.1.2 Integer Arithmetic Instructions

The integer arithmetic operations include four basic operations: ADD, SUB, MUL, and DIV. They also include CMP, CMPM, CMP2, CLR, and NEG. The instruction set includes ADD, CMP, and SUB instructions for both address and data operations with all operand sizes valid for data operations. Address operands consist of 16 or 32 bits. The CLR and NEG instructions apply to all sizes of data operands. Signed and unsigned MUL and DIV instructions include:

- Word multiply to produce a long-word product.
- Long-word multiply to produce a long-word or quad-word product.
- Long word divided by a word divisor (word quotient and word remainder).
- Long word or quad word divided by a long-word divisor (long-word quotient and long-word remainder).

A set of extended instructions provides multiprecision and mixed-size arithmetic: ADDX, SUBX, EXT, and NEGX. Refer to Table 3-3 for a summary of the integer arithmetic operations. In Table 3-3, X refers to the X-bit in the CCR.

Table 3-3. Integer Arithmetic Operation Format

Instruction	Operand Syntax	Operand Size	Operation
ADD	Dn,<ea>	8, 16, 32	Source + Destination ♦ Destination
	<ea>,Dn	8, 16, 32	
ADDA	<ea>,An	16, 32	
ADDI	#<data>,<ea>	8, 16, 32	Immediate Data + Destination ♦ Destination
ADDQ	#<data>,<ea>	8, 16, 32	
ADDX	Dn,Dn	8, 16, 32	Source + Destination + X ♦ Destination
	–(An), –(An)	8, 16, 32	
CLR	<ea>	8, 16, 32	0 ♦ Destination
CMP	<ea>,Dn	8, 16, 32	Destination – Source
CMPA	<ea>,An	16, 32	
CMPI	#<data>,<ea>	8, 16, 32	Destination – Immediate Data
CMPM	(An)+,(An)+	8, 16, 32	Destination – Source
CMP2	<ea>,Rn	8, 16, 32	Lower Bound ≤ Rn ≤ Upper Bound
DIVS/DIVU	<ea>,Dn	32 ÷ 16 ♦ 16,16	Destination ÷ Source ♦ Destination
	<ea>,Dr–Dq	64 ÷ 32 ♦ 32,32	(Signed or Unsigned Quotient, Remainder)
	<ea>,Dq	32 ÷ 32 ♦ 32	
DIVSL/DIVUL	<ea>,Dr–Dq	32 ÷ 32 ♦ 32,32	
EXT	Dn	8 ♦ 16	Sign-Extended Destination ♦ Destination
	Dn	16 ♦ 32	
EXTB	Dn	8 ♦ 32	
MULS/MULU	<ea>,Dn	16 x 16 ♦ 32	Source x Destination ♦ Destination
	<ea>,Dl	32 x 32 ♦ 32	(Signed or Unsigned)
	<ea>,Dh–Dl	32 x 32 ♦ 64	
NEG	<ea>	8, 16, 32	0 – Destination ♦ Destination
NEGX	<ea>	8, 16, 32	0 – Destination – X ♦ Destination
SUB	<ea>,Dn	8, 16, 32	Destination = Source ♦ Destination
	Dn,<ea>	8, 16, 32	
SUBA	<ea>,An	16, 32	
SUBI	#<data>,<ea>	8, 16, 32	Destination – Immediate Data ♦ Destination
SUBQ	#<data>,<ea>	8, 16, 32	
SUBX	Dn,Dn	8, 16, 32	Destination – Source – X ♦ Destination
	–(An), –(An)	8, 16, 32	

3

3.1.3 Logical Instructions

The logical operation instructions (AND, OR, EOR, and NOT) perform logical operations with all sizes of integer data operands. A similar set of immediate instructions (ANDI, ORI, and EORI) provides these logical operations with all sizes of immediate data. Table 3-4 summarizes the logical operations.

Table 3-4. Logical Operation Format

Instruction	Operand Syntax	Operand Size	Operation
AND	<ea>,Dn Dn,<ea>	8, 16, 32 8, 16, 32	Source $\wedge$ Destination $\rightarrow$ Destination
ANDI	#<data>,<ea>	8, 16, 32	Immediate Data $\wedge$ Destination $\rightarrow$ Destination
EOR	Dn,<ea>	8, 16, 32	Source $\oplus$ Destination $\rightarrow$ Destination
EORI	#<data>,<ea>	8, 16, 32	Immediate Data $\oplus$ Destination $\rightarrow$ Destination
NOT	<ea>	8, 16, 32	~ Destination $\rightarrow$ Destination
OR	<ea>,Dn Dn,<ea>	8, 16, 32	Source $\vee$ Destination $\rightarrow$ Destination
ORI	#<data>,<ea>	8, 16, 32	Immediate Data $\vee$ Destination $\rightarrow$ Destination

3.1.4 Shift and Rotate Instructions

The ASR, ASL, LSR, and LSL instructions provide shift operations in both directions. The ROR, ROL, ROXR, and ROXL instructions perform rotate (circular shift) operations, with and without the CCR extend bit (X-bit). All shift and rotate operations can be performed on either registers or memory.

Register shift and rotate operations shift all operand sizes. The shift count can be specified in the instruction operation word (to shift from 1–8 places) or in a register (modulo 64 shift count).

Memory shift and rotate operations shift word operands one bit position only. The SWAP instruction exchanges the 16-bit halves of a register. Fast byte swapping is possible by using the ROR and ROL instructions with a shift count of eight, enhancing the performance of the shift/rotate instructions. Table 3-5 is a summary of the shift and rotate operations. In Table 3-5, C and X refer to the C-bit and X-bit in the CCR.

Table 3-5. Shift and Rotate Operation Format

Instruction	Operand Syntax	Operand Size	Operation
ASL	Dn,Dn #<data>,Dn <ea>	8, 16, 32 8, 16, 32 16	
ASR	Dn,Dn #<data>,Dn <ea>	8, 16, 32 8, 16, 32 16	
LSL	Dn,Dn #<data>,Dn <ea>	8, 16, 32 8, 16, 32 16	
LSR	Dn,Dn #<data>,Dn <ea>	8, 16, 32 8, 16, 32 16	
ROL	Dn,Dn #<data>,Dn <ea>	8, 16, 32 8, 16, 32 16	
ROR	Dn,Dn #<data>,Dn <ea>	8, 16, 32 8, 16, 32 16	
ROXL	Dn,Dn #<data>,Dn <ea>	8, 16, 32 8, 16, 32 16	
ROXR	Dn,Dn #<data>,Dn <ea>	8, 16, 32 8, 16, 32 16	
SWAP	Dn	32	

NOTE: X indicates the extend bit and C the carry bit in the CCR.

3.1.5 Bit Manipulation Instructions

BTST, BSET, BCLR, and BCHG are bit manipulation instructions. All bit manipulation operations can be performed on either registers or memory. The bit number is specified either as immediate data or in the contents of a data register. Register operands are 32 bits long, and memory operands are 8 bits long. Table 3-6 summarizes bit manipulation operations; Z refers to the zero bit of the CCR.

Table 3-6. Bit Manipulation Operation Format

Instruction	Operand Syntax	Operand Size	Operation
BCHG	Dn,<ea> #<data>,<ea>	8, 32 8, 32	~ (<Bit Number> of Destination) ♦ Z ♦ Bit of Destination
BCLR	Dn,<ea> #<data>,<ea>	8, 32 8, 32	~ (<Bit Number> of Destination) ♦ Z; 0 ♦ Bit of Destination
BSET	Dn,<ea> #<data>,<ea>	8, 32 8, 32	~ (<Bit Number> of Destination) ♦ Z; 1 ♦ Bit of Destination
BTST	Dn,<ea> #<data>,<ea>	8, 32 8, 32	~ (<Bit Number> of Destination) ♦ Z

3.1.6 Bit Field Instructions

The M68000 family architecture supports variable-length bit field operations on fields of up to 32 bits. The BFINS instruction inserts a value into a bit field. BFEXTU and BFEXTS extract a value from the field. BFFFO finds the first set bit in a bit field. Also included are instructions analogous to the bit manipulation operations: BFTST, BFSET, BFCLR, and BFCHG. Table 3-7 summarizes bit field operations.

Table 3-7. Bit Field Operation Format

Instruction	Operand Syntax	Operand Size	Operation
BFCHG	<ea> {offset:width}	1–32	~ Field ♦ Field
BFCLR	<ea> {offset:width}	1–32	0's ♦ Field
BFEXTS	<ea> {offset:width}, Dn	1–32	Field ♦ Dn; Sign-Extended
BFEXTU	<ea> {offset:width}, Dn	1–32	Field ♦ Dn; Zero-Extended
BFFFO	<ea> {offset:width}, Dn	1–32	Scan for First Bit Set in Field; Offset ♦ Dn.
BFINS	Dn,<ea> {offset:width}	1–32	Dn ♦ Field
BFSET	<ea> {offset:width}	1–32	1's ♦ Field
BFTST	<ea> {offset:width}	1–32	Field MSB ♦ N; ~ (OR of All Bits in Field) ♦ Z

NOTE: All bit field instructions set the CCR N and Z bits as shown for BFTST before performing the specified operation.

3.1.7 Binary-Coded Decimal Instructions

Five instructions support operations on binary-coded decimal (BCD) numbers. The arithmetic operations on packed BCD numbers are ABCD, SBCD, and NBCD. PACK and UNPK instructions aid in the conversion of byte-encoded numeric data, such as ASCII or EBCDIC strings to BCD data and vice versa. Table 3-8 summarizes BCD operations. In Table 3-8 X refers to the X-bit in the CCR.

Table 3-8. Binary-Coded Decimal Operation Format

Instruction	Operand Syntax	Operand Size	Operation
ABCD	Dn,Dn −(An), −(An)	8 8	$Source_{10}$ + $Destination_{10}$ + X $\bullet$ Destination
NBCD	<ea>	8	$0 - Destination_{10} - X \bullet$ Destination
PACK	−(An), −(An) #<data> Dn,Dn,#<data>	16 $\bullet$ 8 16 $\bullet$ 8	Unpackaged Source + Immediate Data $\bullet$ Packed Destination
SBCD	Dn,Dn −(An), −(An)	8 8	$Destination_{10} - Source_{10} - X \bullet$ Destination
UNPK	−(An),−(An) #<data> Dn,Dn,#<data>	8 $\bullet$ 16 8 $\bullet$ 16	Packed Source $\bullet$ Unpacked Source Unpacked Source + Immediate Data $\bullet$ Unpacked Destination

3.1.8 Program Control Instructions

A set of subroutine call and return instructions and conditional and unconditional branch instructions perform program control operations. Also included are test operand instructions (TST and FTST), which set the integer or floating-point condition codes for use by other program and system control instructions. NOP forces synchronization of the internal pipelines. Table 3-9 summarizes these instructions.

Table 3-9. Program Control Operation Format

Instruction	Operand Syntax	Operand Size	Operation
Integer and Floating-Point Conditional			
Bcc, FBcc	<label>	8, 16, 32	If Condition True, Then PC + d_n ♦ PC
DBcc, FDBcc	Dn,<label>	16	If Condition False, Then Dn − 1 ♦ Dn If Dn ≠ −1, Then PC + d_n ♦ PC
Scc, FScc	<ea>	8	If Condition True, Then 1's ♦ Destination; Else 0's ♦ Destination
Unconditional			
BRA	<label>	8, 16, 32	PC + d_n ♦ PC
BSR	<label>	8, 16, 32	SP − 4 ♦ SP; PC ♦ (SP); PC + d_n ♦ PC
JMP	<ea>	none	Destination ♦ PC
JSR	<ea>	none	SP − 4 ♦ SP; PC ♦ (SP); Destination ♦ PC
NOP	none	none	PC + 2 ♦ PC (Integer Pipeline Synchronized)
FNOP	none	none	PC + 4 ♦ PC (FPU Pipeline Synchronized)
Returns			
RTD	#<data>	16	(SP) ♦ PC; SP + 4 + d_n ♦ SP
RTR	none	none	(SP) ♦ CCR; SP + 2 ♦ SP; (SP) ♦PC; SP + 4 ♦ SP
RTS	none	none	(SP) ♦ PC; SP + 4 ♦ SP
Test Operand			
TST	<ea>	8, 16, 32	Set Integer Condition Codes
FTST	<ea> FPn	B, W, L, S, D, X, P X	Set Floating-Point Condition Codes

Letters cc in the integer instruction mnemonics Bcc, DBcc, and Scc specify testing one of the following conditions:

CC—Carry clear	GE—Greater than or equal
LS—Lower or same	PL—Plus
CS—Carry set	GT—Greater than
LT—Less than	T—Always true*
EQ—Equal	HI—Higher
MI—Minus	VC—Overflow clear
F—Never true*	LE—Less than or equal
NE—Not equal	VS—Overflow set

*Not applicable to the Bcc instructions.

3.1.9 System Control Instructions

Privileged and trapping instructions as well as instructions that use or modify the CCR provide system control operations. FSAVE and FRESTORE save and restore the nonuser visible portion of the FPU during context switches in a virtual memory or multitasking system. The conditional trap instructions, which use the same conditional tests as their corresponding program control instructions, allow an optional 16- or 32-bit immediate operand to be included as part of the instruction for passing parameters to the operating system. These instructions cause the processor to flush the instruction pipe. Table 3-10 summarizes these instructions. See **3.2 Integer Unit Condition Code Computation** for more details on condition codes.

Table 3-10. System Control Operation Format

Instruction	Operand Syntax	Operand Size	Operation
Privileged			
ANDI to SR	#<data>,SR	16	Immediate Data ∧ SR ⬦ SR
EORI to SR	#<data>,SR	16	Immediate Data ⊕ SR ⬦ SR
FRESTORE	<ea>	none	State Frame ⬦ Internal Floating-Point Registers
FSAVE	<ea>	none	Internal Floating-Point Registers ⬦ State Frame
MOVE to SR	<ea>,SR	16	Source ⬦ SR
MOVE from SR	SR,<ea>	16	SR ⬦ Destination
MOVE USP	USP,An	32	USP ⬦ An
	An,USP	32	An ⬦ USP
MOVEC	Rc,Rn	32	Rc ⬦ Rn
	Rn,Rc	32	Rn ⬦ Rc
MOVES	Rn,<ea>	8, 16, 32	Rn ⬦ Destination Using DFC
	<ea>,Rn		Source Using SFC ⬦ Rn
ORI to SR	#<data>,SR	16	Immediate Data ∨ SR ⬦ SR
RESET	none	none	Assert Reset Output
RTE	none	none	(SP) ⬦ SR; SP + 2 ⬦ SP; (SP) ⬦PC; SP + 4 ⬦ SP; Restore Stack According to Format
STOP	#<data>	16	Immediate Data ⬦ SR; STOP
Trap Generating			
BKPT	#<data>	none	Run Breakpoint Cycle
CHK	<ea>,Dn	16, 32	If Dn < 0 or Dn > (<ea>), Then CHK Exception
CHK2	<ea>,Rn	8, 16, 32	If Rn< Lower Bound or Rn > Upper Bound, Then CHK Exception
ILLEGAL	none	none	SSP − 2 ⬦ SSP; Vector Offset ⬦ (SSP); SSP − 4 ⬦ SSP; PC ⬦ (SSP); SSP − 2 ⬦ SSP; SR ⬦ (SSP); Illegal Instruction Vector Address ⬦ PC
TRAP	#<data>	none	SSP − 2 ⬦ SSP; Format and Vector Offset ⬦ (SSP) SSP − 4 ⬦ SSP; PC ⬦ (SSP); SSP − 2 ⬦ SSP; SR ⬦ (SSP); Vector Address ⬦ PC
TRAPcc	none	none	If cc True, Then Trap Exception
	#<data>	16, 32	
FTRAPcc	none	none	If Floating-Point cc True, Then Trap Exception
	#<data>	16, 32	
TRAPV	none	none	If V, Then Take Overflow Trap Exception
Condition Code Register			
ANDI to SR	#<data>,CCR	8	Immediate Data ∧ CCR ⬦ CCR
EORI to SR	#<data>,CCR	8	Immediate Data ⊕ CCR ⬦ CCR
MOVE to SR	<ea>,CCR	16	Source ⬦ CCR
MOVE from SR	CCR,<ea>	16	CCR ⬦ Destination
ORI to SR	#<data>,CCR	8	Immediate Data ∨ CCR ⬦ CCR

Letters cc in the TRAPcc and FTRAPcc specify testing for a condition.

3.1.10 Cache Control Instructions (MC68040)

The cache instructions provide maintenance functions for managing the instruction and data caches. CINV invalidates cache entries in both caches, and CPUSH pushes dirty data from the data cache to update memory. Both instructions can operate on either or both caches and can select a single cache line, all lines in a page, or the entire cache. Table 3-11 summarizes these instructions.

Table 3-11. Cache Control Operation Format

Instruction	Operand Syntax	Operand Size	Operation
CINVL	caches,(An)	none	Invalidate cache line
CINVP	caches, (An)	none	Invalidate cache page
CINVA	caches	none	Invalidate entire cache
CPUSHL CPUSHP CPUSHA	caches,(An) caches, (An) caches	none none none	Push selected dirty data cache lines, then invalidate selected cache lines

3.1.11 Multiprocessor Instructions

The TAS, CAS, and CAS2 instructions coordinate the operations of processors in multiprocessing systems. These instructions use read-modify-write bus cycles to ensure uninterrupted updating of memory. Coprocessor instructions control the coprocessor operations. Table 3-12 summarizes these instructions.

Table 3-12. Multiprocessor Operations

Instruction	Operand Syntax	Operand Size	Operation
Read-Write-Modify			
CAS	Dc,Du,<ea>	8, 16, 32	Destination − Dc $\blacklozenge$ CC If Z, Then Du $\blacklozenge$ Destination Else Destination $\blacklozenge$ Dc
CAS2	Dc1–Dc2, Du1–Du2, (Rn)–(Rn)	16, 32	Dual Operand CAS
TAS	<ea>	8	Destination − 0; Set Condition Codes; 1 $\blacklozenge$ Destination [7]
Coprocessor			
cpBcc	<label>	16, 32	If cpcc True, Then PC + d_n $\blacklozenge$ PC
cpDBcc	<label>,Dn	16	If cpcc False, Then Dn − 1 $\blacklozenge$ Dn If Dn ≠ −1, Then PC + d_n $\blacklozenge$ PC
cpGEN	User Defined	User Defined	Operand $\blacklozenge$ Coprocessor
cpRESTORE	<ea>	none	Restore Coprocessor State from <ea>
cpSAVE	<ea>	none	Save Coprocessor State at <ea>
cpScc	<ea>	8	If cpcc True, Then 1's $\blacklozenge$ Destination; Else 0's $\blacklozenge$ Destination
cpTRAPcc	none #<data>	none 16, 32	If cpcc True, Then TRAPcc Exception

3.1.12 Memory Management Unit (MMU) Instructions

The PFLUSH instructions flush the address translation caches (ATCs) and can optionally select only nonglobal entries for flushing. PTEST performs a search of the address translation tables, stores the results in the MMU status register, and loads the entry into the ATC. Table 3-13 summarizes these instructions.

Table 3-13. MMU Operation Format

Instruction	Processor	Operand Syntax	Operand Size	Operation
PBcc	MC68851	<label>	none	Branch on PMMU Condition
PDBcc	MC68851	Dn,<label>	none	Test, Decrement, and Branch
PFLUSHA	MC68030 MC68040 MC68851	none	none	Invalidate All ATC Entries
PFLUSH	MC68040	(An)	none	Invalidate ATC Entries at Effective Address
PFLUSHN	MC68040	(An)	none	Invalidate Nonglobal ATC Entries at Effective Address
PFLUSHAN	MC68040	none	none	Invalidate All Nonglobal ATC Entries
PFLUSHS	MC68851	none	none	Invalidate All Shared/Global ATC Entries
PFLUSHR	MC68851	<ea>	none	Invalidate ATC and RPT Entries
PLOAD	MC68030 MC68851	FC,<ea>	none	Load an Entry into the ATC
PMOVE	MC68030 MC68851	MRn,<ea> <ea>,MRn	8,16,32,64	Move to/from MMU Registers
PRESTORE	MC68851	<ea>	none	PMMU Restore Function
PSAVE	MC68851	<ea>	none	PMMU Save Function
PScc	MC68851	<ea>	8	Set on PMMU Condition
PTEST	MC68030 MC68040 MC68851	(An)	none	Information About Logical Address ♦ MMU Status Register
PTRAPcc	MC68851	#<data>	16,32	Trap on PMMU Condition

3.1.13 Floating-Point Arithmetic Instructions

The following paragraphs describe the floating-point instructions, organized into two categories of operation: dyadic (requiring two operands) and monadic (requiring one operand).

The dyadic floating-point instructions provide several arithmetic functions that require two input operands, such as add and subtract. For these operations, the first operand can be located in memory, an integer data register, or a floating-point data register. The second operand is always located in a floating-point data register. The results of the operation store in the register specified as the second operand. All FPU operations support all data formats. Results are rounded to either extended-, single-, or double-precision format. Table 3-14 gives the general format of dyadic instructions, and Table 3-15 lists the available operations.

Table 3-14. Dyadic Floating-Point Operation Format

Instruction	Operand Syntax	Operand Format	Operation
F<dop>	<ea>,FPn FPm,FPn	B, W, L, S, D, X, P X	FPn <Function> Source ♦ FPn

NOTE: <dop> is any one of the dyadic operation specifiers.

Table 3-15. Dyadic Floating-Point Operations

Instruction	Operation
FADD, FSADD, FDADD	Add
FCMP	Compare
FDIV, FSDIV, FDDIV	Divide
FMOD	Modulo Remainder
FMUL, FSMUL, FDMUL	Multiply
FREM	IEEE Remainder
FSCALE	Scale Exponent
FSUB, FSSUB, FDSUB	Subtract
FSGLDIV, FSGLMUL	Single-Precision Divide, Multiply

The monadic floating-point instructions provide several arithmetic functions requiring only one input operand. Unlike the integer counterparts to these functions (e.g., NEG <ea>), a source and a destination can be specified. The operation is performed on the source operand and the result is stored in the destination, which is always a floating-point data register. When the source is not a floating-point data register, all data formats are supported. The data format is always extended precision for register-to-register operations. Table 3-16 lists the general format of these instructions, and Table 3-17 lists the available operations.

Table 3-16. Monadic Floating-Point Operation Format

Instruction	Operand Syntax	Operand Format	Operation
F<mop>	<ea>,FPn FPm,FPn FPn	B, W, L, S, D, X, P X X	Source ♦ Function ♦ FPn FPn ♦ Function ♦ FPn

NOTE: <mop> is any one of the monadic operation specifiers.

Table 3-17. Monadic Floating-Point Operations

Instruction	Operation	Instruction	Operation
FABS	Absolute Value	FLOGN	ln(x)
FACOS	Arc Cosine	FLOGNP1	ln(x + 1)
FASIN	Arc Sine	FLOG10	$Log_{10}(x)$
FATAN	Hyperbolic Art Tangent	FLOG2	$Log_2(x)$
FCOS	Cosine	FNEG	Negate
FCOSH	Hyperbolic Cosine	FSIN	Sine
FETOX	e^x	FSINH	Hyperbolic Sine
FETOXM1	$e^x - 1$	FSQRT	Square Root
FGETEXP	Extract Exponent	FTAN	Tangent
FGETMAN	Extract Mantissa	FTANH	Hyperbolic Tangent
FINT	Extract Integer Part	FTENTOX	10^x
FINTRZ	Extract Integer Part, Rounded-to-Zero	FTWOTOX	2^x

3.2 INTEGER UNIT CONDITION CODE COMPUTATION

Many integer instructions affect the CCR to indicate the instruction's results. Program and system control instructions also use certain combinations of these bits to control program and system flow. The condition codes meet consistency criteria across instructions, uses, and instances. They also meet the criteria of meaningful results, where no change occurs unless it provides useful information. Refer to **Section 1 Introduction** for details concerning the CCR.

Table 3-18 lists the integer condition code computations for instructions and Table 3-19 lists the condition names, encodings, and tests for the conditional branch and set instructions. The test associated with each condition is a logical formula using the current states of the condition codes. If this formula evaluates to one, the condition is true. If the formula evaluates to zero, the condition is false. For example, the T condition is always true, and the EQ condition is true only if the Z-bit condition code is currently true.

Table 3-18. Integer Unit Condition Code Computations

Operations	X	N	Z	V	C	Special Definition
ABCD	*	U	?	U	?	C = Decimal Carry $Z = Z \wedge \overline{Rm} \wedge \ldots \wedge \overline{R0}$
ADD, ADDI, ADDQ	*	*	*	?	?	$V = Sm \wedge Dm \wedge \overline{Rm} \vee \overline{Sm} \wedge \overline{Dm} \wedge Rm$ $C = Sm \wedge Dm \vee \overline{Rm} \wedge Dm \vee Sm \wedge \overline{Rm}$
ADDX	*	*	?	?	?	$V = Sm \wedge Dm \wedge \overline{Rm} \vee \overline{Sm} \wedge \overline{Dm} \wedge Rm$ $C = Sm \wedge Dm \vee \overline{Rm} \wedge Dm \vee Sm \wedge \overline{Rm}$ $Z = Z \wedge \overline{Rm} \wedge \ldots \wedge \overline{R0}$
AND, ANDI, EOR, EORI, MOVEQ, MOVE, OR, ORI, CLR, EXT, EXTB, NOT, TAS, TST	—	*	*	0	0	
CHK	—	*	U	U	U	
CHK2, CMP2	—	U	?	U	?	$Z = (R = LB) \vee (R = UB)$ $C = (LB \le UB) \wedge (IR < LB) \vee (R > UB))$ $V = (UB < LB) \wedge (R > UB) \wedge (R < LB)$
SUB, SUBI, SUBQ	*	*	*	?	?	$V = \overline{Sm} \wedge Dm \wedge \overline{Rm} \vee Sm \wedge \overline{Dm} \wedge Rm$ $C = Sm \wedge \overline{Dm} \vee Rm \wedge \overline{Dm} \vee Sm \wedge Rm$
SUBX	*	*	?	?	?	$V = \overline{Sm} \wedge Dm \wedge \overline{Rm} \vee Sm \wedge \overline{Dm} \wedge Rm$ $C = Sm \wedge \overline{Dm} \vee Rm \wedge \overline{Dm} \vee Sm \wedge Rm$ $Z = Z \wedge \overline{Rm} \wedge \ldots \wedge \overline{R0}$
CAS, CAS2, CMP, CMPA, CMPI, CMPM	—	*	*	?	?	$V = \overline{Sm} \wedge Dm \wedge \overline{Rm} \vee Sm \wedge \overline{Dm} \wedge Rm$ $C = Sm \wedge \overline{Dm} \vee Rm \wedge \overline{Dm} \vee Sm \wedge Rm$
DIVS, DUVU	—	*	*	?	0	V = Division Overflow
MULS, MULU	—	*	*	?	0	V = Multiplication Overflow
SBCD, NBCD	*	U	?	U	?	C = Decimal Borrow $Z = Z \wedge \overline{Rm} \wedge \ldots \wedge \overline{R0}$
NEG	*	*	*	?	?	$V = Dm \wedge Rm$ $C = Dm \vee Rm$
NEGX	*	*	?	?	?	$V = Dm \wedge Rm$ $C = Dm \vee Rm$ $Z = Z \wedge \overline{Rm} \wedge \ldots \wedge \overline{R0}$
BTST, BCHG, BSET, BCLR	—	—	?	—	—	$Z = \overline{Dn}$
BFTST, BFCHG, BFSET, BFCLR	—	?	?	0	0	$N = Dm$ $Z = \overline{Dn} \wedge \overline{Dm-1} \wedge \ldots \wedge \overline{D0}$
BFEXTS, BFEXTU, BFFFO	—	?	?	0	0	$N = Sm$ $Z = Sm \wedge \overline{Sm-1} \wedge \ldots \wedge \overline{S0}$
BFINS	—	?	?	0	0	$N = Dm$ $Z = \overline{Dm} \wedge \overline{Dm-1} \wedge \ldots \wedge \overline{D0}$
ASL	*	*	*	?	?	$V = Dm \wedge \overline{Dm-1} \vee \ldots \vee \overline{Dm-r} \vee \overline{Dm} \wedge$ $(DM-1 \vee \ldots + Dm-r)$ $C = \overline{Dm-r+1}$
ASL (r = 0)	—	*	*	0	0	
LSL, ROXL	*	*	*	0	?	$C = Dm - r + 1$

Table 3-18. Integer Unit Condition Code Computations (Continued)

Operations	X	N	Z	V	C	Special Definition
LSR (r = 0)	—	*	*	0	0	
ROXL (r = 0)	—	*	*	0	?	X = C
ROL	—	*	*	0	?	C = Dm − r + 1
ROL (r = 0)	—	*	*	0	0	
ASR, LSR, ROXR	*	*	*	0	?	C = Dr − 1
ASR, LSR (r = 0)	—	*	*	0	0	
ROXR (r = 0)	—	*	*	0	?	X = C
ROR	—	*	*	0	?	C = Dr − 1
ROR (r = 0)	—	*	*	0	0	

? = Other—See Special Definition
N = Result Operand (MSB)
Z = $\overline{Rm} \wedge ... \wedge \overline{R0}$
Sm = Source Operand (MSB)
Dm = Destination Operand (MSB)

Rm = Result Operand (MSB)
$\overline{Rm}$ = Not Result Operand (MSB)
R = Register Tested
r = Shift Count

Table 3-19. Conditional Tests

Mnemonic	Condition	Encoding	Test
T*	True	0000	1
F*	False	0001	0
HI	High	0010	$\overline{C} \wedge \overline{Z}$
LS	Low or Same	0011	$C \vee Z$
CC(HI)	Carry Clear	0100	$\overline{C}$
CS(LO)	Carry Set	0101	C
NE	Not Equal	0110	$\overline{Z}$
EQ	Equal	0111	Z
VC	Overflow Clear	1000	$\overline{V}$
VS	Overflow Set	1001	V
PL	Plus	1010	$\overline{N}$
MI	Minus	1011	N
GE	Greater or Equal	1100	$N \wedge V \vee \overline{N} \wedge \overline{V}$
LT	Less Than	1101	$N \wedge \overline{V} \vee \overline{N} \wedge V$
GT	Greater Than	1110	$N \wedge V \wedge \overline{Z} \vee \overline{N} \wedge \overline{V} \wedge \overline{Z}$
LE	Less or Equal	1111	$Z \vee N \wedge \overline{V} \vee \overline{N} \wedge V$

NOTES:

$\overline{N}$ = Logical Not N
$\overline{V}$ = Logical Not V
$\overline{Z}$ = Logical Not Z
*Not available for the Bcc instruction.

3.3 INSTRUCTION EXAMPLES

The following paragraphs provide examples of how to use selected instructions.

3.3.1 Using the CAS and CAS2 Instructions

The CAS instruction compares the value in a memory location with the value in a data register, and copies a second data register into the memory location if the compared values are equal. This provides a means of updating system counters, history information, and globally shared pointers. The instruction uses an indivisible read-modify-write cycle. After CAS reads the memory location, no other instruction can change that location before CAS has written the new value. This provides security in single-processor systems, in multitasking environments, and in multiprocessor environments. In a single-processor system, the operation is protected from instructions of an interrupt routine. In a multitasking environment, no other task can interfere with writing the new value of a system variable. In a multiprocessor environment, the other processors must wait until the CAS instruction completes before accessing a global pointer.

3.3.2 Using the MOVES Instruction

This instruction moves the byte, word, or long-word operand from the specified general register to a location within the address space specified by the destination function code (DFC) register. It also moves the byte, word, or long-word operand from a location within the address space specified by the source function code (SFC) register to the specified general register.

3.3.3 Nested Subroutine Calls

The LINK instruction pushes an address onto the stack, saves the stack address at which the address is stored, and reserves an area of the stack. Using this instruction in a series of subroutine calls results in a linked list of stack frames.

The UNLK instruction removes a stack frame from the end of the list by loading an address into the stack pointer and pulling the value at that address from the stack. When the operand of the instruction is the address of the link address at the bottom of a stack frame, the effect is to remove the stack frame from the stack and from the linked list.

3.3.4 Bit Field Instructions

One of the data types provided by the MC68030 is the bit field, consisting of as many as 32 consecutive bits. An offset from an effective address and a width value defines a bit field. The offset is a value in the range of -2^{31} through $2^{31} - 1$ from the most significant bit (bit 7) at the effective address. The width is a positive number, 1 through 32. The most significant bit of a bit field is bit 0. The bits number in a direction opposite to the bits of an integer.

The instruction set includes eight instructions that have bit field operands. The insert bit field (BFINS) instruction inserts a bit field stored in a register into a bit field. The extract bit field signed (BFEXTS) instruction loads a bit field into the least significant bits of a register and extends the sign to the left, filling the register. The extract bit field unsigned (BFEXTU) also loads a bit field, but zero fills the unused portion of the destination register.

The set bit field (BFSET) instruction sets all the bits of a field to ones. The clear bit field (BFCLR) instruction clears a field. The change bit field (BFCHG) instruction complements all the bits in a bit field. These three instructions all test the previous value of the bit field, setting the condition codes accordingly. The test bit field (BFTST) instruction tests the value in the field, setting the condition codes appropriately without altering the bit field. The find first one in bit field (BFFFO) instruction scans a bit field from bit 0 to the right until it finds a bit set to one and loads the bit offset of the first set bit into the specified data register. If no bits in the field are set, the field offset and the field width is loaded into the register.

An important application of bit field instructions is the manipulation of the exponent field in a floating-point number. In the IEEE standard format, the most significant bit is the sign bit of the mantissa. The exponent value begins at the next most significant bit position; the exponent field does not begin on a byte boundary. The extract bit field (BFEXTU) instruction and the BFTST instruction are the most useful for this application, but other bit field instructions can also be used.

Programming of input and output operations to peripherals requires testing, setting, and inserting of bit fields in the control registers of the peripherals. This is another application for bit field instructions. However, control register locations are not memory locations; therefore, it is not always possible to insert or extract bit fields of a register without affecting other fields within the register.

Another widely used application for bit field instructions is bit-mapped graphics. Because byte boundaries are ignored in these areas of memory, the field definitions used with bit field instructions are very helpful.

3.3.5 Pipeline Synchronization with the NOP Instruction

Although the no operation (NOP) instruction performs no visible operation, it serves an important purpose. It forces synchronization of the integer unit pipeline by waiting for all pending bus cycles to complete. All previous integer instructions and floating-point external operand accesses complete execution before the NOP begins. The NOP instruction does not synchronize the FPU pipeline—floating-point instructions with floating-point register operand destinations can be executing when the NOP begins. NOP is considered a change of flow instruction and traps for trace on change of flow. A single-cycle nonsynchronizing operation can be affected with the TRAPF instruction.

3.4 FLOATING-POINT INSTRUCTION DETAILS

The following paragraphs describe the operation tables used in the instruction descriptions and the conditional tests that can be used to change program flow based on floating-point conditions. Details on NANs and floating-point condition codes are also discussed. The IEEE 754 standard specifies that each data format must support add, subtract, multiply, divide, remainder, square root, integer part, and compare. In addition to these arithmetic functions, software supports remainder and integer part; the FPU also supports the nontranscendental operations of absolute value, negate, and test.

Most floating-point instruction descriptions include an operation table. This table lists the resulting data types for the instruction based on the operand's input. Table 3-20 is an operation table example for the FADD instruction. The operation table lists the source operand type along the top, and the destination operand type along the side. In-range numbers are normalized, denormalized, unnormalized real numbers, or integers that are converted to normalized or denormalized extended-precision numbers upon entering the FPU.

Table 3-20. Operation Table Example (FADD Instruction)

DESTINATION		SOURCE[1]						
		+	In Range	–	+	Zero	–	+	Infinity	–
In Range	+ –		ADD			ADD		+inf	–inf
Zero	+ –		ADD		+0.0 0.0[2]		0.0[2] –0.0	+inf	–inf
Infinity	+ –		+inf –inf			+inf –inf		+inf NAN[3]	NAN[3] –inf

NOTES:
1. If either operand is a NAN, refer to **1.6.5 NANs** for more information.
2. Returns +0.0 in rounding modes RN, RZ, and RP; returns –0.0 in RM.
3. Sets the OPERR bit in the FPSR exception byte.

For example, Table 3-20 illustrates that if both the source and destination operand are positive zero, the result is also a positive zero. If the source operand is a positive zero and the destination operand is an in-range number, then the ADD algorithm is executed to obtain the result. If a label such as ADD appears in the table, it indicates that the FPU performs the indicated operation and returns the correct result. Since the result of such an operation is undefined, a NAN is returned as the result, and the OPERR bit is set in the FPSR EXC byte.

In addition to the data types covered in the operation tables for each floating-point instruction, NANs can also be used as inputs to an arithmetic operation. The operation tables do not contain a row and column for NANs because NANs are handled the same way for all operations. If either operand, but not both operands, of an operation is a nonsignaling NAN, then that NAN is returned as the result. If both operands are nonsignaling NANs, then the destination operand nonsignaling NAN is returned as the result.

If either operand to an operation is a signaling NAN (SNAN), then the SNAN bit is set in the FPSR EXC byte. If the SNAN exception enable bit is set in the FPCR ENABLE byte, then the exception is taken and the destination is not modified. If the SNAN exception enable bit is not set, setting the SNAN bit in the operand to a one converts the SNAN to a nonsignaling NAN. The operation then continues as described in the preceding paragraph for nonsignaling NANs.

3.5 FLOATING-POINT COMPUTATIONAL ACCURACY

Representing a real number in a binary format of finite precision is problematic. If the number cannot be represented exactly, a round-off error occurs. Furthermore, when two of these inexact numbers are used in a calculation, the result becomes even more inexact. The IEEE 754 standard defines the error bounds for calculating binary floating-point values so that the result obtained by any conforming device can be predicted exactly for a particular precision and rounding mode. The error bound defined by the IEEE 754 standard is one-half unit in the last place of the destination data format in the RN mode, and one unit in last place in the other rounding modes. The operation's data format must have the same input values, rounding mode, and precision. The standard also specifies the maximum allowable error that can be introduced during a calculation and the manner in which rounding of the result is performed.

The single- and double-precision formats provide emulation for devices that only support those precisions. The execution speed of all instructions is the same whether using single- or double-precision rounding. When using these two data formats, the FPU produces the same results as any other device that conforms to the IEEE standard but does not support extended precision. The results are the same when performing the same operation in extended precision and storing the results in single- or double-precision format.

The FPU performs all floating-point internal operations in extended-precision. It supports mixed-mode arithmetic by converting single- and double-precision operands to extended-precision values before performing the specified operation. The FPU converts all memory data formats to the extended-precision data format and stores the value in a floating-point register or uses it as the source operand for an arithmetic operation. The FPU also converts extended-precision data formats in a floating-point data register to any data format and either stores it in a memory destination or in an integer data register.

Additionally if the external operand is a denormalized number, the number is normalized before an operation is performed. However, an external denormalized number moved into a floating-point data register is stored as a denormalized number. The number is first normalized and then denormalized before it is stored in the designated floating-point data register. This method simplifies the handling of all other data formats and types.

If an external operand is an unnormalized number, the number is normalized before it is used in an arithmetic operation. If the external operand is an unnormalized zero (i.e., with a mantissa of all zeros), the number is converted to a normalized zero before the specified operation is performed. The regular use of unnormalized inputs not only defeats the purpose of the IEEE 754 standard, but also can produce gross inaccuracies in the results.

3.5.1 Intermediate Result

All FPU calculations use an intermediate result. When the FPU performs any operation, the calculation is carried out using extended-precision inputs, and the intermediate result is calculated as if to produce infinite precision. After the calculation is complete, the intermediate result is rounded to the selected precision and stored in the destination.

Figure 3-1 illustrates the intermediate result format. The intermediate result's exponent for some dyadic operations (i.e., multiply and divide) can easily overflow or underflow the 15-bit exponent of the designation floating-point register. To simplify the overflow and underflow detection, intermediate results in the FPU maintain a 16-bit (17 bits for the MC68881 and MC68882), twos complement, integer exponent. Detection of an overflow or underflow intermediate result always converts the 16-bit exponent into a 15-bit biased exponent before being stored in a floating-point data register. The FPU internally maintains the 67-bit mantissa for rounding purposes. The mantissa is always rounded to 64 bits (or less, depending on the selected rounding precision) before it is stored in a floating-point data register.

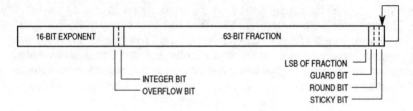

Figure 3-1. Intermediate Result Format

If the destination is a floating-point data register, the result is in the extended-precision format and is rounded to the precision specified by the FPSR PREC bits before being stored. All mantissa bits beyond the selected precision are zero. If the single- or double-precision mode is selected, the exponent value is in the correct range even if it is stored in extended-precision format. If the destination is a memory location, the FPSR PREC bits are ignored. In this case, a number in the extended-precision format is taken from the source floating-point data register, rounded to the destination format precision, and then written to memory.

Depending on the selected rounding mode or destination data format in effect, the location of the least significant bit of the mantissa and the locations of the guard, round, and sticky bits in the 67-bit intermediate result mantissa varies. The guard and round bits are always calculated exactly. The sticky bit is used to create the illusion of an infinitely wide intermediate result. As the arrow illustrates in Figure 3-1, the sticky bit is the logical OR of all the bits in the infinitely precise result to the right of the round bit. During the calculation stage of an arithmetic operation, any non-zero bits generated that are to the right of the round bit set the sticky bit to one. Because of the sticky bit, the rounded intermediate result for all required IEEE arithmetic operations in the RN mode is in error by no more than one half unit in the last place.

3.5.2 Rounding the Result

The FPU supports the four rounding modes specified by the IEEE 754 standard. These modes are round to nearest (RN), round toward zero (RZ), round toward plus infinity (RP), and round toward minus infinity (RM). The RM and RP rounding modes are often referred to as "directed rounding modes" and are useful in interval arithmetic. Rounding is accomplished through the intermediate result. Single-precision results are rounded to a 24-bit boundary; double-precision results are rounded to a 53-bit boundary; and extended-precision results are rounded to a 64-bit boundary. Table 3-21 lists the encodings for the FPCR that denote the rounding and precision modes.

Table 3-21. FPCR Encodings

Rounding Mode (RND Field)	Encoding		Rounding Precision (PREC Field)
To Nearest (RN)	0	0	Extend (X)
To Zero (RZ)	0	1	Single (S)
To Minus Infinity (RM)	1	0	Double (D)
To Plus Infinity (RP)	1	1	Undefined

Rounding the intermediate result's mantissa to the specified precision and checking the 16-bit intermediate exponent to ensure that it is within the representable range of the selected rounding precision accomplishes range control. Range control is a method used to assure correct emulation of a device that only supports single- or double-precision arithmetic. If the intermediate result's exponent exceeds the range of the selected precision, the exponent value appropriate for an underflow or overflow is stored as the result in the 16-bit extended-precision format exponent. For example, if the data format and rounding mode is single precision RM and the result of an arithmetic operation overflows the magnitude of the single-precision format, the largest normalized single-precision value is stored as an extended-precision number in the destination floating-point data register (i.e., an unbiased 15-bit exponent of $00FF and a mantissa of $FFFFFF0000000000). If an infinity is the appropriate result for an underflow or overflow, the infinity value for the destination data format is stored as the result (i.e., an exponent with the maximum value and a mantissa of zero).

Figure 3-2 illustrates the algorithm that the FPU uses to round an intermediate result to the selected rounding precision and destination data format. If the destination is a floating-point register, either the selected rounding precision specified by the FPCR PREC status byte or by the instruction itself determines the rounding boundary. For example, FSADD and FDADD specify single- and double-precision rounding regardless of the precision specified in the FPCR PREC status byte. If the destination is external memory or an integer data register, the destination data format determines the rounding boundary. If the rounded result of an operation is not exact, then the INEX2 bit is set in the FPSR EXC status byte.

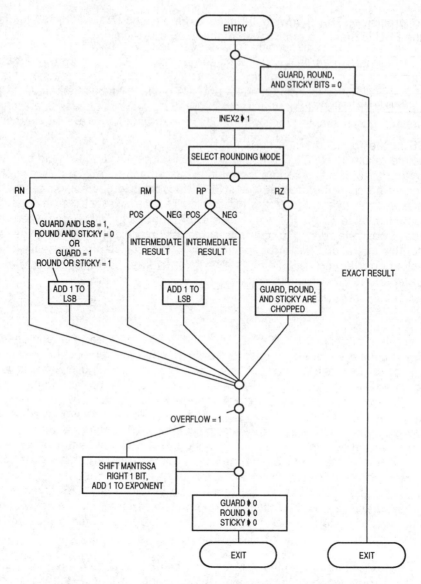

Figure 3-2. Rounding Algorithm Flowchart

The three additional bits beyond the extended-precision format, the difference between the intermediate result's 67-bit mantissa and the storing result's 64-bit mantissa, allow the FPU to perform all calculations as though it were performing calculations using a float engine with infinite bit precision. The result is always correct for the specified destination's data format before performing rounding (unless an overflow or underflow error occurs). The specified rounding operation then produces a number that is as close as possible to the infinitely precise intermediate value and still representable in the selected precision. The following tie-case example shows how the 67-bit mantissa allows the FPU to meet the error bound of the IEEE specification:

Result	Integer	63-Bit Fraction	Guard	Round	Sticky
Intermediate	x	xxx...x00	1	0	0
Rounded-to-Nearest	x	xxx...x00	0	0	0

The LSB of the rounded result does not increment though the guard bit is set in the intermediate result. The IEEE 754 standard specifies that tie cases should be handled in this manner. If the destination data format is extended and there is a difference between the infinitely precise intermediate result and the round-to-nearest result, the relative difference is 2^{-64} (the value of the guard bit). This error is equal to half of the least significant bit's value and is the worst case error that can be introduced when using the RN mode. Thus, the term one-half unit in the last place correctly identifies the error bound for this operation. This error specification is the relative error present in the result; the absolute error bound is equal to $2^{exponent} \times 2^{-64}$. The following example shows the error bound for the other rounding modes:

Result	Integer	63-Bit Fraction	Guard	Round	Sticky
Intermediate	x	xxx...x00	1	1	1
Rounded-to-Nearest	x	xxx...x00	0	0	0

The difference between the infinitely precise result and the rounded result is $2^{-64} + 2^{-65} + 2^{-66}$, which is slightly less than 2^{-63} (the value of the LSB). Thus, the error bound for this operation is not more than one unit in the last place. For all arithmetic operations, the FPU meets these error bounds, providing accurate and repeatable results.

3.6 FLOATING-POINT POSTPROCESSING

Most operations end with a postprocessing step. The FPU provides two steps in postprocessing. First, the condition code bits in the FPSR are set or cleared at the end of each arithmetic operation or move operation to a single floating-point data register. The condition code bits are consistently set based on the result of the operation. Second, the FPU supports 32 conditional tests that allow floating-point conditional instructions to test floating-point conditions in exactly the same way as the integer conditional instructions test the integer condition codes. The combination of consistently set condition code bits and the simple programming of conditional instructions gives the processor a very flexible, high-performance method of altering program flow based on floating-point results. While reading the summary for each instruction, it should be assumed that an instruction performs postprocessing unless the summary specifically states that the instruction does not do so. The following paragraphs describe postprocessing in detail.

3.6.1 Underflow, Round, Overflow

During the calculation of an arithmetic result, the FPU arithmetic logic unit (ALU) has more precision and range than the 80-bit extended precision format. However, the final result of these operations is an extended-precision floating-point value. In some cases, an intermediate result becomes either smaller or larger than can be represented in extended precision. Also, the operation can generate a larger exponent or more bits of precision than can be represented in the chosen rounding precision. For these reasons, every arithmetic instruction ends by rounding the result and checking for overflow and underflow.

At the completion of an arithmetic operation, the intermediate result is checked to see if it is too small to be represented as a normalized number in the selected precision. If so, the underflow (UNFL) bit is set in the FPSR EXC byte. It is also denormalized unless denormalization provides a zero value. Denormalizing a number causes a loss of accuracy, but a zero is not returned unless absolutely necessary. If a number is grossly underflowed, the FPU returns a zero or the smallest denormalized number with the correct sign, depending on the rounding mode in effect.

If no underflow occurs, the intermediate result is rounded according to the user-selected rounding precision and rounding mode. After rounding, the inexact bit (INEX2) is set appropriately. Lastly, the magnitude of the result is checked to see if it is too large to be represented in the current rounding precision. If so, the overflow (OVFL) bit is set and a correctly signed infinity or correctly signed largest normalized number is returned, depending on the rounding mode in effect.

3.6.2 Conditional Testing

Unlike the integer arithmetic condition codes, an instruction either always sets the floating-point condition codes in the same way or it does not change them at all. Therefore, the instruction descriptions do not include floating-point condition code settings. The following paragraphs describe how floating-point condition codes are set for all instructions that modify condition codes.

The condition code bits differ slightly from the integer condition codes. Unlike the operation type dependent integer condition codes, examining the result at the end of the operation sets or clears the floating-point condition codes accordingly. The M68000 family integer condition codes bits N and Z have this characteristic, but the V and C bits are set differently for different instructions. The data type of the operation's result determines how the four condition code bits are set. Table 3-22 lists the condition code bit setting for each data type. Loading the FPCC with one of the other combinations and executing a conditional instruction can produce an unexpected branch condition.

Table 3-22. FPCC Encodings

Data Type	N	Z	I	NAN
+ Normalized or Denormalized	0	0	0	0
− Normalized or Denormalized	1	0	0	0
+ 0	0	1	0	0
− 0	1	1	0	0
+ Infinity	0	0	1	0
− Infinity	1	0	1	0
+ NAN	0	0	0	1
− NAN	1	0	0	1

The inclusion of the NAN data type in the IEEE floating-point number system requires each conditional test to include the NAN condition code bit in its Boolean equation. Because a comparison of a NAN with any other data type is unordered (i.e., it is impossible to determine if a NAN is bigger or smaller than an in-range number), the compare instruction sets the NAN condition code bit when an unordered compare is attempted. All arithmetic instructions also set the NAN bit if the result of an operation is a NAN. The conditional instructions interpret the NAN condition code bit equal to one as the unordered condition.

The IEEE 754 standard defines four conditions: equal to (EQ), greater than (GT), less than (LT), and unordered (UN). In addition, the standard only requires the generation of the condition codes as a result of a floating-point compare operation. The FPU can test these conditions at the end of any operation affecting the condition codes. For purposes of the floating-point conditional branch, set byte on condition, decrement and branch on condition, and trap on condition instructions, the processor logically combines the four FPCC condition codes to form 32 conditional tests. There are three main categories of conditional tests: IEEE nonaware tests, IEEE aware tests, and miscellaneous. The set of IEEE nonaware tests is best used:

- when porting a program from a system that does not support the IEEE standard to a conforming system, or
- when generating high-level language code that does not support IEEE floating-point concepts (i.e., the unordered condition).

The 32 conditional tests are separated into two groups; 16 that cause an exception if an unordered condition is present when the conditional test is attempted and 16 that do not cause an exception. An unordered condition occurs when one or both of the operands in a floating-point compare operation is a NAN. The inclusion of the unordered condition in floating-point branches destroys the familiar trichotomy relationship (greater than, equal, less than) that exists for integers. For example, the opposite of floating-point branch greater than (FBGT) is not floating-point branch less than or equal (FBLE). Rather, the opposite condition is floating-point branch not greater than (FBNGT). If the result of the previous instruction was unordered, FBNGT is true; whereas, both FBGT and FBLE would be false since unordered fails both of these tests (and sets BSUN). Compiler programmers should be particularly careful of the lack of trichotomy in the floating-point branches since it is common for compilers to invert the sense of conditions.

When using the IEEE nonaware tests, the user receives a BSUN exception whenever a branch is attempted and the NAN condition code bit is set, unless the branch is an FBEQ or an FBNE. If the BSUN exception is enabled in the FPCR, the exception causes another exception. Therefore, the IEEE nonaware program is interrupted if an unexpected condition occurs. Compilers and programmers who are knowledgeable of the IEEE 754 standard should use the IEEE aware tests in programs that contain ordered and unordered conditions. Since the ordered or unordered attribute is explicitly included in the conditional test, the BSUN bit is not set in the FPSR EXC byte when the unordered condition occurs. Table 3-23 summarizes the conditional mnemonics, definitions, equations, predicates, and whether the BSUN bit is set in the FPSR EXC byte for the 32 floating-point conditional tests. The equation column lists the combination of FPCC bits for each test in the form of an equation. All condition codes with an overbar indicate cleared bits; all other bits are set.

Table 3-23. Floating-Point Conditional Tests

Mnemonic	Definition	Equation	Predicate	BSUN Bit Set
IEEE Nonaware Tests				
EQ	Equal	Z	000001	No
NE	Not Equal	$\overline{Z}$	001110	No
GT	Greater Than	$\overline{\text{NAN} \vee Z \vee N}$	010010	Yes
NGT	Not Greater Than	$\text{NAN} \vee Z \vee N$	011101	Yes
GE	Greater Than or Equal	$Z \vee (\overline{\text{NAN} \vee N})$	010011	Yes
NGE	Not Greater Than or Equal	$\text{NAN} \vee (N \wedge \overline{Z})$	011100	Yes
LT	Less Than	$N \wedge (\overline{\text{NAN} \vee Z})$	010100	Yes
NLT	Not Less Than	$\text{NAN} \vee (Z \vee \overline{N})$	011011	Yes
LE	Less Than or Equal	$Z \vee (N \wedge \overline{\text{NAN}})$	010101	Yes
NLE	Not Less Than or Equal	$\text{NAN} \vee (\overline{N \vee Z})$	011010	Yes
GL	Greater or Less Than	$\overline{\text{NAN} \vee Z}$	010110	Yes
NGL	Not Greater or Less Than	$\text{NAN} \vee Z$	011001	Yes
GLE	Greater, Less or Equal	$\overline{\text{NAN}}$	010111	Yes
NGLE	Not Greater, Less or Equal	NAN	011000	Yes
IEEE Aware Tests				
EQ	Equal	Z	000001	No
NE	Not Equal	$\overline{Z}$	001110	No
OGT	Ordered Greater Than	$\overline{\text{NAN} \vee Z \vee N}$	000010	No
ULE	Unordered or Less or Equal	$\text{NAN} \vee Z \vee N$	001101	No
OGE	Ordered Greater Than or Equal	$Z \vee (\overline{\text{NAN} \vee N})$	000011	No
ULT	Unordered or Less Than	$\text{NAN} \vee (N \wedge \overline{Z})$	001100	No
OLT	Ordered Less Than	$N \wedge (\overline{\text{NAN} \vee Z})$	000100	No
UGE	Unordered or Greater or Equal	$\text{NAN} \vee Z \vee N$	001011	No
OLE	Ordered Less Than or Equal	$Z \vee (N \wedge \overline{\text{NAN}})$	000101	No
UGT	Unordered or Greater Than	$\text{NAN} \vee (\overline{N \vee Z})$	001010	No
OGL	Ordered Greater or Less Than	$\overline{\text{NAN} \vee Z}$	000110	No
UEQ	Unordered or Equal	$\text{NAN} \vee Z$	001001	No
OR	Ordered	$\overline{\text{NAN}}$	000111	No
UN	Unordered	NAN	001000	No
Miscellaneous Tests				
F	False	False	000000	No
T	True	True	001111	No
SF	Signaling False	False	010000	Yes
ST	Signaling True	True	011111	Yes
SEQ	Signaling Equal	Z	010001	Yes
SNE	Signaling Not Equal	$\overline{Z}$	011110	Yes

3.7 INSTRUCTION DESCRIPTIONS

Section 4, 5, 6, and 7 contain detailed information about each instruction in the M68000 family instruction set. Each section arranges the instruction in alphabetical order by instruction mnemonic and includes descriptions of the instruction's notation and format. Figure 3-3 illustrates the format of the instruction descriptions. Note that the illustration is an amalgamation of the various parts that make up an instruction description. Instruction descriptions for the integer unit differ slightly from those for the floating-point unit; i.e. there are no operation tables included for integer unit instruction descriptions.

The size attribute line specifies the size of the operands of an instruction. When an instruction uses operands of more than one size, the mnemonic of the instruction includes a suffix such as:

.B—Byte Operands

.W—Word Operands

.L—Long-Word Operands

.S—Single-Precision Real Operands

.D—Double-Precision Real Operands

.X—Extended-Precision Real Operands

.P—Packed BCD Real Operands

The instruction format specifies the bit pattern and fields of the operation and command words, and any other words that are always part of the instruction. The effective address extensions are not explicitly illustrated. The extension words, if any, follow immediately after the illustrated portions of the instructions.

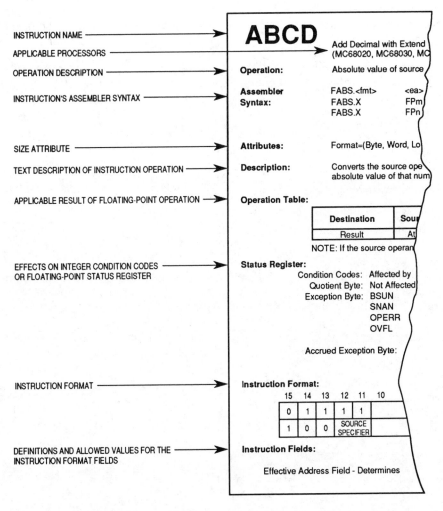

INSTRUCTION NAME

APPLICABLE PROCESSORS

OPERATION DESCRIPTION

INSTRUCTION'S ASSEMBLER SYNTAX

SIZE ATTRIBUTE

TEXT DESCRIPTION OF INSTRUCTION OPERATION

APPLICABLE RESULT OF FLOATING-POINT OPERATION

EFFECTS ON INTEGER CONDITION CODES
OR FLOATING-POINT STATUS REGISTER

INSTRUCTION FORMAT

DEFINITIONS AND ALLOWED VALUES FOR THE
INSTRUCTION FORMAT FIELDS

ABCD

Add Decimal with Extend
(MC68020, MC68030, MC

Operation: Absolute value of source

Assembler FABS.<fmt> <ea>
Syntax: FABS.X FPm
FABS.X FPn

Attributes: Format=(Byte, Word, Lo

Description: Converts the source ope
absolute value of that num

Operation Table:

Destination	Sour
Result	At

NOTE: If the source operan

Status Register:

Condition Codes: Affected by
Quotient Byte: Not Affected
Exception Byte: BSUN
SNAN
OPERR
OVFL

Accrued Exception Byte:

Instruction Format:

15	14	13	12	11	10
0	1	1	1	1	
1	0	0	SOURCE SPECIFIER		

Instruction Fields:

Effective Address Field - Determines

Figure 3-3. Instruction Description Format

3

SECTION 4
INTEGER INSTRUCTIONS

This section contains detailed information about the integer instructions for the M68000 family. A detailed discussion of each instruction description is arranged in alphabetical order by instruction mnemonic.

Each instruction description identifies the differences among the M68000 family for that instruction. Noted under the title of the instruction are all specific processors that apply to that instruction—for example:

Test Bit Field and Change
(MC68030, MC68040)

The MC68HC000 is identical to the MC68000 except for power dissipation; therefore, all instructions that apply to the MC68000 also apply to the MC68HC000. All references to the MC68000, MC68020, and MC68030 include references to the corresponding embedded controllers, MC68EC000, MC68EC020, and MC68EC030. All references to the MC68040 include the MC68LC040 and MC68EC040. This referencing applies throughout this section unless otherwise specified.

Identified within the paragraphs are the specific processors that use different instruction fields, instruction formats, etc.—for example:

MC68020, MC68030, and MC68040 only

(bd,An,Xn)**	110	reg. number:An	(bd,PC,Xn)**	111	011

**Can be used with CPU32 processor.

Appendix A Processor Instruction Summary provides a listing of all processors and the instructions that apply to them for quick reference.

Add Decimal with Extend
(M68000 Family)

Operation: $\text{Source}_{10} + \text{Destination}_{10} + X \rightarrow \text{Destination}$

Assembler ABCD Dy,Dx
Syntax: ABCD –(Ay),–(Ax)

Attributes: Size = (Byte)

Description: Adds the source operand to the destination operand along with the extend bit, and stores the result in the destination location. The addition is performed using binary-coded decimal arithmetic. The operands, which are packed binary-coded decimal numbers, can be addressed in two different ways:

1. Data Register to Data Register: The operands are contained in the data registers specified in the instruction.
2. Memory to Memory: The operands are addressed with the predecrement addressing mode using the address registers specified in the instruction.

This operation is a byte operation only.

Condition Codes:

X	N	Z	V	C
*	U	*	U	*

X—Set the same as the carry bit.
N—Undefined.
Z—Cleared if the result is nonzero; unchanged otherwise.
V—Undefined.
C—Set if a decimal carry was generated; cleared otherwise.

NOTE

Normally, the Z condition code bit is set via programming before the start of an operation. This allows successful tests for zero results upon completion of multiple-precision operations.

ABCD

Add Decimal with Extend
(M68000 Family)

ABCD

Instruction Format:

15	14	13	12	11	10	9	8	7	6	5	4	3	2	1	0
1	1	0	0	REGISTER Rx			1	0	0	0	0	R/M	REGISTER Ry		

Instruction Fields:

Register Rx field—Specifies the destination register.
If R/M = 0, specifies a data register.
If R/M = 1, specifies an address register for the predecrement addressing mode.

R/M field—Specifies the operand addressing mode.
0—The operation is data register to data register.
1—The operation is memory to memory.

Register Ry field—Specifies the source register.
If R/M = 0, specifies a data register.
If R/M = 1, specifies an address register for the predecrement addressing mode.

4

ADD

ADD

Operation: Source + Destination ♦ Destination

Assembler ADD <ea>,Dn
Syntax: ADD Dn,<ea>

Attributes: Size = (Byte, Word, Long)

Description: Adds the source operand to the destination operand using binary addition and stores the result in the destination location. The size of the operation may be specified as byte, word, or long. The mode of the instruction indicates which operand is the source and which is the destination, as well as the operand size.

Condition Codes:

X	N	Z	V	C
*	*	*	*	*

X—Set the same as the carry bit.
N—Set if the result is negative; cleared otherwise.
Z—Set if the result is zero; cleared otherwise.
V—Set if an overflow is generated; cleared otherwise.
C—Set if a carry is generated; cleared otherwise.

Instruction Format:

15	14	13	12	11	10	9	8	7	6	5	4	3	2	1	0
1	1	0	1	REGISTER			OPMODE			EFFECTIVE ADDRESS					
										MODE			REGISTER		

ADD

ADD

Instruction Fields:

Register field—Specifies any of the eight data registers.

Opmode field

Byte	Word	Long	Operation
000	001	010	$<ea> + Dn \rightarrow Dn$
100	101	110	$Dn + <ea> \rightarrow <ea>$

Effective Address field—Determines addressing mode.

a. If the location specified is a source operand, all addressing modes can be used as listed in the following tables:

Addressing Mode	Mode	Register	Addressing Mode	Mode	Register
Dn	000	reg. number:Dn	(xxx).W	111	000
An*	001	reg. number:An	(xxx).L	111	001
(An)	010	reg. number:An	#<data>	111	100
(An) +	011	reg. number:An			
– (An)	100	reg. number:An			
(d_{16},An)	101	reg. number:An	(d_{16},PC)	111	010
(d_8,An,Xn)	110	reg. number:An	(d_8,PC,Xn)	111	011

MC68020, MC68030, and MC68040 only

(bd,An,Xn)**	110	reg. number:An	(bd,PC,Xn)**	111	011
([bd,An,Xn],od)	110	reg. number:An	([bd,PC,Xn],od)	111	011
([bd,An],Xn,od)	110	reg. number:An	([bd,PC],Xn,od)	111	011

*Word and long only.

**Can be used with CPU32.

b. If the location specified is a destination operand, only memory alterable addressing modes can be used as listed in the following tables:

Addressing Mode	Mode	Register
Dn	—	—
An	—	—
(An)	010	reg. number:An
(An) +	011	reg. number:An
− (An)	100	reg. number:An
(d$_{16}$,An)	101	reg. number:An
(d$_8$,An,Xn)	110	reg. number:An

Addressing Mode	Mode	Register
(xxx).W	111	000
(xxx).L	111	001
#<data>	—	—
(d$_{16}$,PC)	—	—
(d$_8$,PC,Xn)	—	—

MC68020, MC68030, and MC68040 only

(bd,An,Xn)*	110	reg. number:An
([bd,An,Xn],od)	110	reg. number:An
([bd,An],Xn,od)	110	reg. number:An

(bd,PC,Xn)*	—	—
([bd,PC,Xn],od)	—	—
([bd,PC],Xn,od)	—	—

*Can be used with CPU32.

NOTE

The Dn mode is used when the destination is a data register; the destination <ea> mode is invalid for a data register.

ADDA is used when the destination is an address register. ADDI and ADDQ are used when the source is immediate data. Most assemblers automatically make this distinction.

ADDA

Add Address
(M68000 Family)

ADDA

Operation: Source + Destination ♦ Destination

Assembler
Syntax: ADDA <ea>, An

Attributes: Size = (Word, Long)

Description: Adds the source operand to the destination address register and stores the result in the address register. The size of the operation may be specified as word or long. The entire destination address register is used regardless of the operation size.

Condition Codes:
Not affected.

Instruction Format:

15	14	13	12	11	10	9	8	7	6	5	4	3	2	1	0
1	1	0	1	REGISTER			OPMODE			EFFECTIVE ADDRESS					
										MODE			REGISTER		

Instruction Fields:

Register field—Specifies any of the eight address registers. This is always the destination.

Opmode field—Specifies the size of the operation.
011—Word operation; the source operand is sign-extended to a long operand and the operation is performed on the address register using all 32 bits.
111—Long operation.

Effective Address field—Specifies the source operand. All addressing modes can be used as listed in the following tables:

Addressing Mode	Mode	Register
Dn	000	reg. number:Dn
An	001	reg. number:An
(An)	010	reg. number:An
(An) +	011	reg. number:An
– (An)	100	reg. number:An
(d_{16},An)	101	reg. number:An
(d_8,An,Xn)	110	reg. number:An

Addressing Mode	Mode	Register
(xxx).W	111	000
(xxx).L	111	001
#<data>	111	100
(d_{16},PC)	111	010
(d_8,PC,Xn)	111	011

MC68020, MC68030, and MC68040 only

(bd,An,Xn)*	110	reg. number:An
([bd,An,Xn],od)	110	reg. number:An
([bd,An],Xn,od)	110	reg. number:An

(bd,PC,Xn)*	111	011
([bd,PC,Xn],od)	111	011
([bd,PC],Xn,od)	111	011

*Can be used with CPU32.

ADDI

Operation: Immediate Data + Destination ⬦ Destination

Assembler
Syntax: ADDI #<data>,<ea>

Attributes: Size = (Byte, Word, Long)

Description: Adds the immediate data to the destination operand and stores the result in the destination location. The size of the operation may be specified as byte, word, or long. The size of the immediate data matches the operation size.

Condition Codes:

X	N	Z	V	C
*	*	*	*	*

X—Set the same as the carry bit.
N—Set if the result is negative; cleared otherwise.
Z—Set if the result is zero; cleared otherwise.
V—Set if an overflow is generated; cleared otherwise.
C—Set if a carry is generated; cleared otherwise.

Instruction Format:

15	14	13	12	11	10	9	8	7	6	5	4	3	2	1	0
0	0	0	0	0	1	1	0	SIZE		EFFECTIVE ADDRESS					
										MODE			REGISTER		
16-BIT WORD DATA								8-BIT BYTE DATA							
32-BIT LONG DATA															

ADDI

Instruction Fields:

Size field—Specifies the size of the operation.
- 00—Byte operation
- 01—Word operation
- 10—Long operation

Effective Address field—Specifies the destination operand. Only data alterable addressing modes can be used as listed in the following tables:

Addressing Mode	Mode	Register	Addressing Mode	Mode	Register
Dn	000	reg. number:Dn	(xxx).W	111	000
An	—	—	(xxx).L	111	001
(An)	010	reg. number:An	#<data>	—	—
(An) +	011	reg. number:An			
– (An)	100	reg. number:An			
(d$_{16}$,An)	101	reg. number:An	(d$_{16}$,PC)	—	—
(d$_8$,An,Xn)	110	reg. number:An	(d$_8$,PC,Xn)	—	—

MC68020, MC68030, and MC68040 only

(bd,An,Xn)*	110	reg. number:An	(bd,PC,Xn)*	—	—
([bd,An,Xn],od)	110	reg. number:An	([bd,PC,Xn],od)	—	—
([bd,An],Xn,od)	110	reg. number:An	([bd,PC],Xn,od)	—	—

*Can be used with CPU32.

Immediate field—Data immediately following the instruction.
- If size = 00, the data is the low-order byte of the immediate word.
- If size = 01, the data is the entire immediate word.
- If size = 10, the data is the next two immediate words.

ADDQ

Add Quick
(M68000 Family)

ADDQ

Operation: Immediate Data + Destination ♦ Destination

**Assembler
Syntax:** ADDQ #<data>,<ea>

Attributes: Size = (Byte, Word, Long)

Description: Adds an immediate value of one to eight to the operand at the destination location. The size of the operation may be specified as byte, word, or long. Word and long operations are also allowed on the address registers. When adding to address registers, the condition codes are not altered, and the entire destination address register is used regardless of the operation size.

Condition Codes:

X	N	Z	V	C
*	*	*	*	*

X—Set the same as the carry bit.
N—Set if the result is negative; cleared otherwise.
Z—Set if the result is zero; cleared otherwise.
V—Set if an overflow occurs; cleared otherwise.
C—Set if a carry occurs; cleared otherwise.

The condition codes are not affected when the destination is an address register.

Instruction Format:

15	14	13	12	11	10	9	8	7	6	5	4	3	2	1	0
0	1	0	1	DATA			0	SIZE		EFFECTIVE ADDRESS					
										MODE			REGISTER		

ADDQ

ADDQ

Add Quick
(M68000 Family)

Instruction Fields:

Data field—Three bits of immediate data representing eight values (0–7), with the immediate value zero representing a value of eight.

Size field—Specifies the size of the operation.
  00—Byte operation
  01—Word operation
  10—Long operation

Effective Address field—Specifies the destination location. Only alterable addressing modes can be used as listed in the following tables:

Addressing Mode	Mode	Register	Addressing Mode	Mode	Register
Dn	000	reg. number:Dn	(xxx).W	111	000
An*	001	reg. number:An	(xxx).L	111	001
(An)	010	reg. number:An	#<data>	—	—
(An) +	011	reg. number:An			
– (An)	100	reg. number:An			
(d_{16},An)	101	reg. number:An	(d_{16},PC)	—	—
(d_8,An,Xn)	110	reg. number:An	(d_8,PC,Xn)	—	—

MC68020, MC68030, and MC68040 only

(bd,An,Xn)**	110	reg. number:An	(bd,PC,Xn)**	—	—
([bd,An,Xn],od)	110	reg. number:An	([bd,PC,Xn],od)	—	—
([bd,An],Xn,od)	110	reg. number:An	([bd,PC],Xn,od)	—	—

*Word and long only.

**Can be used with CPU32.

ADDX

Add Extended
(M68000 Family)

ADDX

Operation: Source + Destination + X ♦ Destination

Assembler ADDX Dy,Dx
Syntax: ADDX –(Ay),–(Ax)

Attributes: Size = (Byte, Word, Long)

Description: Adds the source operand and the extend bit to the destination operand and stores the result in the destination location. The operands can be addressed in two different ways:

1. Data register to data register—The data registers specified in the instruction contain the operands.
2. Memory to memory—The address registers specified in the instruction address the operands using the predecrement addressing mode.

The size of the operation can be specified as byte, word, or long.

Condition Codes:

X	N	Z	V	C
*	*	*	*	*

X—Set the same as the carry bit.
N—Set if the result is negative; cleared otherwise.
Z—Cleared if the result is nonzero; unchanged otherwise.
V—Set if an overflow occurs; cleared otherwise.
C—Set if a carry is generated; cleared otherwise.

NOTE

Normally, the Z condition code bit is set via programming before the start of an operation. This allows successful tests for zero results upon completion of multiple-precision operations.

ADDX

Add Extended
(M68000 Family)

ADDX

Instruction Format:

15	14	13	12	11	10	9	8	7	6	5	4	3	2	1	0
1	1	0	1	REGISTER Rx			1	SIZE		0	0	R/M	REGISTER Ry		

Instruction Fields:

Register Rx field—Specifies the destination register.
   If R/M = 0, specifies a data register.
   If R/M = 1, specifies an address register for the predecrement addressing mode.

Size field—Specifies the size of the operation.
   00—Byte operation
   01—Word operation
   10—Long operation

R/M field—Specifies the operand address mode.
   0—The operation is data register to data register.
   1—The operation is memory to memory.

Register Ry field—Specifies the source register.
   If R/M = 0, specifies a data register.
   If R/M = 1, specifies an address register for the predecrement addressing mode.

AND

AND Logical
(M68000 Family)

AND

Operation: Source Λ Destination ♦ Destination

Assembler   AND <ea>,Dn
Syntax: AND Dn,<ea>

Attributes: Size = (Byte, Word, Long)

Description: Performs an AND operation of the source operand with the destination operand and stores the result in the destination location. The size of the operation can be specified as byte, word, or long. The contents of an address register may not be used as an operand.

Condition Codes:

X	N	Z	V	C
—	*	*	0	0

X—Not affected.
N—Set if the most significant bit of the result is set; cleared otherwise.
Z—Set if the result is zero; cleared otherwise.
V—Always cleared.
C—Always cleared.

Instruction Format:

15	14	13	12	11	10	9	8	7	6	5	4	3	2	1	0
1	1	0	0	REGISTER			OPMODE			EFFECTIVE ADDRESS					
										MODE			REGISTER		

Instruction Fields:

Register field—Specifies any of the eight data registers.

Opmode field

Byte	Word	Long	Operation
000	001	010	<ea> Λ Dn ♦ Dn
100	101	110	Dn Λ <ea> ♦ <ea>

Effective Address field—Determines addressing mode.

   a. If the location specified is a source operand, only data addressing modes can be used as listed in the following tables:

Addressing Mode	Mode	Register
Dn	000	reg. number:Dn
An	—	—
(An)	010	reg. number:An
(An) +	011	reg. number:An
− (An)	100	reg. number:An
(d_{16},An)	101	reg. number:An
(d_8,An,Xn)	110	reg. number:An

Addressing Mode	Mode	Register
(xxx).W	111	000
(xxx).L	111	001
#<data>	111	100
(d_{16},PC)	111	010
(d_8,PC,Xn)	111	011

MC68020, MC68030, and MC68040 only

(bd,An,Xn)*	110	reg. number:An
([bd,An,Xn],od)	110	reg. number:An
([bd,An],Xn,od)	110	reg. number:An

(bd,PC,Xn)*	111	011
([bd,PC,Xn],od)	111	011
([bd,PC],Xn,od)	111	011

*Can be used with CPU32.

b. If the location specified is a destination operand, only memory alterable addressing modes can be used as listed in the following tables:

Addressing Mode	Mode	Register	Addressing Mode	Mode	Register
Dn	—	—	(xxx).W	111	000
An	—	—	(xxx).L	111	001
(An)	010	reg. number:An	#<data>	—	—
(An) +	011	reg. number:An			
– (An)	100	reg. number:An			
(d$_{16}$,An)	101	reg. number:An	(d$_{16}$,PC)	—	—
(d$_8$,An,Xn)	110	reg. number:An	(d$_8$,PC,Xn)	—	—

MC68020, MC68030, and MC68040 only

(bd,An,Xn)*	110	reg. number:An	(bd,PC,Xn)*	—	—
([bd,An,Xn],od)	110	reg. number:An	([bd,PC,Xn],od)	—	—
([bd,An],Xn,od)	110	reg. number:An	([bd,PC],Xn,od)	—	—

*Can be used with CPU32.

NOTE

The Dn mode is used when the destination is a data register; the destination <ea> mode is invalid for a data register.

Most assemblers use ANDI when the source is immediate data.

ANDI

AND Immediate
(M68000 Family)

ANDI

Operation: Immediate Data Λ Destination ♦ Destination

Assembler
Syntax: ANDI #<data>,<ea>

Attributes: Size = (Byte, Word, Long)

Description: Performs an AND operation of the immediate data with the destination operand and stores the result in the destination location. The size of the operation can be specified as byte, word, or long. The size of the immediate data matches the operation size.

Condition Codes:

X	N	Z	V	C
—	*	*	0	0

X—Not affected.
N—Set if the most significant bit of the result is set; cleared otherwise.
Z—Set if the result is zero; cleared otherwise.
V—Always cleared.
C—Always cleared.

Instruction Format:

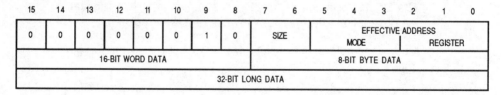

Instruction Fields:

Size field—Specifies the size of the operation.
 00—Byte operation
 01—Word operation
 10—Long operation

Effective Address field—Specifies the destination operand. Only data alterable addressing modes can be used as listed in the following tables:

Addressing Mode	Mode	Register	Addressing Mode	Mode	Register
Dn	000	reg. number:Dn	(xxx).W	111	000
An	—	—	(xxx).L	111	001
(An)	010	reg. number:An	#<data>	—	—
(An) +	011	reg. number:An			
– (An)	100	reg. number:An			
(d$_{16}$,An)	101	reg. number:An	(d$_{16}$,PC)	—	—
(d$_8$,An,Xn)	110	reg. number:An	(d$_8$,PC,Xn)	—	—

MC68020, MC68030, and MC68040 only

(bd,An,Xn)*	110	reg. number:An	(bd,PC,Xn)*	—	—
([bd,An,Xn],od)	110	reg. number:An	([bd,PC,Xn],od)	—	—
([bd,An],Xn,od)	110	reg. number:An	([bd,PC],Xn,od)	—	—

*Can be used with CPU32.

Immediate field—Data immediately following the instruction.
 If size = 00, the data is the low-order byte of the immediate word.
 If size = 01, the data is the entire immediate word.
 If size = 10, the data is the next two immediate words.

ANDI
to CCR

AND Immediate to Condition Codes
(M68000 Family)

Operation: Source $\wedge$ CCR $\rightarrow$ CCR

**Assembler
Syntax:**   ANDI #<data>,CCR

Attributes: Size = (Byte)

Description: Performs an AND operation of the immediate operand with the condition codes and stores the result in the low-order byte of the status register.

Condition Codes:

X	N	Z	V	C
*	*	*	*	*

X—Cleared if bit 4 of immediate operand is zero; unchanged otherwise.
N—Cleared if bit 3 of immediate operand is zero; unchanged otherwise.
Z—Cleared if bit 2 of immediate operand is zero; unchanged otherwise.
V—Cleared if bit 1 of immediate operand is zero; unchanged otherwise.
C—Cleared if bit 0 of immediate operand is zero; unchanged otherwise.

Instruction Format:

15	14	13	12	11	10	9	8	7	6	5	4	3	2	1	0
0	0	0	0	0	0	1	0	0	0	1	1	1	1	0	0
0	0	0	0	0	0	0	0	8-BIT BYTE DATA							

ASL, ASR   Arithmetic Shift   ASL, ASR
(M68000 Family)

Operation: Destination Shifted By Count ◆ Destination

Assembler   ASd Dx,Dy
Syntax: ASd #<data>,Dy
    ASd <ea>
    where d is direction, L or R

Attributes: Size = (Byte, Word, Long)

Description: Arithmetically shifts the bits of the operand in the direction (L or R) specified. The carry bit receives the last bit shifted out of the operand. The shift count for the shifting of a register may be specified in two different ways:

1. Immediate—The shift count is specified in the instruction (shift range, 1–8).
2. Register—The shift count is the value in the data register specified in instruction modulo 64.

The size of the operation can be specified as byte, word, or long. An operand in memory can be shifted one bit only, and the operand size is restricted to a word.

For ASL, the operand is shifted left; the number of positions shifted is the shift count. Bits shifted out of the high-order bit go to both the carry and the extend bits; zeros are shifted into the low-order bit. The overflow bit indicates if any sign changes occur during the shift.

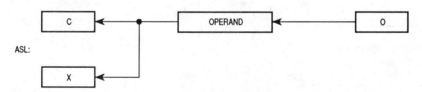

ASL:

ASL, ASR   Arithmetic Shift   ASL, ASR
(M68000 Family)

For ASR, the operand is shifted right; the number of positions shifted is the shift count. Bits shifted out of the low-order bit go to both the carry and the extend bits; the sign bit (MSB) is shifted into the high-order bit.

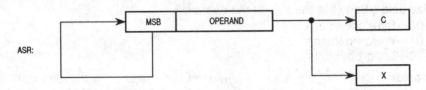

Condition Codes:

X	N	Z	V	C
*	*	*	*	*

X—Set according to the last bit shifted out of the operand; unaffected for a shift count of zero.

N—Set if the most significant bit of the result is set; cleared otherwise.

Z—Set if the result is zero; cleared otherwise.

V—Set if the most significant bit is changed at any time during the shift operation; cleared otherwise.

C—Set according to the last bit shifted out of the operand; cleared for a shift count of zero.

Instruction Format:

Register Shifts

15	14	13	12	11	10	9	8	7	6	5	4	3	2	1	0
1	1	1	0	COUNT/ REGISTER			dr	SIZE		i/r	0	0	REGISTER		

Instruction Fields:

Count/Register field—Specifies shift count or register that contains the shift count:

If i/r = 0, this field contains the shift count. The values 1–7 represent counts of 1–7; a value of zero represents a count of eight.

If i/r = 1, this field specifies the data register that contains the shift count (modulo 64).

dr field—Specifies the direction of the shift.
   0—Shift right
   1—Shift left

Size field—Specifies the size of the operation.
   00—Byte operation
   01—Word operation
   10—Long operation

i/r field
   If i/r = 0, specifies immediate shift count.
   If i/r = 1, specifies register shift count.

Register field—Specifies a data register to be shifted.

Instruction Format:

Memory Shifts

15	14	13	12	11	10	9	8	7	6	5	4	3	2	1	0
1	1	1	0	0	0	0	dr	1	1	|EFFECTIVE ADDRESS|					
										MODE			REGISTER		

Instruction Fields:

dr field—Specifies the direction of the shift.
   0—Shift right
   1—Shift left

Effective Address field—Specifies the operand to be shifted. Only memory alterable addressing modes can be used as listed in the following tables:

Addressing Mode	Mode	Register
Dn	—	—
An	—	—
(An)	010	reg. number:An
(An) +	011	reg. number:An
– (An)	100	reg. number:An
(d$_{16}$,An)	101	reg. number:An
(d$_8$,An,Xn)	110	reg. number:An

Addressing Mode	Mode	Register
(xxx).W	111	000
(xxx).L	111	001
#<data>	—	—
(d$_{16}$,PC)	—	—
(d$_8$,PC,Xn)	—	—

MC68020, MC68030, and MC68040 only

Addressing Mode	Mode	Register
(bd,An,Xn)*	110	reg. number:An
([bd,An,Xn],od)	110	reg. number:An
([bd,An],Xn,od)	110	reg. number:An

Addressing Mode	Mode	Register
(bd,PC,Xn)*	—	—
([bd,PC,Xn],od)	—	—
([bd,PC],Xn,od)	—	—

*Can be used with CPU32.

Bcc

Operation: If Condition True
Then PC + d_n → PC

**Assembler
Syntax:**   Bcc <label>

Attributes: Size = (Byte, Word, Long*)

*(MC68020, MC68030, and MC68040 only)

Description: If the specified condition is true, program execution continues at location (PC) + displacement. The program counter contains the address of the instruction word for the Bcc instruction plus two. The displacement is a twos-complement integer that represents the relative distance in bytes from the current program counter to the destination program counter. If the 8-bit displacement field in the instruction word is zero, a 16-bit displacement (the word immediately following the instruction) is used. If the 8-bit displacement field in the instruction word is all ones ($FF), the 32-bit displacement (long word immediately following the instruction) is used. Condition code cc specifies one of the following conditional tests (refer to Table 3-19 for more information on these conditional tests):

Mnemonic	Condition	Mnemonic	Condition
CC(HI)	Carry Clear	LS	Low or Same
CS(LO)	Carry Set	LT	Less Than
EQ	Equal	MI	Minus
GE	Greater or Equal	NE	Not Equal
GT	Greater Than	PL	Plus
HI	High	VC	Overflow Clear
LE	Less or Equal	VS	Overflow Set

Condition Codes:
Not affected.

Branch Conditionally
(M68000 Family)

Instruction Format:

15	14	13	12	11	10	9	8	7	6	5	4	3	2	1	0
0	1	1	0		CONDITION					8-BIT DISPLACEMENT					
16-BIT DISPLACEMENT IF 8-BIT DISPLACEMENT = $00															
32-BIT DISPLACEMENT IF 8-BIT DISPLACEMENT = $FF															

Instruction Fields:

Condition field—The binary code for one of the conditions listed in the table.

8-Bit Displacement field—Twos complement integer specifying the number of bytes between the branch instruction and the next instruction to be executed if the condition is met.

16-Bit Displacement field—Used for the displacement when the 8-bit displacement field contains $00.

32-Bit Displacement field—Used for the displacement when the 8-bit displacement field contains $FF.

NOTE

A branch to the immediately following instruction automatically uses the 16-bit displacement format because the 8-bit displacement field contains $00 (zero offset).

BCHG

Test a Bit and Change
(M68000 Family)

Operation: TEST (<number> of Destination) ♦ Z;
TEST (<number> of Destination) ♦ <bit number> of Destination

Assembler BCHG Dn,<ea>
Syntax: BCHG #<data>,<ea>

Attributes: Size = (Byte, Long)

Description: Tests a bit in the destination operand and sets the Z condition code appropriately, then inverts the specified bit in the destination. When the destination is a data register, any of the 32 bits can be specified by the modulo 32-bit number. When the destination is a memory location, the operation is a byte operation, and the bit number is modulo 8. In all cases, bit zero refers to the least significant bit. The bit number for this operation may be specified in either of two ways:

1. Immediate—The bit number is specified in a second word of the instruction.
2. Register—The specified data register contains the bit number.

Condition Codes:

X	N	Z	V	C
—	—	*	—	—

X—Not affected.
N—Not affected.
Z—Set if the bit tested is zero; cleared otherwise.
V—Not affected.
C—Not affected.

BCHG

Test a Bit and Change
(M68000 Family)

BCHG

Instruction Format:

Bit Number Dynamic, Specified in a Register

15	14	13	12	11	10	9	8	7	6	5	4	3	2	1	0
0	0	0	0	REGISTER			1	0	1	EFFECTIVE ADDRESS					
										MODE			REGISTER		

Instruction Fields:

Register field—Specifies the data register that contains the bit number.

Effective Address field—Specifies the destination location. Only data alterable addressing modes can be used as listed in the following tables:

Addressing Mode	Mode	Register	Addressing Mode	Mode	Register
Dn*	000	reg. number:Dn	(xxx).W	111	000
An	—	—	(xxx).L	111	001
(An)	010	reg. number:An	#<data>	—	—
(An) +	011	reg. number:An			
– (An)	100	reg. number:An			
(d$_{16}$,An)	101	reg. number:An	(d$_{16}$,PC)	—	—
(d$_8$,An,Xn)	110	reg. number:An	(d$_8$,PC,Xn)	—	—

MC68020, MC68030, and MC68040 only

(bd,An,Xn)**	110	reg. number:An	(bd,PC,Xn)**	—	—
([bd,An,Xn],od)	110	reg. number:An	([bd,PC,Xn],od)	—	—
([bd,An],Xn,od)	110	reg. number:An	([bd,PC],Xn,od)	—	—

*Long only; all others are byte only.

**Can be used with CPU32.

Instruction Format:

Bit Number Static, Specified as Immediate Data

15	14	13	12	11	10	9	8	7	6	5	4	3	2	1	0
0	0	0	0	1	0	0	0	0	1		EFFECTIVE ADDRESS				
											MODE		REGISTER		
0	0	0	0	0	0	0	0				BIT NUMBER				

Instruction Fields:

Effective Address field—Specifies the destination location. Only data alterable addressing modes can be used as listed in the following tables:

Addressing Mode	Mode	Register
Dn*	000	reg. number:Dn
An	—	—
(An)	010	reg. number:An
(An) +	011	reg. number:An
– (An)	100	reg. number:An
(d_{16},An)	101	reg. number:An
(d_8,An,Xn)	110	reg. number:An

Addressing Mode	Mode	Register
(xxx).W	111	000
(xxx).L	111	001
#<data>	—	—
(d_{16},PC)	—	—
(d_8,PC,Xn)	—	—

MC68020, MC68030, and MC68040 only

(bd,An,Xn)**	110	reg. number:An
([bd,An,Xn],od)	110	reg. number:An
([bd,An],Xn,od)	110	reg. number:An

(bd,PC,Xn)**	—	—
([bd,PC,Xn],od)	—	—
([bd,PC],Xn,od)	—	—

*Long only; all others are byte only.

**Can be used with CPU32.

Bit Number field—Specifies the bit number.

Test a Bit and Clear
(M68000 Family)

Operation: TEST (<bit number> of Destination) ♦ Z; 0 ♦ <bit number> of Destination

Assembler   BCLR Dn,<ea>
Syntax: BCLR #<data>,<ea>

Attributes: Size = (Byte, Long)

Description: Tests a bit in the destination operand and sets the Z condition code appropriately, then clears the specified bit in the destination. When a data register is the destination, any of the 32 bits can be specified by a modulo 32-bit number. When a memory location is the destination, the operation is a byte operation, and the bit number is modulo 8. In all cases, bit zero refers to the least significant bit. The bit number for this operation can be specified in either of two ways:

1. Immediate—The bit number is specified in a second word of the instruction.
2. Register—The specified data register contains the bit number.

Condition Codes:

X	N	Z	V	C
—	—	*	—	—

X—Not affected.
N—Not affected.
Z—Set if the bit tested is zero; cleared otherwise.
V—Not affected.
C—Not affected.

BCLR

BCLR

Instruction Format:

Bit Number Dynamic, Specified in a Register

15	14	13	12	11	10	9	8	7	6	5	4	3	2	1	0
0	0	0	0	REGISTER			1	1	0	EFFECTIVE ADDRESS					
										MODE			REGISTER		

Instruction Fields:

Register field—Specifies the data register that contains the bit number.

Effective Address field—Specifies the destination location. Only data alterable addressing modes can be used as listed in the following tables:

Addressing Mode	Mode	Register
Dn*	000	reg. number:Dn
An	—	—
(An)	010	reg. number:An
(An) +	011	reg. number:An
– (An)	100	reg. number:An
(d_{16},An)	101	reg. number:An
(d_8,An,Xn)	110	reg. number:An

Addressing Mode	Mode	Register
(xxx).W	111	000
(xxx).L	111	001
#<data>	—	—
(d_{16},PC)	—	—
(d_8,PC,Xn)	—	—

MC68020, MC68030, and MC68040 only

(bd,An,Xn)**	110	reg. number:An
([bd,An,Xn],od)	110	reg. number:An
([bd,An],Xn,od)	110	reg. number:An

(bd,PC,Xn)**	—	—
([bd,PC,Xn],od)	—	—
([bd,PC],Xn,od)	—	—

*Long only; all others are byte only.
**Can be used with CPU32.

BCLR

Test a Bit and Clear
(M68000 Family)

BCLR

Instruction Format:

Bit Number Static, Specified as Immediate Data

15	14	13	12	11	10	9	8	7	6	5	4	3	2	1	0
0	0	0	0	1	0	0	0	1	0	EFFECTIVE ADDRESS MODE				REGISTER	
0	0	0	0	0	0	0	0	BIT NUMBER							

Instruction Fields:

Effective Address field—Specifies the destination location. Only data alterable addressing modes can be used as listed in the following tables:

Addressing Mode	Mode	Register	Addressing Mode	Mode	Register
Dn*	000	reg. number:Dn	(xxx).W	111	000
An	—	—	(xxx).L	111	001
(An)	010	reg. number:An	#<data>	—	—
(An)+	011	reg. number:An			
–(An)	100	reg. number:An			
(d$_{16}$,An)	101	reg. number:An	(d$_{16}$,PC)	—	—
(d$_8$,An,Xn)	110	reg. number:An	(d$_8$,PC,Xn)	—	—

MC68020, MC68030, and MC68040 only

(bd,An,Xn)**	110	reg. number:An	(bd,PC,Xn)**	—	—
([bd,An,Xn],od)	110	reg. number:An	([bd,PC,Xn],od)	—	—
([bd,An],Xn,od)	110	reg. number:An	([bd,PC],Xn,od)	—	—

*Long only; all others are byte only.

**Can be used with CPU32.

Bit Number field—Specifies the bit number.

Operation: TEST (<bit field> of Destination) ♦ <bit field> of Destination

**Assembler
Syntax**:   BFCHG <ea>{offset:width}

Attributes: Unsized

Description: Sets the condition codes according to the value in a bit field at the specified effective address, then complements the field.

A field offset and a field width select the field. The field offset specifies the starting bit of the field. The field width determines the number of bits in the field.

Condition Codes:

X	N	Z	V	C
—	*	*	0	0

X—Not affected.
N—Set if the most significant bit of the field is set; cleared otherwise.
Z—Set if all bits of the field are zero; cleared otherwise.
V—Always cleared.
C—Always cleared.

Instruction Format:

15	14	13	12	11	10	9	8	7	6	5	4	3	2	1	0
1	1	1	0	1	0	1	0	1	1		EFFECTIVE ADDRESS				
											MODE		REGISTER		
0	0	0	0	Do			OFFSET			Dw			WIDTH		

NOTE

For the MC68020, MC68030, and MC68040, all bit field instructions access only those bytes in memory that contain some portion of the bit field. The possible accesses are byte, word, 3-byte, long word, and long word with byte (for a 5-byte access).

BFCHG

Test Bit Field and Change
(MC68020, MC68030, MC68040)

BFCHG

Instruction Fields:

Effective Address field—Specifies the base location for the bit field. Only data register direct or control alterable addressing modes can be used as listed in the following table:

Addressing Mode	Mode	Register	Addressing Mode	Mode	Register
Dn	000	reg. number:Dn	(xxx).W	111	000
An	—	—	(xxx).L	111	001
(An)	010	reg. number:An	#<data>	—	—
(An) +	—	—			
– (An)	—	—			
(d$_{16}$,An)	101	reg. number:An	(d$_{16}$,PC)	—	—
(d$_8$,An,Xn)	110	reg. number:An	(d$_8$,PC,Xn)	—	—
(bd,An,Xn)	110	reg. number:An	(bd,PC,Xn)	—	—
([bd,An,Xn],od)	110	reg. number:An	([bd,PC,Xn],od)	—	—
([bd,An],Xn,od)	110	reg. number:An	([bd,PC],Xn,od)	—	—

Do field—Determines how the field offset is specified.
  0—The offset field contains the bit field offset.
  1—Bits 8–6 of the extension word specify a data register that contains the offset; bits 10–9 are zero.

Offset field—Specifies the field offset, depending on Do.
  If Do = 0, the offset field is an immediate operand; the operand value is in the range 0–31.
  If Do = 1, the offset field specifies a data register that contains the offset. The value is in the range of -2^{31} to $2^{31} - 1$.

Dw field—Determines how the field width is specified.
  0—The width field contains the bit field width.
  1—Bits 2–0 of the extension word specify a data register that contains the width; bits 3–4 are zero.

Width field—Specifies the field width, depending on Dw.
  If Dw = 0, the width field is an immediate operand; an operand value in the range 1–31 specifies a field width of 1–31, and a value of zero specifies a width of 32.
  If Dw = 1, the width field specifies a data register that contains the width. The value is modulo 32; values of 1–31 specify field widths of 1–31, and a value of zero specifies a width of 32.

BFCLR

Operation: 0 ♦ <bit field> of Destination

**Assembler
Syntax:** BFCLR <ea>{offset:width}

Attributes: Unsized

Description: Sets condition codes according to the value in a bit field at the specified effective address and clears the field.

The field offset and field width select the field. The field offset specifies the starting bit of the field. The field width determines the number of bits in the field.

Condition Codes:

X	N	Z	V	C
—	*	*	0	0

X—Not affected.
N—Set if the most significant bit of the field is set; cleared otherwise.
Z—Set if all bits of the field are zero; cleared otherwise.
V—Always cleared.
C—Always cleared.

Instruction Format:

15	14	13	12	11	10	9	8	7	6	5	4	3	2	1	0
1	1	1	0	1	1	0	0	1	1	\multicolumn{6}{EFFECTIVE ADDRESS}					

15	14	13	12	11	10	9	8	7	6	5	4	3	2	1	0
1	1	1	0	1	1	0	0	1	1	MODE			REGISTER		
0	0	0	0	Do	OFFSET				Dw	WIDTH					

Instruction Fields:

Effective Address field—Specifies the base location for the bit field. Only data register direct or control alterable addressing modes can be used as listed in the following table:

Addressing Mode	Mode	Register	Addressing Mode	Mode	Register
Dn	000	reg. number:Dn	(xxx).W	111	000
An	—	—	(xxx).L	111	001
(An)	010	reg. number:An	#<data>	—	—
(An) +	—	—			
– (An)	—	—			
(d_{16},An)	101	reg. number:An	(d_{16},PC)	—	—
(d_8,An,Xn)	110	reg. number:An	(d_8,PC,Xn)	—	—
(bd,An,Xn)	110	reg. number:An	(bd,PC,Xn)	—	—
([bd,An,Xn],od)	110	reg. number:An	([bd,PC,Xn],od)	—	—
([bd,An],Xn,od)	110	reg. number:An	([bd,PC],Xn,od)	—	—

Do field—Determines how the field offset is specified.

0—The offset field contains the bit field offset.

1—Bits 8–6 of the extension word specify a data register that contains the offset; bits 10–9 are zero.

Offset field—Specifies the field offset, depending on Do.

If Do = 0, the offset field is an immediate operand; the operand value is in the range of 0–31.

If Do = 1, the offset field specifies a data register that contains the offset. The value is in the range of -2^{31} to $2^{31}-1$.

Dw field—Determines how the field width is specified.

0—The width field contains the bit field width.

1—Bits 2–0 of the extension word specify a data register that contains the width; bits 3–4 are zero.

Width field—Specifies the field width, depending on Dw.

If Dw = 0, the width field is an immediate operand; operand values in the range of 1–31 specify a field width of 1–31, and a value of zero specifies a width of 32.

If Dw = 1, the width field specifies a data register that contains the width. The value is modulo 32; values of 1–31 specify field widths of 1–31, and a value of zero specifies a width of 32.

BFEXTS

Extract Bit Field Signed
(MC68020, MC68030, MC68040)

BFEXTS

Operation: <bit field> of Source ♦ Dn

**Assembler
Syntax:**   BFEXTS <ea>{offset:width},Dn

Attributes: Unsized

Description: Extracts a bit field from the specified effective address location, sign extends to 32 bits, and loads the result into the destination data register.

The field offset and field width select the bit field. The field offset specifies the starting bit of the field. The field width determines the number of bits in the field.

Condition Codes:

X	N	Z	V	C
—	*	*	0	0

X—Not affected.
N—Set if the most significant bit of the field is set; cleared otherwise.
Z—Set if all bits of the field are zero; cleared otherwise.
V—Always cleared.
C—Always cleared.

Instruction Format:

15	14	13	12	11	10	9	8	7	6	5	4	3	2	1	0
1	1	1	0	1	0	1	1	1	1	EFFECTIVE ADDRESS MODE			REGISTER		
0	REGISTER		Do	OFFSET						Dw	WIDTH				

Instruction Fields:

Effective Address field—Specifies the base location for the bit field. Only data register direct or control addressing modes can be used as listed in the following table:

Addressing Mode	Mode	Register	Addressing Mode	Mode	Register
Dn	000	reg. number:Dn	(xxx).W	111	000
An	—	—	(xxx).L	111	001
(An)	010	reg. number:An	#<data>	—	—
(An) +	—	—			
– (An)	—	—			
(d$_{16}$,An)	101	reg. number:An	(d$_{16}$,PC)	111	010
(d$_8$,An,Xn)	110	reg. number:An	(d$_8$,PC,Xn)	111	011
(bd,An,Xn)	110	reg. number:An	(bd,PC,Xn)	111	011
([bd,An,Xn],od)	110	reg. number:An	([bd,PC,Xn],od)	111	011
([bd,An],Xn,od)	110	reg. number:An	([bd,PC],Xn,od)	111	011

Register field—Specifies the destination register.

Do field—Determines how the field offset is specified.
  0—The offset field contains the bit field offset.
  1—Bits 8–6 of the extension word specify a data register that contains the offset; bits 10–9 are zero.

Offset field—Specifies the field offset, depending on Do.
  If Do = 0, the offset field is an immediate operand; the operand value is in the range of 0–31.
  If Do = 1, the offset field specifies a data register that contains the offset. The value is in the range of -2^{31} to $2^{31}-1$.

Dw field—Determines how the field width is specified.
  0—The width field contains the bit field width.
  1—Bits 2–0 of the extension word specify a data register that contains the width; bits 4–3 are zero.

BFEXTS

Extract Bit Field Signed
(MC68020, MC68030, MC68040)

BFEXTS

Width field—Specifies the field width, depending on Dw.

If Dw = 0, the width field is an immediate operand; operand values in the range of 1–31 specify a field width of 1–31, and a value of zero specifies a width of 32.

If Dw = 1, the width field specifies a data register that contains the width. The value is modulo 32; values of 1–31 specify field widths of 1–31, and a value of zero specifies a width of 32.

4

BFEXTU

Extract Bit Field Unsigned
(MC68020, MC68030, MC68040)

BFEXTU

Operation: <bit offset> of Source → Dn

**Assembler
Syntax:** BFEXTU <ea>{offset:width},Dn

Attributes: Unsized

Description: Extracts a bit field from the specified effective address location, zero extends to 32 bits, and loads the results into the destination data register.

The field offset and field width select the field. The field offset specifies the starting bit of the field. The field width determines the number of bits in the field.

Condition Codes:

X	N	Z	V	C
—	*	*	0	0

X—Not affected.
N—Set if the most significant bit of the source field is set; cleared otherwise.
Z—Set if all bits of the field are zero; cleared otherwise.
V—Always cleared.
C—Always cleared.

Instruction Format:

15	14	13	12	11	10	9	8	7	6	5	4	3	2	1	0
1	1	1	0	1	0	0	1	1	1	EFFECTIVE ADDRESS MODE			REGISTER		
0	REGISTER			Do	OFFSET					Dw	WIDTH				

Instruction Fields:

Effective Address field—Specifies the base location for the bit field. Only data register direct or control addressing modes can be used as listed in the following table:

Addressing Mode	Mode	Register	Addressing Mode	Mode	Register
Dn	000	reg. number:Dn	(xxx).W	111	000
An	—	—	(xxx).L	111	001
(An)	010	reg. number:An	#<data>	—	—
(An) +	—	—			
– (An)	—	—			
(d$_{16}$,An)	101	reg. number:An	(d$_{16}$,PC)	111	010
(d$_8$,An,Xn)	110	reg. number:An	(d$_8$,PC,Xn)	111	011
(bd,An,Xn)	110	reg. number:An	(bd,PC,Xn)	111	011
([bd,An,Xn],od)	110	reg. number:An	([bd,PC,Xn],od)	111	011
([bd,An],Xn,od)	110	reg. number:An	([bd,PC],Xn,od)	111	011

Register field—Specifies the destination data register.

Do field—Determines how the field offset is specified.
   0—The offset field contains the bit field offset.
   1—Bits 8–6 of the extension word specify a data register that contains the offset; bits 10–9 are zero.

Offset field—Specifies the field offset, depending on Do.
   If Do = 0, the offset field is an immediate operand; the operand value is in the range of 0–31.
   If Do = 1, the offset field specifies a data register that contains the offset. The value is in the range of -2^{31} to $2^{31}-1$.

Dw field—Determines how the field width is specified.
   0—The width field contains the bit field width.
   1—Bits 2–0 of the extension word specify a data register that contains the width; bits 4–3 are zero.

Width field—Specifies the field width, depending on Dw.

If Dw = 0, the width field is an immediate operand; operand values in the range of 1–31 specify a field width of 1–31, and a value of zero specifies a width of 32.

If Dw = 1, the width field specifies a data register that contains the width. The value is modulo 32; values of 1–31 specify field widths of 1–31, and a value of zero specifies a width of 32.

BFFFO

Operation: <bit offset> of Source Bit Scan ♦ Dn

**Assembler
Syntax**:   BFFFO <ea>{offset:width},Dn

Attributes: Unsized

Description: Searches the source operand for the most significant bit that is set to a value of one. The bit offset of that bit (the bit offset in the instruction plus the offset of the first one bit) is placed in Dn. If no bit in the bit field is set to one, the value in Dn is the field offset plus the field width. The instruction sets the condition codes according to the bit field value.

The field offset and field width select the field. The field offset specifies the starting bit of the field. The field width determines the number of bits in the field.

Condition Codes:

X	N	Z	V	C
—	*	*	0	0

X—Not affected.
N—Set if the most significant bit of the field is set; cleared otherwise.
Z—Set if all bits of the field are zero; cleared otherwise.
V—Always cleared.
C—Always cleared.

Instruction Format:

15	14	13	12	11	10	9	8	7	6	5	4	3	2	1	0
1	1	1	0	1	1	0	1	1	1	— EFFECTIVE ADDRESS					
										MODE			REGISTER		
0	REGISTER		Do	OFFSET						Dw	WIDTH				

Instruction Fields:

Effective Address field—Specifies the base location for the bit field. Only data register direct or control addressing modes can be used as listed in the following table:

Addressing Mode	Mode	Register	Addressing Mode	Mode	Register
Dn	000	reg. number:Dn	(xxx).W	111	000
An	—	—	(xxx).L	111	001
(An)	010	reg. number:An	#<data>	—	—
(An) +	—	—			
– (An)	—	—			
(d_{16},An)	101	reg. number:An	(d_{16},PC)	111	010
(d_8,An,Xn)	110	reg. number:An	(d_8,PC,Xn)	111	011
(bd,An,Xn)	110	reg. number:An	(bd,PC,Xn)	111	011
([bd,An,Xn],od)	110	reg. number:An	([bd,PC,Xn],od)	111	011
([bd,An],Xn,od)	110	reg. number:An	([bd,PC],Xn,od)	111	011

Register field—Specifies the destination data register operand.

Do field—Determines how the field offset is specified.
  0—The offset field contains the bit field offset.
  1—Bits 8–6 of the extension word specify a data register that contains the offset; bits 10–9 are zero.

Offset field—Specifies the field offset, depending on Do.
  If Do = 0, the offset field is an immediate operand; the operand value is in the range of 0–31.
  If Do = 1, the offset field specifies a data register that contains the offset. The value is in the range of -2^{31} to $2^{31} - 1$.

Dw field—Determines how the field width is specified.
  0—The width field contains the bit field width.
  1—Bits 2–0 of the extension word specify a data register that contains the width; bits 4–3 are zero.

Find First One in Bit Field
(MC68020, MC68030, MC68040)

Width field—Specifies the field width, depending on Dw.

If Dw = 0, the width field is an immediate operand; operand values in the range of 1–31 specify a field width of 1–31, and a value of zero specifies a width of 32.

If Dw = 1, the width field specifies a data register that contains the width. The value is modulo 32; values of 1–31 specify field widths of 1–31, and a value of zero specifies a width of 32.

4

Operation: Dn ♦ <bit field> of Destination

**Assembler
Syntax**:   BFINS Dn,<ea>{offset:width}

Attributes: Unsized

Description: Inserts a bit field taken from the low-order bits of the specified data register into a bit field at the effective address location. The instruction sets the condition codes according to the inserted value.

The field offset and field width select the field. The field offset specifies the starting bit of the field. The field width determines the number of bits in the field.

Condition Codes:

X	N	Z	V	C
—	*	*	0	0

X—Not affected.
N—Set if the most significant bit of the field is set; cleared otherwise.
Z—Set if all bits of the field are zero; cleared otherwise.
V—Always cleared.
C—Always cleared.

Instruction Format:

15	14	13	12	11	10	9	8	7	6	5	4	3	2	1	0
1	1	1	0	1	1	1	1	1	1	_ EFFECTIVE ADDRESS _					
										MODE			REGISTER		
0	REGISTER			Do	OFFSET					Dw	WIDTH				

Insert Bit Field
(MC68020, MC68030, MC68040)

Instruction Fields:

Effective Address field—Specifies the base location for the bit field. Only data register direct or control alterable addressing modes can be used as listed in the following table:

Addressing Mode	Mode	Register	Addressing Mode	Mode	Register
Dn	000	reg. number:Dn	(xxx).W	111	000
An	—	—	(xxx).L	111	001
(An)	010	reg. number:An	#<data>	—	—
(An) +	—	—			
– (An)	—	—			
(d_{16},An)	101	reg. number:An	(d_{16},PC)	—	—
(d_8,An,Xn)	110	reg. number:An	(d_8,PC,Xn)	—	—
(bd,An,Xn)	110	reg. number:An	(bd,PC,Xn)	—	—
([bd,An,Xn],od)	110	reg. number:An	([bd,PC,Xn],od)	—	—
([bd,An],Xn,od)	110	reg. number:An	([bd,PC],Xn,od)	—	—

Register field—Specifies the source data register operand.

Do field—Determines how the field offset is specified.
0—The offset field contains the bit field offset.
1—Bits 8–6 of the extension word specify a data register that contains the offset; bits 10–9 are zero.

Offset field—Specifies the field offset, depending on Do.
If Do = 0, the offset field is an immediate operand; the operand value is in the range of 0–31.
If Do = 1, the offset field specifies a data register that contains the offset. The value is in the range of -2^{31} to $2^{31} - 1$.

Dw field—Determines how the field width is specified.
0—The width field contains the bit field width.
1—Bits 2–0 of the extension word specify a data register that contains the width; bits 4–3 are zero.

Insert Bit Field
(MC68020, MC68030, MC68040)

Width field—Specifies the field width, depending on Dw.

If Dw = 0, the width field is an immediate operand; operand values in the range of 1–31 specify a field width of 1–31, and a value of zero specifies a width of 32.

If Dw = 1, the width field specifies a data register that contains the width. The value is modulo 32; values of 1–31 specify field widths of 1–31, and a value of zero specifies a width of 32.

BFSET

Test Bit Field and Set
(MC68020, MC68030, MC68040)

Operation: 1 ♦ \<bit field\> of Destination

Assembler
Syntax: BFSET \<ea\>{offset:width}

Attributes: Unsized

Description: Sets the condition codes according to the value in a bit field at the specified effective address, then sets each bit in the field.

The field offset and the field width select the field. The field offset specifies the starting bit of the field. The field width determines the number of bits in the field.

4

Condition Codes:

X	N	Z	V	C
—	*	*	0	0

X—Not affected.
N—Set if the most significant bit of the field is set; cleared otherwise.
Z—Set if all bits of the field are zero; cleared otherwise.
V—Always cleared.
C—Always cleared.

Instruction Format:

15	14	13	12	11	10	9	8	7	6	5	4	3	2	1	0
1	1	1	0	1	1	1	0	1	1	EFFECTIVE ADDRESS					

15	14	13	12	11	10	9	8	7	6	5	4	3	2	1	0
1	1	1	0	1	1	1	0	1	1	MODE			REGISTER		
0	0	0	0	Do	OFFSET					Dw	WIDTH				

Instruction Fields:

Effective Address field—Specifies the base location for the bit field. Only data register direct or control alterable addressing modes can be used as listed in the following table:

Addressing Mode	Mode	Register	Addressing Mode	Mode	Register
Dn	000	reg. number:Dn	(xxx).W	111	000
An	—	—	(xxx).L	111	001
(An)	010	reg. number:An	#<data>	—	—
(An) +	—	—			
– (An)	—	—			
(d$_{16}$,An)	101	reg. number:An	(d$_{16}$,PC)	—	—
(d$_8$,An,Xn)	110	reg. number:An	(d$_8$,PC,Xn)	—	—
(bd,An,Xn)	110	reg. number:An	(bd,PC,Xn)	—	—
([bd,An,Xn],od)	110	reg. number:An	([bd,PC,Xn],od)	—	—
([bd,An],Xn,od)	110	reg. number:An	([bd,PC],Xn,od)	—	—

Do field—Determines how the field offset is specified.
    0—The offset field contains the bit field offset.
    1—Bits 8–6 of the extension word specify a data register that contains the offset; bits 10–9 are zero.

Offset field—Specifies the field offset, depending on Do.
    If Do = 0, the offset field is an immediate operand; the operand value is in the range of 0–31.
    If Do = 1, the offset field specifies a data register that contains the offset. The value is in the range of -2^{31} to $2^{31} - 1$.

Dw field—Determines how the field width is specified.
    0—The width field contains the bit field width.
    1—Bits 2–0 of the extension word specify a data register that contains the width; bits 4–3 are zero.

Width field—Specifies the field width, depending on Dw.
    If Dw = 0, the width field is an immediate operand; operand values in the range of 1–31 specify a field width of 1–31, and a value of zero specifies a width of 32.
    If Dw = 1, the width field specifies a data register that contains the width. The value is modulo 32; values of 1–31 specify field widths of 1–31, and a value of zero specifies a width of 32.

BFTST

Operation: \<bit field\> of Destination

**Assembler
Syntax:**   BFTST \<ea\>{offset:width}

Attributes: Unsized

Description: Sets the condition codes according to the value in a bit field at the specified effective address location.

The field offset and field width select the field. The field offset specifies the starting bit of the field. The field width determines the number of bits in the field.

Condition Codes:

X	N	Z	V	C
—	*	*	0	0

X—Not affected.
N—Set if the most significant bit of the field is set; cleared otherwise.
Z—Set if all bits of the field are zero; cleared otherwise.
V—Always cleared.
C—Always cleared.

Instruction Format:

15	14	13	12	11	10	9	8	7	6	5	4	3	2	1	0
1	1	1	0	1	0	0	0	1	1	EFFECTIVE ADDRESS					
										MODE			REGISTER		
0	0	0	0	Do	OFFSET					Dw	WIDTH				

Instruction Fields:

Effective Address field—Specifies the base location for the bit field. Only data register direct or control addressing modes can be used as listed in the following table:

Addressing Mode	Mode	Register	Addressing Mode	Mode	Register
Dn	000	reg. number:Dn	(xxx).W	111	000
An	—	—	(xxx).L	111	001
(An)	010	reg. number:An	#<data>	—	—
(An) +	—	—			
– (An)	—	—			
(d_{16},An)	101	reg. number:An	(d_{16},PC)	111	010
(d_8,An,Xn)	110	reg. number:An	(d_8,PC,Xn)	111	011
(bd,An,Xn)	110	reg. number:An	(bd,PC,Xn)	111	011
([bd,An,Xn],od)	110	reg. number:An	([bd,PC,Xn],od)	111	011
([bd,An],Xn,od)	110	reg. number:An	([bd,PC],Xn,od)	111	011

Do field—Determines how the field offset is specified.
  0—The offset field contains the bit field offset.
  1—Bits 8–6 of the extension word specify a data register that contains the offset; bits 10–9 are zero.

Offset field—Specifies the field offset, depending on Do.
  If Do = 0, the offset field is an immediate operand; the operand value is in the range of 0–31.
  If Do = 1, the offset field specifies a data register that contains the offset. The value is in the range of -2^{31} to $2^{31} - 1$.

Dw field—Determines how the field width is specified.
  0—The width field contains the bit field width.
  1—Bits 2–0 of the extension word specify a data register that contains the width; bits 4–3 are zero.

Width field—Specifies the field width, depending on Dw.
  If Dw = 0, the width field is an immediate operand, operand values in the range of 1–31 specify a field width of 1–31, and a value of zero specifies a width of 32.
  If Dw = 1, the width field specifies a data register that contains the width. The value is modulo 32; values of 1–31 specify field widths of 1–31, and a value of zero specifies a width of 32.

BKPT

BKPT
Breakpoint
(MC68EC000, MC68010, MC68020,
MC68030, MC68040, CPU32)

BKPT

Operation: Run Breakpoint Acknowledge Cycle; TRAP As Illegal Instruction

**Assembler
Syntax**: BKPT #<data>

Attributes: Unsized

Description: For the MC68010, a breakpoint acknowledge bus cycle is run with function codes driven high and zeros on all address lines. Whether the breakpoint acknowledge bus cycle is terminated with $\overline{DTACK}$, $\overline{BERR}$, or $\overline{VPA}$, the processor always takes an illegal instruction exception. During exception processing, a debug monitor can distinguish different software breakpoints by decoding the field in the BKPT instruction. For the MC68000 and MC68008, the breakpoint cycle is not run, but an illegal instruction exception is taken.

For the MC68020, MC68030, and CPU32, a breakpoint acknowledge bus cycle is executed with the immediate data (value 0–7) on bits 2–4 of the address bus and zeros on bits 0 and 1 of the address bus. The breakpoint acknowledge bus cycle accesses the CPU space, addressing type 0, and provides the breakpoint number specified by the instruction on address lines A2–A4. If the external hardware terminates the cycle with $\overline{DSACKx}$ or $\overline{STERM}$, the data on the bus (an instruction word) is inserted into the instruction pipe and is executed after the breakpoint instruction. The breakpoint instruction requires a word to be transferred so, if the first bus cycle accesses an 8-bit port, a second bus cycle is required. If the external logic terminates the breakpoint acknowledge bus cycle with $\overline{BERR}$ (i.e., no instruction word available), the processor takes an illegal instruction exception.

For the MC68040, this instruction executes a breakpoint acknowledge bus cycle. Regardless of the cycle termination, the MC68040 takes an illegal instruction exception.

For more information on the breakpoint instruction refer to the appropriate user's manual on bus operation.

This instruction supports breakpoints for debug monitors and real-time hardware emulators.

Breakpoint
(MC68EC000, MC68010, MC68020,
MC68030, MC68040, CPU32)

Condition Codes:
Not affected.

Instruction Format:

15	14	13	12	11	10	9	8	7	6	5	4	3	2	1	0
0	1	0	0	1	0	0	0	0	1	0	0	1		VECTOR	

Instruction Field:

Vector field—Contains the immediate data, a value in the range of 0–7. This is the breakpoint number.

BRA

Operation: $PC + d_n \rightarrow PC$

**Assembler
Syntax:** BRA <label>

Attributes: Size = (Byte, Word, Long*)

*(MC68020, MC68030, MC68040 only)

Description: Program execution continues at location (PC) + displacement. The program counter contains the address of the instruction word of the BRA instruction plus two. The displacement is a twos complement integer that represents the relative distance in bytes from the current program counter to the destination program counter. If the 8-bit displacement field in the instruction word is zero, a 16-bit displacement (the word immediately following the instruction) is used. If the 8-bit displacement field in the instruction word is all ones ($FF), the 32-bit displacement (long word immediately following the instruction) is used.

Condition Codes:
Not affected.

Instruction Format:

15	14	13	12	11	10	9	8	7	6	5	4	3	2	1	0
0	1	1	0	0	0	0	0			8-BIT DISPLACEMENT					
16-BIT DISPLACEMENT IF 8-BIT DISPLACEMENT = $00															
32-BIT DISPLACEMENT IF 8-BIT DISPLACEMENT = $FF															

Instruction Fields:

8-Bit Displacement field—Twos complement integer specifying the number of bytes between the branch instruction and the next instruction to be executed.

16-Bit Displacement field—Used for a larger displacement when the 8-bit displacement is equal to $00.

32-Bit Displacement field—Used for a larger displacement when the 8-bit displacement is equal to $FF.

NOTE

A branch to the immediately following instruction automatically uses the 16-bit displacement format because the 8-bit displacement field contains $00 (zero offset).

Operation: TEST (<bit number> of Destination) ♦ Z; 1 ♦ <bit number> of
Destination

Assembler BSET Dn,<ea>
Syntax: BSET #<data>,<ea>

Attributes: Size = (Byte, Long)

Description: Tests a bit in the destination operand and sets the Z condition code
appropriately, then sets the specified bit in the destination operand. When a data
register is the destination, any of the 32 bits can be specified by a modulo 32-bit
number. When a memory location is the destination, the operation is a byte
operation, and the bit number is modulo 8. In all cases, bit zero refers to the least
significant bit. The bit number for this operation can be specified in either of two
ways:

1. Immediate—The bit number is specified in the second word of the instruction.
2. Register—The specified data register contains the bit number.

Condition Codes:

X	N	Z	V	C
—	—	*	—	—

X—Not affected.
N—Not affected.
Z—Set if the bit tested is zero; cleared otherwise.
V—Not affected.
C—Not affected.

Instruction Format:

Bit Number Dynamic, Specified in a Register

15	14	13	12	11	10	9	8	7	6	5	4	3	2	1	0
0	0	0	0	REGISTER			1	1	1	EFFECTIVE ADDRESS					
										MODE			REGISTER		

Instruction Fields:

Register field—Specifies the data register that contains the bit number.

Effective Address field—Specifies the destination location. Only data alterable addressing modes can be used as listed in the following tables:

Addressing Mode	Mode	Register	Addressing Mode	Mode	Register
Dn*	000	reg. number:Dn	(xxx).W	111	000
An	—	—	(xxx).L	111	001
(An)	010	reg. number:An	#<data>	—	—
(An) +	011	reg. number:An			
– (An)	100	reg. number:An			
(d$_{16}$,An)	101	reg. number:An	(d$_{16}$,PC)	—	—
(d$_8$,An,Xn)	110	reg. number:An	(d$_8$,PC,Xn)	—	—

MC68020, MC68030, and MC68040 only

(bd,An,Xn)**	110	reg. number:An	(bd,PC,Xn)**	—	—
([bd,An,Xn],od)	110	reg. number:An	([bd,PC,Xn],od)	—	—
([bd,An],Xn,od)	110	reg. number:An	([bd,PC],Xn,od)	—	—

*Long only; all others are byte only.

**Can be used with CPU32.

BSET

Test a Bit and Set
(M68000 Family)

Instruction Format:

Bit Number Static, Specified as Immediate Data

15	14	13	12	11	10	9	8	7	6	5	4	3	2	1	0
0	0	0	0	1	0	0	0	1	1	EFFECTIVE ADDRESS					

15	14	13	12	11	10	9	8	7	6	5	4	3	2	1	0
0	0	0	0	1	0	0	0	1	1	MODE			REGISTER		
0	0	0	0	0	0	0	BIT NUMBER								

Instruction Fields:

Effective Address field—Specifies the destination location. Only data alterable addressing modes can be used as listed in the following tables:

Addressing Mode	Mode	Register		Addressing Mode	Mode	Register
Dn*	000	reg. number:Dn		(xxx).W	111	000
An	—	—		(xxx).L	111	001
(An)	010	reg. number:An		#<data>	—	—
(An) +	011	reg. number:An				
– (An)	100	reg. number:An				
(d$_{16}$,An)	101	reg. number:An		(d$_{16}$,PC)	—	—
(d$_8$,An,Xn)	110	reg. number:An		(d$_8$,PC,Xn)	—	—

MC68020, MC68030, and MC68040 only

Addressing Mode	Mode	Register		Addressing Mode	Mode	Register
(bd,An,Xn)**	110	reg. number:An		(bd,PC,Xn)**	—	—
([bd,An,Xn],od)	110	reg. number:An		([bd,PC,Xn],od)	—	—
([bd,An],Xn,od)	110	reg. number:An		([bd,PC],Xn,od)	—	—

*Long only; all others are byte only.

**Can be used with CPU32.

Bit Number field—Specifies the bit number.

BSR

Branch to Subroutine
(M68000 Family)

Operation: $SP - 4 \rightarrow SP; PC \rightarrow (SP); PC + d_n \rightarrow PC$

**Assembler
Syntax:**   BSR <label>

Attributes: Size = (Byte, Word, Long*)

*(MC68020, MC68030, MC68040 only)

Description: Pushes the long-word address of the instruction immediately following the BSR instruction onto the system stack. The program counter contains the address of the instruction word plus two. Program execution then continues at location (PC) + displacement. The displacement is a twos complement integer that represents the relative distance in bytes from the current program counter to the destination program counter. If the 8-bit displacement field in the instruction word is zero, a 16-bit displacement (the word immediately following the instruction) is used. If the 8-bit displacement field in the instruction word is all ones ($FF), the 32-bit displacement (long word immediately following the instruction) is used.

Condition Codes:
Not affected.

Instruction Format:

15	14	13	12	11	10	9	8	7	6	5	4	3	2	1	0
0	1	1	0	0	0	0	1				8-BIT DISPLACEMENT				
16-BIT DISPLACEMENT IF 8-BIT DISPLACEMENT = $00															
32-BIT DISPLACEMENT IF 8-BIT DISPLACEMENT = $FF															

Instruction Fields:

8-Bit Displacement field—Twos complement integer specifying the number of bytes between the branch instruction and the next instruction to be executed.

16-Bit Displacement field—Used for a larger displacement when the 8-bit displacement is equal to $00.

32-Bit Displacement field—Used for a larger displacement when the 8-bit displacement is equal to $FF.

NOTE

A branch to the immediately following instruction automatically uses the 16-bit displacement format because the 8-bit displacement field contains $00 (zero offset).

4

Operation: TEST (<bit number> of Destination) ♦ Z

Assembler BTST Dn,<ea>
Syntax: BTST #<data>,<ea>

Attributes: Size = (Byte, Long)

Description: Tests a bit in the destination operand and sets the Z condition code appropriately. When a data register is the destination, any of the 32 bits can be specified by a modulo 32-bit number. When a memory location is the destination, the operation is a byte operation, and the bit number is modulo 8. In all cases, bit zero refers to the least significant bit. The bit number for this operation can be specified in either of two ways:

1. Immediate—The bit number is specified in a second word of the instruction.
2. Register—The specified data register contains the bit number.

Condition Codes:

X	N	Z	V	C
—	—	*	—	—

X—Not affected.
N—Not affected.
Z—Set if the bit tested is zero; cleared otherwise.
V—Not affected.
C—Not affected.

BTST

Test a Bit
(M68000 Family)

BTST

Instruction Format:

Bit Number Dynamic, Specified in a Register

15	14	13	12	11	10	9	8	7	6	5	4	3	2	1	0
0	0	0	0	REGISTER			1	0	0	EFFECTIVE ADDRESS					
										MODE			REGISTER		

Instruction Fields:

Register field—Specifies the data register that contains the bit number.

Effective Address field—Specifies the destination location. Only data addressing modes can be used as listed in the following tables:

Addressing Mode	Mode	Register		Addressing Mode	Mode	Register
Dn*	000	reg. number:Dn		(xxx).W	111	000
An	—	—		(xxx).L	111	001
(An)	010	reg. number:An		#<data>	111	100
(An) +	011	reg. number:An				
– (An)	100	reg. number:An				
(d$_{16}$,An)	101	reg. number:An		(d$_{16}$,PC)	111	010
(d$_8$,An,Xn)	110	reg. number:An		(d$_8$,PC,Xn)	111	011

MC68020, MC68030, and MC68040 only

Addressing Mode	Mode	Register		Addressing Mode	Mode	Register
(bd,An,Xn)**	110	reg. number:An		(bd,PC,Xn)**	111	011
([bd,An,Xn],od)	110	reg. number:An		([bd,PC,Xn],od)	111	011
([bd,An],Xn,od)	110	reg. number:An		([bd,PC],Xn,od)	111	011

*Long only; all others are byte only.

**Can be used with CPU32.

BTST

Test a Bit
(M68000 Family)

Instruction Format:

Bit Number Static, Specified as Immediate Data

15	14	13	12	11	10	9	8	7	6	5	4	3	2	1	0
0	0	0	0	1	0	0	0	0	0	EFFECTIVE ADDRESS					

15	14	13	12	11	10	9	8	7	6	5	4	3	2	1	0
0	0	0	0	1	0	0	0	0	0	MODE			REGISTER		
0	0	0	0	0	0	0	0	BIT NUMBER							

Instruction Fields:

Effective Address field—Specifies the destination location. Only data addressing modes can be used as listed in the following tables:

Addressing Mode	Mode	Register
Dn	000	reg. number:Dn
An	—	—
(An)	010	reg. number:An
(An) +	011	reg. number:An
− (An)	100	reg. number:An
(d_{16},An)	101	reg. number:An
(d_8,An,Xn)	110	reg. number:An

Addressing Mode	Mode	Register
(xxx).W	111	000
(xxx).L	111	001
#<data>	—	—
(d_{16},PC)	111	010
(d_8,PC,Xn)	111	011

MC68020, MC68030, and MC68040 only

Addressing Mode	Mode	Register
(bd,An,Xn)*	110	reg. number:An
([bd,An,Xn],od)	110	reg. number:An
([bd,An],Xn,od)	110	reg. number:An

Addressing Mode	Mode	Register
(bd,PC,Xn)*	111	011
([bd,PC,Xn],od)	111	011
([bd,PC],Xn,od)	111	011

*Can be used with CPU32.

Bit Number field—Specifies the bit number.

CALLM

CALLM

Operation: Save Current Module State on Stack; Load New Module State from Destination

Assembler
Syntax: CALLM #<data>, <ea>

Attributes: Unsized

Description: The effective address of the instruction is the location of an external module descriptor. A module frame is created on the top of the stack, and the current module state is saved in the frame. The immediate operand specifies the number of bytes of arguments to be passed to the called module. A new module state is loaded from the descriptor addressed by the effective address.

Condition Codes:
Not affected.

Instruction Format:

15	14	13	12	11	10	9	8	7	6	5	4	3	2	1	0
0	0	0	0	0	1	1	0	1	1	\multicolumn{2}{EFFECTIVE ADDRESS MODE}			REGISTER	
0	0	0	0	0	0	0	0	ARGUMENT COUNT							

Instruction Fields:

Effective Address field—Specifies the address of the module descriptor. Only control addressing modes can be used as listed in the following table:

Addressing Mode	Mode	Register	Addressing Mode	Mode	Register
Dn	—	—	(xxx).W	111	000
An	—	—	(xxx).L	111	001
(An)	010	reg. number:An	#<data>	—	—
(An) +	—	—			
– (An)	—	—			
(d_{16},An)	101	reg. number:An	(d_{16},PC)	111	010
(d_8,An,Xn)	110	reg. number:An	(d_8,PC,Xn)	111	011
(bd,An,Xn)	110	reg. number:An	(bd,PC,Xn)	111	011
([bd,An,Xn],od)	110	reg. number:An	([bd,PC,Xn],od)	111	011
([bd,An],Xn,od)	110	reg. number:An	([bd,PC],Xn,od)	111	011

Argument Count field—Specifies the number of bytes of arguments to be passed to the called module. The 8-bit field can specify from 0 to 255 bytes of arguments. The same number of bytes is removed from the stack by the RTM instruction.

Compare and Swap with Operand
(MC68020, MC68030, MC68040)

Operation: CAS Destination – Compare Operand ♦ cc;
   If Z, Update Operand ♦ Destination
   Else Destination ♦ Compare Operand
CAS2 Destination 1 – Compare 1 ♦ cc;
   If Z, Destination 2 – Compare 2 ♦ cc
   If Z, Update 1 ♦ Destination 1; Update 2 ♦ Destination 2
   Else Destination 1 ♦ Compare 1; Destination 2 ♦ Compare 2

Assembler   CAS Dc,Du,<ea>
Syntax: CAS2 Dc1:Dc2,Du1:Du2,(Rn1):(Rn2)

Attributes: Size = (Byte†, Word, Long)

Description: CAS compares the effective address operand to the compare operand (Dc). If the operands are equal, the instruction writes the update operand (Du) to the effective address operand; otherwise, the instruction writes the effective address operand to the compare operand (Dc).

CAS2 compares memory operand 1 (Rn1) to compare operand 1 (Dc1). If the operands are equal, the instruction compares memory operand 2 (Rn2) to compare operand 2 (Dc2). If these operands are also equal, the instruction writes the update operands (Du1 and Du2) to the memory operands (Rn1 and Rn2). If either comparison fails, the instruction writes the memory operands (Rn1 and Rn2) to the compare operands (Dc1 and Dc2).

Both operations access memory using locked or read-modify-write transfer sequences, providing a means of synchronizing several processors.

Condition Codes:

X	N	Z	V	C
—	*	*	*	*

X—Not affected.
N—Set if the result is negative; cleared otherwise.
Z—Set if the result is zero; cleared otherwise.
V—Set if an overflow is generated; cleared otherwise.
C—Set if a borrow is generated; cleared otherwise.

---

†CAS2 cannot use byte operands.

CAS
CAS2

Compare and Swap with Operand
(MC68020, MC68030, MC68040)

Instruction Format:

CAS

15	14	13	12	11	10	9	8	7	6	5	4	3	2	1	0
0	0	0	0	1	SIZE		0	1	1	EFFECTIVE ADDRESS					

15	14	13	12	11	10	9	8	7	6	5	4	3	2	1	0
											EFFECTIVE ADDRESS				
0	0	0	0	1	SIZE		0	1	1	MODE			REGISTER		
0	0	0	0	0	0	0	Du			0	0	0	Dc		

Instruction Fields:

Size field—Specifies the size of the operation.
    01—Byte operation
    10—Word operation
    11—Long operation

Effective Address field—Specifies the location of the memory operand. Only memory alterable addressing modes can be used as listed in the following table:

Addressing Mode	Mode	Register	Addressing Mode	Mode	Register
Dn	—	—	(xxx).W	111	000
An	—	—	(xxx).L	111	001
(An)	010	reg. number:An	#<data>	—	—
(An) +	011	reg. number:An			
– (An)	100	reg. number:An			
(d_{16},An)	101	reg. number:An	(d_{16},PC)	—	—
(d_8,An,Xn)	110	reg. number:An	(d_8,PC,Xn)	—	—
(bd,An,Xn)	110	reg. number:An	(bd,PC,Xn)	—	—
([bd,An,Xn],od)	110	reg. number:An	([bd,PC,Xn],od)	—	—
([bd,An],Xn,od)	110	reg. number:An	([bd,PC],Xn,od)	—	—

Du field—Specifies the data register that contains the update value to be written to the memory operand location if the comparison is successful.

Dc field—Specifies the data register that contains the value to be compared to the memory operand.

MOTOROLA   M68000 FAMILY PROGRAMMER'S REFERENCE MANUAL   4-67

CAS
CAS2

Compare and Swap with Operand
(MC68020, MC68030, MC68040)

Instruction Format:

CAS2

15	14	13	12	11	10	9	8	7	6	5	4	3	2	1	0
0	0	0	0	1	SIZE		0	1	1	1	1	1	1	0	0
D/A1	Rn1			0	0	0	Du1			0	0	0	Dc1		
D/A2	Rn2			0	0	0	Du2			0	0	0	Dc2		

Instruction Fields:

Size field—Specifies the size of the operation.
   10—Word operation
   11—Long operation

D/A1, D/A2 fields—Specify whether Rn1 and Rn2 reference data or address registers, respectively.
   0—The corresponding register is a data register.
   1—The corresponding register is an address register.

Rn1, Rn2 fields—Specify the numbers of the registers that contain the addresses of the first and second memory operands, respectively. If the operands overlap in memory, the results of any memory update are undefined.

Du1, Du2 fields—Specify the data registers that contain the update values to be written to the first and second memory operand locations if the comparison is successful.

Dc1, Dc2 fields—Specify the data registers that contain the test values to be compared to the first and second memory operands, respectively. If Dc1 and Dc2 specify the same data register and the comparison fails, memory operand 1 is stored in the data register.

NOTE

The CAS and CAS2 instructions can be used to perform secure update operations on system control data structures in a multiprocessing environment.

In the MC68040 if the operands are not equal, the destination or destination 1 operand is written back to memory to complete the locked access for CAS or CAS2, respectively.

Check Register Against Bounds
(M68000 Family)

Operation: If Dn < 0 or Dn > Source
Then TRAP

**Assembler
Syntax:** CHK <ea>,Dn

Attributes: Size = (Word, Long*)

*(MC68020, MC68030, MC68040 only)

Description: Compares the value in the data register specified in the instruction to zero and to the upper bound (effective address operand). The upper bound is a twos complement integer. If the register value is less than zero or greater than the upper bound, a CHK instruction exception (vector number 6) occurs.

Condition Codes:

X	N	Z	V	C
—	*	U	U	U

X—Not affected.
N—Set if Dn < 0; cleared if Dn > effective address operand;
   undefined otherwise.
Z—Undefined.
V—Undefined.
C—Undefined.

Instruction Format:

15	14	13	12	11	10	9	8	7	6	5	4	3	2	1	0
0	1	0	0	REGISTER			SIZE		0	EFFECTIVE ADDRESS					
										MODE			REGISTER		

Check Register Against Bounds
(M68000 Family)

Instruction Fields:

Register field—Specifies the data register that contains the value to be checked.

Size field—Specifies the size of the operation.
11—Word operation
10—Long operation

Effective Address field—Specifies the upper bound operand. Only data addressing modes can be used as listed in the following tables:

Addressing Mode	Mode	Register	Addressing Mode	Mode	Register
Dn	000	reg. number:Dn	(xxx).W	111	000
An	—	—	(xxx).L	111	001
(An)	010	reg. number:An	#<data>	111	100
(An) +	011	reg. number:An			
– (An)	100	reg. number:An			
(d_{16},An)	101	reg. number:An	(d_{16},PC)	111	010
(d_8,An,Xn)	110	reg. number:An	(d_8,PC,Xn)	111	011

MC68020, MC68030, and MC68040 only

(bd,An,Xn)*	110	reg. number:An	(bd,PC,Xn)*	111	011
([bd,An,Xn],od)	110	reg. number:An	([bd,PC,Xn],od)	111	011
([bd,An],Xn,od)	110	reg. number:An	([bd,PC],Xn,od)	111	011

*Can be used with CPU32.

Operation: If Rn < LB or Rn > UB
Then TRAP

**Assembler
Syntax**: CHK2 <ea>,Rn

Attributes: Size = (Byte, Word, Long)

Description: Compares the value in Rn to each bound. The effective address contains the bounds pair: the upper bound following the lower bound. For signed comparisons, the arithmetically smaller value should be used as the lower bound. For unsigned comparisons, the logically smaller value should be the lower bound.

The size of the data and the bounds can be specified as byte, word, or long. If Rn is a data register and the operation size is byte or word, only the appropriate low-order part of Rn is checked. If Rn is an address register and the operation size is byte or word, the bounds operands are sign-extended to 32 bits, and the resultant operands are compared to the full 32 bits of An.

If the upper bound equals the lower bound, the valid range is a single value. If the register value is less than the lower bound or greater than the upper bound, a CHK instruction exception (vector number 6) occurs.

Condition Codes:

X	N	Z	V	C
—	U	*	U	*

X—Not affected.
N—Undefined.
Z—Set if Rn is equal to either bound; cleared otherwise.
V—Undefined.
C—Set if Rn is out of bounds; cleared otherwise.

Instruction Format:

15	14	13	12	11	10	9	8	7	6	5	4	3	2	1	0
											EFFECTIVE ADDRESS				
0	0	0	0	0	SIZE		0	1	1		MODE			REGISTER	
D/A	REGISTER			1	0	0	0	0	0	0	0	0	0	0	0

Instruction Fields:

Size field—Specifies the size of the operation.
> 00—Byte operation
> 01—Word operation
> 10—Long operation

Effective Address field—Specifies the location of the bounds operands. Only control addressing modes can be used as listed in the following tables:

Addressing Mode	Mode	Register	Addressing Mode	Mode	Register
Dn	—	—	(xxx).W	111	000
An	—	—	(xxx).L	111	001
(An)	010	reg. number:An	#<data>	—	—
(An) +	—	—			
– (An)	—	—			
(d$_{16}$,An)	101	reg. number:An	(d$_{16}$,PC)	111	010
(d$_8$,An,Xn)	110	reg. number:An	(d$_8$,PC,Xn)	111	011
(bd,An,Xn)	110	reg. number:An	(bd,PC,Xn)	111	011

MC68020, MC68030, and MC68040 only

([bd,An,Xn],od)	110	reg. number:An	([bd,PC,Xn],od)	111	011
([bd,An],Xn,od)	110	reg. number:An	([bd,PC],Xn,od)	111	011

D/A field—Specifies whether an address register or data register is to be checked.
> 0—Data register
> 1—Address register

Register field—Specifies the address or data register that contains the value to be checked.

CLR

Clear an Operand
(M68000 Family)

CLR

Operation: 0 → Destination

**Assembler
Syntax:**   CLR <ea>

Attributes: Size = (Byte, Word, Long)

Description: Clears the destination operand to zero. The size of the operation may be specified as byte, word, or long.

Condition Codes:

X	N	Z	V	C
—	0	1	0	0

X—Not affected.
N—Always cleared.
Z—Always set.
V—Always cleared.
C—Always cleared.

Instruction Format:

15	14	13	12	11	10	9	8	7	6	5	4	3	2	1	0
0	1	0	0	0	0	1	0	SIZE		EFFECTIVE ADDRESS MODE			REGISTER		

Clear an Operand
(M68000 Family)

Instruction Fields:

Size field—Specifies the size of the operation.
00—Byte operation
01—Word operation
10—Long operation

Effective Address field—Specifies the destination location. Only data alterable addressing modes can be used as listed in the following tables:

Addressing Mode	Mode	Register	Addressing Mode	Mode	Register
Dn	000	reg. number:Dn	(xxx).W	111	000
An	—	—	(xxx).L	111	001
(An)	010	reg. number:An	#<data>	—	—
(An) +	011	reg. number:An			
– (An)	100	reg. number:An			
(d$_{16}$,An)	101	reg. number:An	(d$_{16}$,PC)	—	—
(d$_8$,An,Xn)	110	reg. number:An	(d$_8$,PC,Xn)	—	—

MC68020, MC68030, and MC68040 only

(bd,An,Xn)*	110	reg. number:An	(bd,PC,Xn)*	—	—
([bd,An,Xn],od)	110	reg. number:An	([bd,PC,Xn],od)	—	—
([bd,An],Xn,od)	110	reg. number:An	([bd,PC],Xn,od)	—	—

*Can be used with CPU32.

NOTE

In the MC68000 and MC68008 a memory location is read before it is cleared.

CMP

Compare
(M68000 Family)

Operation: Destination − Source ♦ cc

Assembler
Syntax: CMP <ea>, Dn

Attributes: Size = (Byte, Word, Long)

Description: Subtracts the source operand from the destination data register and sets the condition codes according to the result; the data register is not changed. The size of the operation can be byte, word, or long.

Condition Codes:

X	N	Z	V	C
—	*	*	*	*

X—Not affected.
N—Set if the result is negative; cleared otherwise.
Z—Set if the result is zero; cleared otherwise.
V—Set if an overflow occurs; cleared otherwise.
C—Set if a borrow occurs; cleared otherwise.

Instruction Format:

15	14	13	12	11	10	9	8	7	6	5	4	3	2	1	0
1	0	1	1	REGISTER			OPMODE			EFFECTIVE ADDRESS					
										MODE			REGISTER		

Instruction Fields:

Register field—Specifies the destination data register.

Opmode field

Byte	Word	Long	Operation
000	001	010	Dn − <ea>

Effective Address field—Specifies the source operand. All addressing modes can be used as listed in the following tables:

Addressing Mode	Mode	Register	Addressing Mode	Mode	Register
Dn	000	reg. number:Dn	(xxx).W	111	000
An*	001	reg. number:An	(xxx).L	111	001
(An)	010	reg. number:An	#<data>	111	100
(An) +	011	reg. number:An			
– (An)	100	reg. number:An			
(d_{16},An)	101	reg. number:An	(d_{16},PC)	111	010
(d_8,An,Xn)	110	reg. number:An	(d_8,PC,Xn)	111	011

MC68020, MC68030, and MC68040 only

Addressing Mode	Mode	Register	Addressing Mode	Mode	Register
(bd,An,Xn)**	110	reg. number:An	(bd,PC,Xn)**	111	011
([bd,An,Xn],od)	110	reg. number:An	([bd,PC,Xn],od)	111	011
([bd,An],Xn,od)	110	reg. number:An	([bd,PC],Xn,od)	111	011

*Word and Long only.
**Can be used with CPU32.

NOTE

CMPA is used when the destination is an address register. CMPI is used when the source is immediate data. CMPM is used for memory-to-memory compares. Most assemblers automatically make the distinction.

CMPA

Operation: Destination − Source ♦ cc

**Assembler
Syntax:** CMPA <ea>, An

Attributes Size = (Word, Long)

Description Subtracts the source operand from the destination address register and sets the condition codes according to the result; the address register is not changed. The size of the operation can be specified as word or long. Word length source operands are sign-extended to 32 bits for comparison.

Condition Codes:

X	N	Z	V	C
—	*	*	*	*

X—Not affected.
N—Set if the result is negative; cleared otherwise.
Z—Set if the result is zero; cleared otherwise.
V—Set if an overflow is generated; cleared otherwise.
C—Set if a borrow is generated; cleared otherwise.

Instruction Format:

15	14	13	12	11	10	9	8	7	6	5	4	3	2	1	0
1	0	1	1	REGISTER			OPMODE			EFFECTIVE ADDRESS					
										MODE			REGISTER		

Compare Address
(M68000 Family)

Instruction Fields:

Register field—Specifies the destination address register.

Opmode field—Specifies the size of the operation.
011—Word operation; the source operand is sign-extended to a long operand, and the operation is performed on the address register using all 32 bits.
111—Long operation.

Effective Address field—Specifies the source operand. All addressing modes can be used as listed in the following tables:

Addressing Mode	Mode	Register
Dn	000	reg. number:Dn
An	001	reg. number:An
(An)	010	reg. number:An
(An) +	011	reg. number:An
– (An)	100	reg. number:An
(d_{16},An)	101	reg. number:An
(d_8,An,Xn)	110	reg. number:An

Addressing Mode	Mode	Register
(xxx).W	111	000
(xxx).L	111	001
#<data>	111	100
(d_{16},PC)	111	010
(d_8,PC,Xn)	111	011

MC68020, MC68030, and MC68040 only

(bd,An,Xn)*	110	reg. number:An
([bd,An,Xn],od)	110	reg. number:An
([bd,An],Xn,od)	110	reg. number:An

(bd,PC,Xn)*	111	011
([bd,PC,Xn],od)	111	011
([bd,PC],Xn,od)	111	011

*Can be used with CPU32.

CMPI

Compare Immediate
(M68000 Family)

CMPI

Operation: Destination − Immediate Data ✦ cc

Assembler
Syntax: CMPI #<data>,<ea>

Attributes: Size = (Byte, Word, Long)

Description: Subtracts the immediate data from the destination operand and sets the condition codes according to the result; the destination location is not changed. The size of the operation may be specified as byte, word, or long. The size of the immediate data matches the operation size.

Condition Codes:

X	N	Z	V	C
—	*	*	*	*

X—Not affected.
N—Set if the result is negative; cleared otherwise.
Z—Set if the result is zero; cleared otherwise.
V—Set if an overflow occurs; cleared otherwise.
C—Set if a borrow occurs; cleared otherwise.

Instruction Format:

15	14	13	12	11	10	9	8	7	6	5	4	3	2	1	0
0	0	0	0	1	1	0	0	SIZE		EFFECTIVE ADDRESS					

15	14	13	12	11	10	9	8	7	6	5	4	3	2	1	0
0	0	0	0	1	1	0	0	SIZE		MODE			REGISTER		
16-BIT WORD DATA								8-BIT BYTE DATA							
32-BIT LONG DATA															

Instruction Fields:

Size field—Specifies the size of the operation.
  00—Byte operation
  01—Word operation
  10—Long operation

Effective Address field—Specifies the destination operand. Only data addressing modes can be used as listed in the following tables:

Addressing Mode	Mode	Register
Dn	000	reg. number:Dn
An	—	—
(An)	010	reg. number:An
(An) +	011	reg. number:An
– (An)	100	reg. number:An
(d_{16},An)	101	reg. number:An
(d_8,An,Xn)	110	reg. number:An

Addressing Mode	Mode	Register
(xxx).W	111	000
(xxx).L	111	001
#<data>	—	—
(d_{16},PC)*	111	010
(d_8,PC,Xn)*	111	011

MC68020, MC68030, and MC68040 only

(bd,An,Xn)**	110	reg. number:An	(bd,PC,Xn)**	111	011
([bd,An,Xn],od)	110	reg. number:An	([bd,PC,Xn],od)	111	011
([bd,An],Xn,od)	110	reg. number:An	([bd,PC],Xn,od)	111	011

*PC relative addressing modes do not apply to MC68000, MC680008, or MC68010.

**Can be used with CPU32.

Immediate field—Data immediately following the instruction.
  If size = 00, the data is the low-order byte of the immediate word.
  If size = 01, the data is the entire immediate word.
  If size = 10, the data is the next two immediate words.

CMPM

Operation: Destination − Source ⧫ cc

**Assembler
Syntax:** CMPM (Ay)+ ,(Ax)+

Attributes: Size = (Byte, Word, Long)

Description: Subtracts the source operand from the destination operand and sets the
condition codes according to the results; the destination location is not changed.
The operands are always addressed with the postincrement addressing mode,
using the address registers specified in the instruction. The size of the operation
may be specified as byte, word, or long.

Condition Codes:

X	N	Z	V	C
—	*	*	*	*

X—Not affected.
N—Set if the result is negative; cleared otherwise.
Z—Set if the result is zero; cleared otherwise.
V—Set if an overflow is generated; cleared otherwise.
C—Set if a borrow is generated; cleared otherwise.

Instruction Format:

15	14	13	12	11	10	9	8	7	6	5	4	3	2	1	0
1	0	1	1		REGISTER Ax		1		SIZE	0	0	1		REGISTER Ay	

Instruction Fields:

Register Ax field—(always the destination) Specifies an address register in the
postincrement addressing mode.

Size field—Specifies the size of the operation.
   00—Byte operation
   01—Word operation
   10—Long operation

Register Ay field—(always the source) Specifies an address register in the
postincrement addressing mode.

CMP2

Compare Register Against Bounds
(MC68020, MC68030, MC68040, CPU32)

CMP2

Operation: Compare Rn < LB or Rn > UB and Set Condition Codes

**Assembler
Syntax:** CMP2 <ea>,Rn

Attributes: Size = (Byte, Word, Long)

Description: Compares the value in Rn to each bound. The effective address contains the bounds pair: upper bound following the lower bound. For signed comparisons, the arithmetically smaller value should be used as the lower bound. For unsigned comparisons, the logically smaller value should be the lower bound.

The size of the data and the bounds can be specified as byte, word, or long. If Rn is a data register and the operation size is byte or word, only the appropriate low-order part of Rn is checked. If Rn is an address register and the operation size is byte or word, the bounds operands are sign-extended to 32 bits, and the resultant operands are compared to the full 32 bits of An.

If the upper bound equals the lower bound, the valid range is a single value.

NOTE

This instruction is identical to CHK2 except that it sets condition codes rather than taking an exception when the value in Rn is out of bounds.

Condition Codes:

X	N	Z	V	C
—	U	*	U	*

X—Not affected.
N—Undefined.
Z—Set if Rn is equal to either bound; cleared otherwise.
V—Undefined.
C—Set if Rn is out of bounds; cleared otherwise.

CMP2

Compare Register Against Bounds
(MC68020, MC68030, MC68040, CPU32)

CMP2

Instruction Format:

15	14	13	12	11	10	9	8	7	6	5	4	3	2	1	0
0	0	0	0	0	SIZE		0	1	1	EFFECTIVE ADDRESS					
										MODE			REGISTER		
D/A	REGISTER			0	0	0	0	0	0	0	0	0	0	0	0

Instruction Fields:

Size field—Specifies the size of the operation.
   00—Byte operation
   01—Word operation
   10—Long operation

Effective Address field—Specifies the location of the bounds pair. Only control addressing modes can be used as listed in the following tables:

Addressing Mode	Mode	Register	Addressing Mode	Mode	Register
Dn	—	—	(xxx).W	111	000
An	—	—	(xxx).L	111	001
(An)	010	reg. number:An	#<data>	—	—
(An) +	—	—			
– (An)	—	—			
(d_{16},An)	101	reg. number:An	(d_{16},PC)	111	010
(d_8,An,Xn)	110	reg. number:An	(d_8,PC,Xn)	111	011
(bd,An,Xn)	110	reg. number:An	(bd,PC,Xn)	111	011

MC68020, MC68030, and MC68040 only

([bd,An,Xn],od)	110	reg. number:An	([bd,PC,Xn],od)	111	011
([bd,An],Xn,od)	110	reg. number:An	([bd,PC],Xn,od)	111	011

D/A field—Specifies whether an address register or data register is compared.
   0—Data register
   1—Address register

Register field—Specifies the address or data register that contains the value to be checked.

Branch on Coprocessor Condition
(MC68020, MC68030)

Operation: If cpcc True
                   Then Scan PC + d$_n$ $\rightarrow$ PC

Assembler
Syntax: cpBcc <label>

Attributes: Size = (Word, Long)

Description: If the specified coprocessor condition is true, program execution continues at location scan PC + displacement. The value of the scan PC is the address of the first displacement word. The displacement is a twos complement integer that represents the relative distance in bytes from the scan PC to the destination program counter. The displacement can be either 16 or 32 bits. The coprocessor determines the specific condition from the condition field in the operation word.

Condition Codes:
Not affected.

Instruction Format:

15	14	13	12	11	10	9	8	7	6	5	4	3	2	1	0
1	1	1	1	COPROCESSOR ID			0	1	SIZE	COPROCESSOR CONDITION					
OPTIONAL COPROCESSOR-DEFINED EXTENSION WORDS															
WORD OR															
LONG-WORD DISPLACEMENT															

Instruction Fields:

Coprocessor ID field—Identifies the coprocessor for this operation. Coprocessor ID of 000 results in an F-line exception for the MC68030.

Size field—Specifies the size of the displacement.
   0—The displacement is 16 bits.
   1—The displacement is 32 bits.

Coprocessor Condition field—Specifies the coprocessor condition to be tested. This field is passed to the coprocessor, which provides directives to the main processor for processing this instruction.

16-Bit Displacement field—The displacement value occupies 16 bits.

32-Bit Displacement field—The displacement value occupies 32 bits.

cpDBcc

Test Coprocessor Condition
Decrement and Branch
(MC68020, MC68030)

cpDBcc

Operation: If cpcc False
Then (Dn − 1 ♦ Dn; If Dn ≠ − 1 Then Scan PC + d_n ♦ PC)

**Assembler
Syntax:** cpDBcc Dn,<label>

Attributes: Size = (Word)

Description: If the specified coprocessor condition is true, execution continues with the next instruction. Otherwise, the low-order word in the specified data register is decremented by one. If the result is equal to −1, execution continues with the next instruction. If the result is not equal to −1, execution continues at the location indicated by the value of the scan PC plus the sign-extended 16-bit displacement. The value of the scan PC is the address of the displacement word. The displacement is a twos complement integer that represents the relative distance in bytes from the scan PC to the destination program counter. The coprocessor determines the specific condition from the condition word that follows the operation word.

Condition Codes:
Not affected.

Instruction Format:

15	14	13	12	11	10	9	8	7	6	5	4	3	2	1	0
1	1	1	1	COPROCESSOR ID			0	0	1	0	0	1	REGISTER		
0	0	0	0	0	0	0	0	0	0	COPROCESSOR CONDITION					
OPTIONAL COPROCESSOR-DEFINED EXTENSION WORDS															
16-BIT DISPLACEMENT															

Instruction Fields:

Coprocessor ID field—Identifies the coprocessor for this operation; coprocessor ID of 000 results in an F-line exception for the MC68030.

Register field—Specifies the data register used as the counter.

Coprocessor Condition field—Specifies the coprocessor condition to be tested. This field is passed to the coprocessor, which provides directives to the main processor for processing this instruction.

Displacement field—Specifies the distance of the branch (in bytes).

Operation: Pass Command Word to Coprocessor

Assembler
Syntax: cpGEN <parameters as defined by coprocessor>

Attributes: Unsized

Description: Transfers the command word that follows the operation word to the specified coprocessor. The coprocessor determines the specific operation from the command word. Usually a coprocessor defines specific instances of this instruction to provide its instruction set.

Condition Codes:
   May be modified by coprocessor; unchanged otherwise.

Instruction Format:

15	14	13	12	11	10	9	8	7	6	5	4	3	2	1	0
1	1	1	1	COPROCESSOR ID			0	0	0	EFFECTIVE ADDRESS					
										MODE			REGISTER		
COPROCESSOR-DEPENDENT COMMAND WORD															
OPTIONAL EFFECTIVE ADDRESS OR COPROCESSOR-DEFINED EXTENSION WORDS															

Instruction Fields:

Coprocessor ID field—Identifies the coprocessor for this operation; note that coprocessor ID of 000 is reserved for MMU instructions for the MC68030.

Effective Address field—Specifies the location of any operand not resident in the coprocessor. The allowable addressing modes are determined by the operation to be performed.

Coprocessor Command field—Specifies the coprocessor operation to be performed. This word is passed to the coprocessor, which in turn provides directives to the main processor for processing this instruction.

cpScc

Set on Coprocessor Condition
(MC68020, MC68030)

cpScc

Operation: If cpcc True
                     Then 1s ♦ Destination
                   Else 0s ♦ Destination

**Assembler
Syntax:**   cpScc <ea>

Attributes   Size = (Byte)

Description: Tests the specified coprocessor condition code. If the condition is true, the byte specified by the effective address is set to TRUE (all ones); otherwise, that byte is set to FALSE (all zeros). The coprocessor determines the specific condition from the condition word that follows the operation word.

Condition Codes:
   Not affected.

Instruction Format:

15	14	13	12	11	10	9	8	7	6	5	4	3	2	1	0
1	1	1	1	COPROCESSOR D			0	0	1	EFFECTIVE ADDRESS MODE			REGISTER		
0	0	0	0	0	0	0	0	0	0	COPROCESSOR CONDITION					
OPTIONAL EFFECTIVE ADDRESS OR COPROCESSOR-DEFINED EXTENSION WORDS															

Instruction Fields:

Coprocessor ID field—Identifies the coprocessor for this operation. Coprocessor ID of 000 results in an F-line exception for the MC68030.

Effective Address field—Specifies the destination location. Only data alterable addressing modes can be used as listed in the following table:

Addressing Mode	Mode	Register	Addressing Mode	Mode	Register
Dn	000	reg. number:Dn	(xxx).W	111	000
An	—	—	(xxx).L	111	001
(An)	010	reg. number:An	#<data>	—	—
(An) +	011	reg. number:An			
– (An)	100	reg. number:An			
(d_{16},An)	101	reg. number:An	(d_{16},PC)	—	—
(d_8,An,Xn)	110	reg. number:An	(d_8,PC,Xn)	—	—
(bd,An,Xn)	110	reg. number:An	(bd,PC,Xn)	—	—
([bd,An,Xn],od)	110	reg. number:An	([bd,PC,Xn],od)	—	—
([bd,An],Xn,od)	110	reg. number:An	([bd,PC],Xn,od)	—	—

Coprocessor Condition field—Specifies the coprocessor condition to be tested. This field is passed to the coprocessor, which in turn provides directives to the main processor for processing this instruction.

cpTRAPcc   Trap on Coprocessor Condition   cpTRAPcc
(MC68020, MC68030)

Operation: If cpcc True
                    Then TRAP

Assembler   cpTRAPcc
Syntax: cpTRAPcc #<data>

Attributes: Unsized or Size = (Word, Long)

Description: Tests the specified coprocessor condition code; if the selected coprocessor condition is true, the processor initiates a cpTRAPcc exception, vector number 7. The program counter value placed on the stack is the address of the next instruction. If the selected condition is not true, no operation is performed, and execution continues with the next instruction. The coprocessor determines the specific condition from the condition word that follows the operation word. Following the condition word is a user-defined data operand specified as immediate data to be used by the trap handler.

Condition Codes:
Not affected.

Instruction Format:

15	14	13	12	11	10	9	8	7	6	5	4	3	2	1	0
1	1	1	1	COPROCESSOR D			0	0	1	1	1	1	OPMODE		
0	0	0	0	0	0	0	0	0	0	COPROCESSOR CONDITION					
OPTIONAL COPROCESSOR-DEFINED EXTENSION WORDS															
OPTIONAL WORD															
OR LONG-WORD OPERAND															

Instruction Fields:

Coprocessor ID field—Identifies the coprocessor for this operation; coprocessor ID of 000 results in an F-line exception for the MC68030.

Opmode field—Selects the instruction form.
   010—Instruction is followed by one operand word.
   011—Instruction is followed by two operand words.
   100—Instruction has no following operand words.

Coprocessor Condition field—Specifies the coprocessor condition to be tested. This field is passed to the coprocessor, which provides directives to the main processor for processing this instruction.

Operation: If Condition False
Then (Dn − 1 $\rightarrow$ Dn; If Dn ≠ − 1 Then PC + d_n $\rightarrow$ PC)

**Assembler
Syntax:** DBcc Dn,<label>

Attributes: Size = (Word)

Description: Controls a loop of instructions. The parameters are a condition code, a data register (counter), and a displacement value. The instruction first tests the condition for termination; if it is true, no operation is performed. If the termination condition is not true, the low-order 16 bits of the counter data register decrement by one. If the result is −1, execution continues with the next instruction. If the result is not equal to −1, execution continues at the location indicated by the current value of the program counter plus the sign-extended 16-bit displacement. The value in the program counter is the address of the instruction word of the DBcc instruction plus two. The displacement is a twos complement integer that represents the relative distance in bytes from the current program counter to the destination program counter. Condition code cc specifies one of the following conditional tests (refer to Table 3-19 for more information on these conditional tests):

Mnemonic	Condition	Mnemonic	Condition
CC(HI)	Carry Clear	LS	Low or Same
CS(LO)	Carry Set	LT	Less Than
EQ	Equal	MI	Minus
F	False	NE	Not Equal
GE	Greater or Equal	PL	Plus
GT	Greater Than	T	True
HI	High	VC	Overflow Clear
LE	Less or Equal	VS	Overflow Set

Condition Codes:
Not affected.

Instruction Format:

15	14	13	12	11	10	9	8	7	6	5	4	3	2	1	0
0	1	0	1		CONDITION			1	1	0	0	1		REGISTER	
16-BIT DISPLACEMENT															

Instruction Fields:

Condition field—The binary code for one of the conditions listed in the table.

Register field—Specifies the data register used as the counter.

Displacement field—Specifies the number of bytes to branch.

NOTE

The terminating condition is similar to the UNTIL loop clauses of high-level languages. For example: DBMI can be stated as "decrement and branch until minus".

Most assemblers accept DBRA for DBF for use when only a count terminates the loop (no condition is tested).

A program can enter a loop at the beginning or by branching to the trailing DBcc instruction. Entering the loop at the beginning is useful for indexed addressing modes and dynamically specified bit operations. In this case, the control index count must be one less than the desired number of loop executions. However, when entering a loop by branching directly to the trailing DBcc instruction, the control count should equal the loop execution count. In this case, if a zero count occurs, the DBcc instruction does not branch, and the main loop is not executed.

Signed Divide
(M68000 Family)

Operation: Destination ÷ Source ♦ Destination

Assembler   DIVS.W \<ea>,Dn   32/16 ♦ 16r–16q
Syntax: *DIVS.L \<ea>,Dq   32/32 ♦ 32q
                 *DIVS.L \<ea>,Dr:Dq   64/32 ♦ 32r–32q
                 *DIVSL.L \<ea>,Dr:Dq   32/32 ♦ 32r–32q

   *Applies to MC68020, MC68030, MC68040, CPU32 only

Attributes: Size = (Word, Long)

Description: Divides the signed destination operand by the signed source operand and stores the signed result in the destination. The instruction uses one of four forms. The word form of the instruction divides a long word by a word. The result is a quotient in the lower word (least significant 16 bits) and a remainder in the upper word (most significant 16 bits). The sign of the remainder is the same as the sign of the dividend.

The first long form divides a long word by a long word. The result is a long quotient; the remainder is discarded.

The second long form divides a quad word (in any two data registers) by a long word. The result is a long-word quotient and a long-word remainder.

The third long form divides a long word by a long word. The result is a long-word quotient and a long-word remainder.

Two special conditions may arise during the operation:
   1. Division by zero causes a trap.
   2. Overflow may be detected and set before the instruction completes. If the instruction detects an overflow, it sets the overflow condition code, and the operands are unaffected.

Condition Codes:

X	N	Z	V	C
—	*	*	*	0

X—Not affected.
N—Set if the quotient is negative; cleared otherwise; undefined if overflow or divide by zero occurs.
Z—Set if the quotient is zero; cleared otherwise; undefined if overflow or divide by zero occurs.
V—Set if division overflow occurs; undefined if divide by zero occurs; cleared otherwise.
C—Always cleared.

DIVS, DIVSL

Signed Divide
(M68000 Family)

Instruction Format:

Word

15	14	13	12	11	10	9	8	7	6	5	4	3	2	1	0
1	0	0	0	\multicolumn{3}{c|}{REGISTER}	1	1	1	\multicolumn{3}{c|}{MODE}	\multicolumn{3}{c|}{REGISTER}

Effective address: MODE | REGISTER

Instruction Fields:

Register field—Specifies any of the eight data registers. This field always specifies the destination operand.

Effective Address field—Specifies the source operand. Only data alterable addressing modes can be used as listed in the following tables:

Addressing Mode	Mode	Register
Dn	000	reg. number:Dn
An	—	—
(An)	010	reg. number:An
(An) +	011	reg. number:An
– (An)	100	reg. number:An
(d$_{16}$,An)	101	reg. number:An
(d$_8$,An,Xn)	110	reg. number:An

Addressing Mode	Mode	Register
(xxx).W	111	000
(xxx).L	111	001
#<data>	111	100
(d$_{16}$,PC)	111	010
(d$_8$,PC,Xn)	111	011

MC68020, MC68030, and MC68040 only

Addressing Mode	Mode	Register
(bd,An,Xn)*	110	reg. number:An
([bd,An,Xn],od)	110	reg. number:An
([bd,An],Xn,od)	110	reg. number:An

Addressing Mode	Mode	Register
(bd,PC,Xn)*	111	011
([bd,PC,Xn],od)	111	011
([bd,PC],Xn,od)	111	011

*Can be used with CPU32.

NOTE

Overflow occurs if the quotient is larger than a 16-bit signed integer.

DIVS, DIVSL

Signed Divide
(M68000 Family)

DIVS, DIVSL

Instruction Format:

Long

15	14	13	12	11	10	9	8	7	6	5	4	3	2	1	0
0	1	0	0	1	1	0	0	0	1	EFFECTIVE ADDRESS					

0	1	0	0	1	1	0	0	0	1	MODE		REGISTER			
0	REGISTER Dq			1	SIZE	0	0	0	0	0	0	0	REGISTER Dr		

Instruction Fields:

Effective Address field—Specifies the source operand. Only data alterable addressing modes can be used as listed in the following tables:

MC68020, MC68030, MC68040, and CPU32 only

Addressing Mode	Mode	Register	Addressing Mode	Mode	Register
Dn	000	reg. number:Dn	(xxx).W	111	000
An	—	—	(xxx).L	111	001
(An)	010	reg. number:An	#<data>	111	100
(An) +	011	reg. number:An			
– (An)	100	reg. number:An			
(d_{16},An)	101	reg. number:An	(d_{16},PC)	111	010
(d_8,An,Xn)	110	reg. number:An	(d_8,PC,Xn)	111	011
(bd,An,Xn)	110	reg. number:An	(bd,PC,Xn)	111	011

MC68020, MC68030, and MC68040 only

([bd,An,Xn],od)	110	reg. number:An	([bd,PC,Xn],od)	111	011
([bd,An],Xn,od)	110	reg. number:An	([bd,PC],Xn,od)	111	011

Register Dq field—Specifies a data register for the destination operand. The low-order 32 bits of the dividend comes from this register, and the 32-bit quotient is loaded into this register.

Size field—Selects a 32- or 64-bit division operation.

0—32-bit dividend is in register Dq.
1—64-bit dividend is in Dr–Dq.

Register Dr field—After the division, this register contains the 32-bit remainder. If Dr and Dq are the same register, only the quotient is returned. If the size field is 1, this field also specifies the data register that contains the high-order 32 bits of the dividend.

NOTE

Overflow occurs if the quotient is larger than a 32-bit signed integer.

4

Operation: Destination ÷ Source ♦ Destination

Assembler Syntax:

DIVU.W \<ea\>,Dn	32/16 ♦ 16r–16q
*DIVU.L \<ea\>,Dq	32/32 ♦ 32q
*DIVU.L \<ea\>,Dr:Dq	64/32 ♦ 32r–32q
*DIVUL.L \<ea\>,Dr:Dq	32/32 ♦ 32r–32q

*Applies to MC68020, MC68030, MC68040, CPU32 only.

Attributes: Size = (Word, Long)

Description Divides the unsigned destination operand by the unsigned source operand and stores the unsigned result in the destination. The instruction uses one of four forms. The word form of the instruction divides a long word by a word. The result is a quotient in the lower word (least significant 16 bits) and a remainder in the upper word (most significant 16 bits).

The first long form divides a long word by a long word. The result is a long quotient; the remainder is discarded.

The second long form divides a quad word (in any two data registers) by a long word. The result is a long-word quotient and a long-word remainder.

The third long form divides a long word by a long word. The result is a long-word quotient and a long-word remainder.

Two special conditions may arise during the operation:

1. Division by zero causes a trap.
2. Overflow may be detected and set before the instruction completes. If the instruction detects an overflow, it sets the overflow condition code, and the operands are unaffected.

Condition Codes:

X	N	Z	V	C
—	*	*	*	0

X—Not affected.

N—Set if the quotient is negative; cleared otherwise; undefined if overflow or divide by zero occurs.

Z—Set if the quotient is zero; cleared otherwise; undefined if overflow or divide by zero occurs.

V—Set if division overflow occurs; cleared otherwise; undefined if divide by zero occurs.

C—Always cleared.

Instruction Format:

Word

15	14	13	12	11	10	9	8	7	6	5	4	3	2	1	0
1	0	0	0	REGISTER			0	1	1	EFFECTIVE ADDRESS					
										MODE			REGISTER		

Instruction Fields:

Register field—Specifies any of the eight data registers; this field always specifies the destination operand.

Effective Address field—Specifies the source operand. Only data addressing modes can be used as listed in the following tables:

MC68020, MC68030, MC68040, and CPU32 only

Addressing Mode	Mode	Register	Addressing Mode	Mode	Register
Dn	000	reg. number:Dn	(xxx).W	111	000
An	—	—	(xxx).L	111	001
(An)	010	reg. number:An	#<data>	111	100
(An)+	011	reg. number:An			
-(An)	100	reg. number:An			
(d_{16},An)	101	reg. number:An	(d_{16},PC)	111	010
(d_8,An,Xn)	110	reg. number:An	(d_8,PC,Xn)	111	011

MC68020, MC68030, and MC68040 only

(bd,An,Xn)*	110	reg. number:An	(bd,PC,Xn)*	111	011
([bd,An,Xn],od)	110	reg. number:An	([bd,PC,Xn],od)	111	011
([bd,An],Xn,od)	110	reg. number:An	([bd,PC],Xn,od)	111	011

*Can be used with CPU32.

NOTE

Overflow occurs if the quotient is larger than a 16-bit signed integer.

DIVU, DIVUL   Unsigned Divide (M68000 Family)   DIVU, DIVUL

Instruction Format:

Long

15	14	13	12	11	10	9	8	7	6	5	4	3	2	1	0
0	1	0	0	1	1	0	0	0	1	EFFECTIVE ADDRESS MODE				REGISTER	
0	REGISTER Dq			0	SIZE	0	0	0	0	0	0	0	REGISTER Dr		

Instruction Fields:

Effective Address field—Specifies the source operand. Only data addressing modes can be used as listed in the following tables:

MC68020, MC68030, MC68040, and CPU32 only

Addressing Mode	Mode	Register	Addressing Mode	Mode	Register
Dn	000	reg. number:Dn	(xxx).W	111	000
An	—	—	(xxx).L	111	001
(An)	010	reg. number:An	#<data>	111	100
(An)+	011	reg. number:An			
–(An)	100	reg. number:An			
(d_{16},An)	101	reg. number:An	(d_{16},PC)	111	010
(d_8,An,Xn)	110	reg. number:An	(d_8,PC,Xn)	111	011
(bd,An,Xn)*	110	reg. number:An	(bd,PC,Xn)*	111	011

MC68020, MC68030, and MC68040 only

([bd,An,Xn],od)	110	reg. number:An	([bd,PC,Xn],od)	111	011
([bd,An],Xn,od)	110	reg. number:An	([bd,PC],Xn,od)	111	011

Register Dq field—Specifies a data register for the destination operand. The low-order 32 bits of the dividend comes from this register, and the 32-bit quotient is loaded into this register.

Size field—Selects a 32- or 64-bit division operation.

0—32-bit dividend is in register Dq.

1—64-bit dividend is in Dr–Dq.

DIVU, DIVUL   Unsigned Divide   DIVU, DIVUL
(M68000 Family)

Register Dr field—After the division, this register contains the 32-bit remainder. If Dr and Dq are the same register, only the quotient is returned. If the size field is 1, this field also specifies the data register that contains the high-order 32 bits of the dividend.

NOTE

Overflow occurs if the quotient is larger than a 32-bit unsigned integer.

4

EOR

Exclusive-OR Logical
(M68000 Family)

EOR

Operation: Source $\oplus$ Destination $\rightarrow$ Destination

Assembler Syntax: EOR Dn,<ea>

Attributes: Size = (Byte, Word, Long)

Description: Performs an exclusive-OR operation on the destination operand using the source operand and stores the result in the destination location. The size of the operation may be specified to be byte, word, or long. The source operand must be a data register. The destination operand is specified in the effective address field.

Condition Codes:

X	N	Z	V	C
—	*	*	0	0

X—Not affected.
N—Set if the most significant bit of the result is set; cleared otherwise.
Z—Set if the result is zero; cleared otherwise.
V—Always cleared.
C—Always cleared.

Instruction Format:

Word

15	14	13	12	11	10	9	8	7	6	5	4	3	2	1	0
1	0	1	1	REGISTER			OPMODE			EFFECTIVE ADDRESS					
										MODE			REGISTER		

Instruction Fields:

Register field—Specifies any of the eight data registers.

Opmode field

Byte	Word	Long	Operation
100	101	110	<ea> $\oplus$ Dn $\rightarrow$ <ea>

Effective Address field—Specifies the destination operand. Only data alterable addressing modes can be used as listed in the following tables:

Addressing Mode	Mode	Register	Addressing Mode	Mode	Register
Dn	000	reg. number:Dn	(xxx).W	111	000
An	—	—	(xxx).L	111	001
(An)	010	reg. number:An	#<data>	—	—
(An) +	011	reg. number:An			
− (An)	100	reg. number:An			
(d_{16},An)	101	reg. number:An	(d_{16},PC)	—	—
(d_8,An,Xn)	110	reg. number:An	(d_8,PC,Xn)	—	—

MC68020, MC68030, and MC68040 only

(bd,An,Xn)*	110	reg. number:An	(bd,PC,Xn)*	—	—
([bd,An,Xn],od)	110	reg. number:An	([bd,PC,Xn],od)	—	—
([bd,An],Xn,od)	110	reg. number:An	([bd,PC],Xn,od)	—	—

*Can be used with CPU32.

NOTE

Memory-to-data-register operations are not allowed. Most assemblers use EORI when the source is immediate data.

Operation: Immediate Data ⊕ Destination ♦ Destination

Assembler
Syntax: EORI #<data>,<ea>

Attributes: Size = (Byte, Word, Long)

Description: Performs an exclusive-OR operation on the destination operand using the immediate data and the destination operand and stores the result in the destination location. The size of the operation may be specified as byte, word, or long. The size of the immediate data matches the operation size.

Condition Codes:

X	N	Z	V	C
—	*	*	0	0

X—Not affected.
N—Set if the most significant bit of the result is set; cleared otherwise.
Z—Set if the result is zero; cleared otherwise.
V—Always cleared.
C—Always cleared.

Instruction Format:

15	14	13	12	11	10	9	8	7	6	5	4	3	2	1	0
0	0	0	0	1	0	1	0	SIZE		EFFECTIVE ADDRESS MODE			REGISTER		
16-BIT WORD DATA								8-BIT BYTE DATA							
32-BIT LONG DATA															

Instruction Fields:

Size field—Specifies the size of the operation.
   00—Byte operation
   01—Word operation
   10—Long operation

Effective Address field—Specifies the destination operand. Only data alterable addressing modes can be used as listed in the following tables:

Addressing Mode	Mode	Register	Addressing Mode	Mode	Register
Dn	000	reg. number:Dn	(xxx).W	111	000
An	—	—	(xxx).L	111	001
(An)	010	reg. number:An	#<data>	—	—
(An) +	011	reg. number:An			
– (An)	100	reg. number:An			
(d$_{16}$,An)	101	reg. number:An	(d$_{16}$,PC)	—	—
(d$_8$,An,Xn)	110	reg. number:An	(d$_8$,PC,Xn)	—	—

MC68020, MC68030, and MC68040 only

(bd,An,Xn)*	110	reg. number:An	(bd,PC,Xn)*	—	—
([bd,An,Xn],od)	110	reg. number:An	([bd,PC,Xn],od)	—	—
([bd,An],Xn,od)	110	reg. number:An	([bd,PC],Xn,od)	—	—

*Can be used with CPU32.

Immediate field—Data immediately following the instruction.
   If size = 00, the data is the low-order byte of the immediate word.
   If size = 01, the data is the entire immediate word.
   If size = 10, the data is next two immediate words.

Exclusive-OR Immediate
to Condition Code
(M68000 Family)

Operation: Source $\oplus$ CCR $\rightarrow$ CCR

**Assembler
Syntax:** EORI #<data>,CCR

Attributes: Size = (Byte)

Description: Performs an exclusive-OR operation on the condition code register using the immediate operand and stores the result in the condition code register (low-order byte of the status register). All implemented bits of the condition code register are affected.

Condition Codes:

X	N	Z	V	C
*	*	*	*	*

X—Changed if bit 4 of immediate operand is one; unchanged otherwise.
N—Changed if bit 3 of immediate operand is one; unchanged otherwise.
Z—Changed if bit 2 of immediate operand is one; unchanged otherwise.
V—Changed if bit 1 of immediate operand is one; unchanged otherwise.
C—Changed if bit 0 of immediate operand is one; unchanged otherwise.

Instruction Format:

15	14	13	12	11	10	9	8	7	6	5	4	3	2	1	0
0	0	0	0	1	0	1	0	0	0	1	1	1	1	0	0
0	0	0	0	0	0	0	0	8-BIT BYTE DATA							

EXG

Exchange Registers
(M68000 Family)

Operation: Rx ◆◆ Ry

Assembler   EXG Dx,Dy
Syntax: EXG Ax,Ay
   EXG Dx,Ay

Attributes: Size = (Long)

Description: Exchanges the contents of two 32-bit registers. The instruction performs three types of exchanges.

   1. Exchange data registers.
   2. Exchange address registers.
   3. Exchange a data register and an address register.

Condition Codes:
   Not affected.

Instruction Format:

15	14	13	12	11	10	9	8	7	6	5	4	3	2	1	0
1	1	0	0	REGISTER Rx			1	OPMODE					REGISTER Ry		

Instruction Fields:

Register Rx field—Specifies either a data register or an address register depending on the mode. If the exchange is between data and address registers, this field always specifies the data register.

Opmode field—Specifies the type of exchange.
   01000—Data registers
   01001—Address registers
   10001—Data register and address register

Register Ry field—Specifies either a data register or an address register depending on the mode. If the exchange is between data and address registers, this field always specifies the address register.

EXT, EXTB

Operation: Destination Sign-Extended ♦ Destination

Assembler   EXT.W Dn   extend byte to word
Syntax: EXT.L Dn   extend word to long word
                EXTB.L Dn   extend byte to long word (MC68020, MC68030,
                                  MC68040, CPU32)

Attributes: Size = (Word, Long)

Description: Extends a byte in a data register to a word or a long word, or a word in a
data register to a long word, by replicating the sign bit to the left. If the operation
extends a byte to a word, bit 7 of the designated data register is copied to bits 15–8
of that data register. If the operation extends a word to a long word, bit 15 of the
designated data register is copied to bits 31–16 of the data register. The EXTB form
copies bit 7 of the designated register to bits 31–8 of the data register.

Condition Codes:

X	N	Z	V	C
—	*	*	0	0

X—Not affected.
N—Set if the result is negative; cleared otherwise.
Z—Set if the result is zero; cleared otherwise.
V—Always cleared.
C—Always cleared.

Instruction Format:

15	14	13	12	11	10	9	8	7	6	5	4	3	2	1	0
0	1	0	0	1	0	0		OPMODE		0	0	0		REGISTER	

Instruction Fields:

Opmode field—Specifies the size of the sign-extension operation.
    010—Sign-extend low-order byte of data register to word.
    011—Sign-extend low-order word of data register to long.
    111—Sign-extend low-order byte of data register to long.

Register field—Specifies the data register is to be sign-extended.

ILLEGAL Take Illegal Instruction Trap ILLEGAL
(M68000 Family)

Operation: *SSP – 2 ◆ SSP; Vector Offset ◆ (SSP);
SSP – 4 ◆ SSP; PC ◆ (SSP);
SSP – 2 ◆ SSP; SR ◆ (SSP);
Illegal Instruction Vector Address ◆ PC

*The MC68000 and MC68008 cannot write the vector offset and format
code to the system stack.

**Assembler
Syntax:** ILLEGAL

Attributes: Unsized

Description: Forces an illegal instruction exception, vector number 4. All other illegal
instruction bit patterns are reserved for future extension of the instruction set and
should not be used to force an exception.

Condition Codes:
Not affected.

Instruction Format:

15	14	13	12	11	10	9	8	7	6	5	4	3	2	1	0
0	1	0	0	1	0	1	0	1	1	1	1	1	1	0	0

JMP

Jump
(M68000 Family)

Operation: Destination Address → PC

**Assembler
Syntax**: JMP <ea>

Attributes: Unsized

Description: Program execution continues at the effective address specified by the instruction. The addressing mode for the effective address must be a control addressing mode.

Condition Codes:
Not affected.

Instruction Format:

15	14	13	12	11	10	9	8	7	6	5	4	3	2	1	0
0	1	0	0	1	1	1	0	1	1	EFFECTIVE ADDRESS					

| | | | | | | | | | | MODE | | | REGISTER | | |

Instruction Field:

Effective Address field—Specifies the address of the next instruction. Only control addressing modes can be used as listed in the following tables:

Addressing Mode	Mode	Register		Addressing Mode	Mode	Register
Dn	—	—		(xxx).W	111	000
An	—	—		(xxx).L	111	001
(An)	010	reg. number:An		#<data>	—	—
(An) +	—	—				
– (An)	—	—				
(d$_{16}$,An)	101	reg. number:An		(d$_{16}$,PC)	111	010
(d$_8$,An,Xn)	110	reg. number:An		(d$_8$,PC,Xn)	111	011

MC68020, MC68030, and MC68040 only

Addressing Mode	Mode	Register		Addressing Mode	Mode	Register
(bd,An,Xn)*	110	reg. number:An		(bd,PC,Xn)*	111	011
([bd,An,Xn],od)	110	reg. number:An		([bd,PC,Xn],od)	111	011
([bd,An],Xn,od)	110	reg. number:An		([bd,PC],Xn,od)	111	011

*Can be used with CPU32.

JSR

Jump to Subroutine
(M68000 Family)

Operation: SP – 4 ♦ Sp; PC ♦ (SP); Destination Address ♦ PC

Assembler
Syntax: JSR <ea>

Attributes: Unsized

Description: Pushes the long-word address of the instruction immediately following the JSR instruction onto the system stack. Program execution then continues at the address specified in the instruction.

Condition Codes:
Not affected.

Instruction Format:

15	14	13	12	11	10	9	8	7	6	5	4	3	2	1	0
0	1	0	0	1	1	1	0	1	0	EFFECTIVE ADDRESS						

| | | | | | | | | | | | MODE | | | REGISTER | |

Instruction Field:

Effective Address field—Specifies the address of the next instruction. Only control addressing modes can be used as listed in the following tables:

Addressing Mode	Mode	Register		Addressing Mode	Mode	Register
Dn	—	—		(xxx).W	111	000
An	—	—		(xxx).L	111	001
(An)	010	reg. number:An		#<data>	—	—
(An) +	—	—				
– (An)	—	—				
(d$_{16}$,An)	101	reg. number:An		(d$_{16}$,PC)	111	010
(d$_8$,An,Xn)	110	reg. number:An		(d$_8$,PC,Xn)	111	011

MC68020, MC68030, and MC68040 only

(bd,An,Xn)*	110	reg. number:An		(bd,PC,Xn)*	111	011
([bd,An,Xn],od)	110	reg. number:An		([bd,PC,Xn],od)	111	011
([bd,An],Xn,od)	110	reg. number:An		([bd,PC],Xn,od)	111	011

*Can be used with CPU32.

LEA

Load Effective Address
(M68000 Family)

Operation: <ea> ♦ An

**Assembler
Syntax**: LEA <ea>,An

Attributes: Size = (Long)

Description: Loads the effective address into the specified address register. All 32 bits of the address register are affected by this instruction.

Condition Codes:
Not affected.

Instruction Format:

15	14	13	12	11	10	9	8	7	6	5	4	3	2	1	0
0	1	0	0		REGISTER		1	1	1		EFFECTIVE ADDRESS MODE			REGISTER	

Instruction Fields:

Register field—Specifies the address register to be updated with the effective address.

Effective Address field—Specifies the address to be loaded into the address register. Only control addressing modes can be used as listed in the following tables:

Addressing Mode	Mode	Register
Dn	—	—
An	—	—
(An)	010	reg. number:An
(An) +	—	—
– (An)	—	—
(d₁₆,An)	101	reg. number:An
(d₈,An,Xn)	110	reg. number:An

Addressing Mode	Mode	Register
(xxx).W	111	000
(xxx).L	111	001
#<data>	—	—
(d₁₆,PC)	111	010
(d₈,PC,Xn)	111	011

MC68020, MC68030, and MC68040 only

Addressing Mode	Mode	Register
(bd,An,Xn)*	110	reg. number:An
([bd,An,Xn],od)	110	reg. number:An
([bd,An],Xn,od)	110	reg. number:An

Addressing Mode	Mode	Register
(bd,PC,Xn)*	111	011
([bd,PC,Xn],od)	111	011
([bd,PC],Xn,od)	111	011

*Can be used with CPU32.

LINK

Link and Allocate
(M68000 Family)

LINK

Operation: SP − 4 $\rightarrow$ SP; An $\rightarrow$ (SP); SP $\rightarrow$ An; SP + d_n $\rightarrow$ SP

Assembler
Syntax: LINK An, #<displacement>

Attributes: Size = (Word, Long*)

*MC68020, MC68030, MC68040 and CPU32 only.

Description: Pushes the contents of the specified address register onto the stack. Then loads the updated stack pointer into the address register. Finally, adds the displacement value to the stack pointer. For word-size operation, the displacement is the sign-extended word following the operation word. For long size operation, the displacement is the long word following the operation word. The address register occupies one long word on the stack. The user should specify a negative displacement in order to allocate stack area.

Condition Codes:

Not affected.

Instruction Format:

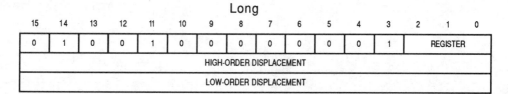

Word

15	14	13	12	11	10	9	8	7	6	5	4	3	2	1	0
0	1	0	0	1	1	1	0	0	1	0	1	0		REGISTER	
WORD DISPLACEMENT															

Instruction Format:

Long

15	14	13	12	11	10	9	8	7	6	5	4	3	2	1	0
0	1	0	0	1	0	0	0	0	0	0	0	1		REGISTER	
HIGH-ORDER DISPLACEMENT															
LOW-ORDER DISPLACEMENT															

Link and Allocate
(M68000 Family)

Instruction Fields:

Register field—Specifies the address register for the link.

Displacement field—Specifies the twos complement integer to be added to the stack pointer.

NOTE

LINK and UNLK can be used to maintain a linked list of local data and parameter areas on the stack for nested subroutine calls.

4

Logical Shift
(M68000 Family)

LSL, LSR

Operation: Destination Shifted By Count ♦ Destination

Assembler   LSd Dx,Dy
Syntax: LSd #<data>,Dy
                  LSd <ea>
                  where d is direction, L or R

Attributes: Size = (Byte, Word, Long)

Description: Shifts the bits of the operand in the direction specified (L or R). The carry bit receives the last bit shifted out of the operand. The shift count for the shifting of a register is specified in two different ways:

1. Immediate—The shift count (1–8) is specified in the instruction.
2. Register—The shift count is the value in the data register specified in the instruction modulo 64.

The size of the operation for register destinations may be specified as byte, word, or long. The contents of memory, <ea>, can be shifted one bit only, and the operand size is restricted to a word.

The LSL instruction shifts the operand to the left the number of positions specified as the shift count. Bits shifted out of the high-order bit go to both the carry and the extend bits; zeros are shifted into the low-order bit.

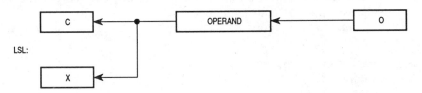

The LSR instruction shifts the operand to the right the number of positions specified as the shift count. Bits shifted out of the low-order bit go to both the carry and the extend bits; zeros are shifted into the high-order bit.

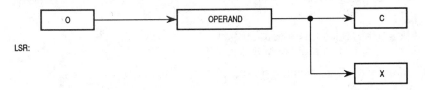

LSL, LSR

LSL, LSR

Condition Codes:

X	N	Z	V	C
*	*	*	0	*

X—Set according to the last bit shifted out of the operand; unaffected for a shift count of zero.

N—Set if the result is negative; cleared otherwise.

Z—Set if the result is zero; cleared otherwise.

V—Always cleared.

C—Set according to the last bit shifted out of the operand; cleared for a shift count of zero.

Instruction Format:

Register Shifts

15	14	13	12	11	10	9	8	7	6	5	4	3	2	1	0
1	1	1	0	COUNT/ REGISTER			dr	SIZE		i/r	0	1	REGISTER		

Instruction Fields:

Count/Register field

If i/r = 0, this field contains the shift count. The values 1–7 represent shifts of 1–7; value of zero specifies a shift count of eight.

If i/r = 1, the data register specified in this field contains the shift count (modulo 64).

dr field—Specifies the direction of the shift.

0—Shift right
1—Shift left

Size field—Specifies the size of the operation.

00—Byte operation
01—Word operation
10—Long operation

i/r field

If i/r = 0, specifies immediate shift count.
If i/r = 1, specifies register shift count.

Register field—Specifies a data register to be shifted.

Instruction Format:

Memory Shifts

15	14	13	12	11	10	9	8	7	6	5	4	3	2	1	0
1	1	1	0	0	0	1	dr	1	1		EFFECTIVE ADDRESS MODE			REGISTER	

Instruction Fields:

dr field—Specifies the direction of the shift.
   0—Shift right
   1—Shift left

Effective Address field—Specifies the operand to be shifted. Only memory alterable addressing modes can be used as listed in the following tables:

Addressing Mode	Mode	Register
Dn	—	—
An	—	—
(An)	010	reg. number:An
(An) +	011	reg. number:An
– (An)	100	reg. number:An
(d$_{16}$,An)	101	reg. number:An
(d$_8$,An,Xn)	110	reg. number:An

Addressing Mode	Mode	Register
(xxx).W	111	000
(xxx).L	111	001
#<data>	—	—
(d$_{16}$,PC)	—	—
(d$_8$,PC,Xn)	—	—

MC68020, MC68030, and MC68040 only

(bd,An,Xn)*	110	reg. number:An
([bd,An,Xn],od)	110	reg. number:An
([bd,An],Xn,od)	110	reg. number:An

(bd,PC,Xn)*	—	—
([bd,PC,Xn],od)	—	—
([bd,PC],Xn,od)	—	—

*Can be used with CPU32.

Operation: Source ◆ Destination

Assembler
Syntax: MOVE <ea>,<ea>

Attributes: Size = (Byte, Word, Long)

Description: Moves the data at the source to the destination location and sets the condition codes according to the data. The size of the operation may be specified as byte, word, or long.

Condition Codes:

X	N	Z	V	C
—	*	*	0	0

X—Not affected.
N—Set if the result is negative; cleared otherwise.
Z—Set if the result is zero; cleared otherwise.
V—Always cleared.
C—Always cleared.

Instruction Format:

15	14	13	12	11	10	9	8	7	6	5	4	3	2	1	0
0	0	SIZE		DESTINATION						SOURCE					
				REGISTER			MODE			MODE			REGISTER		

Instruction Fields:

Size field—Specifies the size of the operand to be moved.
   01—Byte operation
   11—Word operation
   10—Long operation

Destination Effective Address field—Specifies the destination location. Only data alterable addressing modes can be used as listed in the following tables:

Addressing Mode	Mode	Register
Dn	000	reg. number:Dn
An	—	—
(An)	010	reg. number:An
(An) +	011	reg. number:An
– (An)	100	reg. number:An
(d_{16},An)	101	reg. number:An
(d_8,An,Xn)	110	reg. number:An

Addressing Mode	Mode	Register
(xxx).W	111	000
(xxx).L	111	001
#<data>	—	—
(d_{16},PC)	—	—
(d_8,PC,Xn)	—	—

MC68020, MC68030, and MC68040 only

(bd,An,Xn)*	110	reg. number:An
([bd,An,Xn],od)	110	reg. number:An
([bd,An],Xn,od)	110	reg. number:An

(bd,PC,Xn)*	—	—
([bd,PC,Xn],od)	—	—
([bd,PC],Xn,od)	—	—

*Can be used with CPU32.

4

MOVE   Move Data from Source to Destination   MOVE
(M68000 Family)

Source Effective Address field—Specifies the source operand. All addressing modes can be used as listed in the following tables:

Addressing Mode	Mode	Register
Dn	000	reg. number:Dn
An*	001	reg. number:An
(An)	010	reg. number:An
(An) +	011	reg. number:An
– (An)	100	reg. number:An
(d_{16},An)	101	reg. number:An
(d_8,An,Xn)	110	reg. number:An

Addressing Mode	Mode	Register
(xxx).W	111	000
(xxx).L	111	001
#<data>	111	100
(d_{16},PC)	111	010
(d_8,PC,Xn)	111	011

MC68020, MC68030, and MC68040 only

(bd,An,Xn)**	110	reg. number:An	(bd,PC,Xn)**	111	011
([bd,An,Xn],od)	110	reg. number:An	([bd,PC,Xn],od)	111	011
([bd,An],Xn,od)	110	reg. number:An	([bd,PC],Xn,od)	111	011

*For byte size operation, address register direct is not allowed.
**Can be used with CPU32.

NOTE

Most assemblers use MOVEA when the destination is an address register.

MOVEQ can be used to move an immediate 8-bit value to a data register.

MOVEA

Move Address
(M68000 Family)

MOVEA

Operation: Source ♦ Destination

Assembler
Syntax: MOVEA <ea>,An

Attributes: Size = (Word, Long)

Description: Moves the contents of the source to the destination address register. The size of the operation is specified as word or long. Word-size source operands are sign-extended to 32-bit quantities.

Condition Codes:
Not affected.

Instruction Format:

15	14	13	12	11	10	9	8	7	6	5	4	3	2	1	0
0	0	SIZE		DESTINATION REGISTER			0	0	1	SOURCE					
										MODE			REGISTER		

Instruction Fields:

Size field—Specifies the size of the operand to be moved.

11—Word operation; the source operand is sign-extended to a long operand and all 32 bits are loaded into the address register.

10—Long operation.

Destination Register field—Specifies the destination address register.

Effective Address field—Specifies the location of the source operand. All addressing modes can be used as listed in the following tables:

Addressing Mode	Mode	Register		Addressing Mode	Mode	Register
Dn	000	reg. number:Dn		(xxx).W	111	000
An	001	reg. number:An		(xxx).L	111	001
(An)	010	reg. number:An		#<data>	111	100
(An) +	011	reg. number:An				
– (An)	100	reg. number:An				
(d$_{16}$,An)	101	reg. number:An		(d$_{16}$,PC)	111	010
(d$_8$,An,Xn)	110	reg. number:An		(d$_8$,PC,Xn)	111	011

MC68020, MC68030, and MC68040 only

Addressing Mode	Mode	Register		Addressing Mode	Mode	Register
(bd,An,Xn)*	110	reg. number:An		(bd,PC,Xn)*	111	011
([bd,An,Xn],od)	110	reg. number:An		([bd,PC,Xn],od)	111	011
([bd,An],Xn,od)	110	reg. number:An		([bd,PC],Xn,od)	111	011

*Can be used with CPU32.

MOVE
from CCR

MOVE
from CCR

**Move from the
Condition Code Register**

(MC68010, MC68020, MC68030, MC68040, CPU32)

Operation: CCR → Destination

**Assembler
Syntax:**   MOVE CCR,<ea>

Attributes: Size = (Word)

Description: Moves the condition code bits (zero-extended to word size) to the destination location. The operand size is a word. Unimplemented bits are read as zeros.

Condition Codes:
Not affected.

Instruction Format:

15	14	13	12	11	10	9	8	7	6	5	4	3	2	1	0
0	1	0	0	0	0	1	0	1	1	EFFECTIVE ADDRESS					
										MODE			REGISTER		

MOVE
from CCR

Move from the
Condition Code Register
(MC68010, MC68020, MC68030, MC68040, CPU32)

MOVE
from CCR

Instruction Field:

Effective Address field—Specifies the destination location. Only data alterable addressing modes can be used as listed in the following tables:

Addressing Mode	Mode	Register	Addressing Mode	Mode	Register
Dn	000	reg. number:Dn	(xxx).W	111	000
An	—	—	(xxx).L	111	001
(An)	010	reg. number:An	#<data>	—	—
(An) +	011	reg. number:An			
– (An)	100	reg. number:An			
(d$_{16}$,An)	101	reg. number:An	(d$_{16}$,PC)	—	—
(d$_8$,An,Xn)	110	reg. number:An	(d$_8$,PC,Xn)	—	—

MC68020, MC68030, and MC68040 only

(bd,An,Xn)*	110	reg. number:An	(bd,PC,Xn)*	—	—
([bd,An,Xn],od)	110	reg. number:An	([bd,PC,Xn],od)	—	—
([bd,An],Xn,od)	110	reg. number:An	([bd,PC],Xn,od)	—	—

*Can be used with CPU32.

NOTE

MOVE from CCR is a word operation. ANDI, ORI, and EORI to CCR are byte operations.

MOVE
to CCR

Move to Condition Code Register
(M68000 Family)

MOVE
to CCR

Operation: Source ♦ CCR

Assembler
Syntax: MOVE <ea>,CCR

Attributes: Size = (Word)

Description: Moves the low-order byte of the source operand to the condition code register. The upper byte of the source operand is ignored; the upper byte of the status register is not altered.

Condition Codes:

X	N	Z	V	C
*	*	*	*	*

X—Set to the value of bit 4 of the source operand.
N—Set to the value of bit 3 of the source operand.
Z—Set to the value of bit 2 of the source operand.
V—Set to the value of bit 1 of the source operand.
C—Set to the value of bit 0 of the source operand.

Instruction Format:

15	14	13	12	11	10	9	8	7	6	5	4	3	2	1	0
0	1	0	0	0	1	0	0	1	1	EFFECTIVE ADDRESS					
										MODE			REGISTER		

MOVE
to CCR

Move to Condition Code Register
(M68000 Family)

MOVE
to CCR

Instruction Field:

Effective Address field—Specifies the location of the source operand. Only data addressing modes can be used as listed in the following tables:

Addressing Mode	Mode	Register
Dn	000	reg. number:Dn
An	—	—
(An)	010	reg. number:An
(An) +	011	reg. number:An
– (An)	100	reg. number:An
(d_{16},An)	101	reg. number:An
(d_8,An,Xn)	110	reg. number:An

Addressing Mode	Mode	Register
(xxx).W	111	000
(xxx).L	111	001
#<data>	111	100
(d_{16},PC)	111	010
(d_8,PC,Xn)	111	011

MC68020, MC68030, and MC68040 only

(bd,An,Xn)*	110	reg. number:An	(bd,PC,Xn)*	111	011
([bd,An,Xn],od)	110	reg. number:An	([bd,PC,Xn],od)	111	011
([bd,An],Xn,od)	110	reg. number:An	([bd,PC],Xn,od)	111	011

*Can be used with CPU32.

NOTE

MOVE to CCR is a word operation. ANDI, ORI, and EORI to CCR are byte operations.

Move from the Status Register
(MC68000, MC68008)

Operation: SR ♦ Destination

**Assembler
Syntax**:   MOVE SR,<ea>

Attributes: Size = (Word)

Description: Moves the data in the status register to the destination location. The destination is word length. Unimplemented bits are read as zeros.

Condition Codes:
Not affected.

Instruction Format:

15	14	13	12	11	10	9	8	7	6	5	4	3	2	1	0
0	1	0	0	0	0	0	0	1	1	EFFECTIVE ADDRESS					

| | | | | | | | | | | MODE | | | REGISTER | | |

Instruction Fields:

Effective Address field—Specifies the destination location. Only data alterable addressing modes can be used as listed in the following table:

Addressing Mode	Mode	Register	Addressing Mode	Mode	Register
Dn	000	reg. number:Dn	(xxx).W	111	000
An	—	—	(xxx).L	111	001
(An)	010	reg. number:An	#<data>	—	—
(An) +	011	reg. number:An			
– (An)	100	reg. number:An			
(d$_{16}$,An)	101	reg. number:An	(d$_{16}$,PC)	—	—
(d$_8$,An,Xn)	110	reg. number:An	(d$_8$,PC,Xn)	—	—

NOTE

Use the MOVE from CCR instruction to access only the condition codes. Memory destination is read before it is written to.

MOVE16   Move 16-Byte Block   MOVE16
(MC68040)

Operation: Source Block ◆ Destination Block

Assembler   MOVE16 (Ax)+,(Ay)+
Syntax: MOVE16 (xxx).L,(An)
                  MOVE16 (xxx).L,(An)+
                  MOVE16 (An),(xxx).L
                  MOVE16 (An)+,(xxx).L

Attributes: Size = (Line)

Description: Moves the source line to the destination line. The lines are aligned to 16-byte boundaries. Applications for this instruction include coprocessor communications, memory initialization, and fast block copy operations.

MOVE16 has two formats. The postincrement format uses the postincrement addressing mode for both source and destination; whereas, the absolute format specifies an absolute long address for either the source or destination.

Line transfers are performed using burst reads and writes, which begin with the long word pointed to by the effective address of the source and destination, respectively. An address register used in the postincrement addressing mode is incremented by 16 after the transfer.

Example: MOVE16 (A0) + $FE802   A0 = $1400F

The line at address $14000 is read into a temporary holding register by a burst read transfer starting with long-word $14000. Address values in A0 of $14000–$1400F cause the same line to be read, starting at different long words. The line is then written to the line at address $FE800 beginning with long-word $FE800 after the instruction A0 contains $1401F.

Source line at $14000:

$14000	$14004	$14008	$1400C
LONG WORD 0	LONG WORD 1	LONG WORD 2	LONG WORD 3

Destination line at $FE8000:

$FE800	$FE804	$FE808	$FE80C
LONG WORD 0	LONG WORD 1	LONG WORD 2	LONG WORD 3

Condition Codes:

Not affected.

Instruction Format:

Postincrement Source and Destination

15	14	13	12	11	10	9	8	7	6	5	4	3	2	1	0
1	1	1	1	0	1	1	0	0	0	1	0	0	REGISTER Ax		
1	REGISTER Ay		0	0	0	0	0	0	0	0	0	0	0	0	0

Instruction Fields:

Register Ax—Specifies a source address register for the postincrement addressing mode.

Register Ay—Specifies a destination address register for the postincrement addressing mode.

Instruction Format:

Absolute Long Address Source or Destination

15	14	13	12	11	10	9	8	7	6	5	4	3	2	1	0
1	1	1	1	0	1	1	0	0	0	0	OPMODE		REGISTER Ay		
HIGH-ORDER ADDRESS															
LOW-ORDER ADDRESS															

Instruction Fields:

Opmode field—Specifies the addressing modes used for source and destination:

Opmode	Source	Destination	Assembler Syntax
0 0	(Ay)+	(xxx).L	MOVE16 (Ay)+,(xxx).L
0 1	(xxx).L	(Ay) +	MOVE16 (xxx).L,(Ay) +
1 0	(Ay)	(xxx).L	MOVE16 (Ay),(xxx).L
1 1	(xxx).L	(Ay)	MOVE16 (xxx).L,(Ay)

Register Ay—Specifies an address register for the indirect and postincrement addressing mode used as a source or destination.

32-Bit Address field—Specifies the absolute address used as a source or destination.

MOVEM

Move Multiple Registers
(M68000 Family)

MOVEM

Operation: Registers ♦ Destination; Source ♦ Registers

Assembler
Syntax:
MOVEM <list>,<ea>
MOVEM <ea>,<list>

Attributes: Size = (Word, Long)

Description: Moves the contents of selected registers to or from consecutive memory locations starting at the location specified by the effective address. A register is selected if the bit in the mask field corresponding to that register is set. The instruction size determines whether 16 or 32 bits of each register are transferred. In the case of a word transfer to either address or data registers, each word is sign-extended to 32 bits, and the resulting long word is loaded into the associated register.

Selecting the addressing mode also selects the mode of operation of the MOVEM instruction, and only the control modes, the predecrement mode, and the postincrement mode are valid. If the effective address is specified by one of the control modes, the registers are transferred starting at the specified address, and the address is incremented by the operand length (2 or 4) following each transfer. The order of the registers is from D0 to D7, then from A0 to A7.

If the effective address is specified by the predecrement mode, only a register-to-memory operation is allowed. The registers are stored starting at the specified address minus the operand length (2 or 4), and the address is decremented by the operand length following each transfer. The order of storing is from A7 to A0, then from D7 to D0. When the instruction has completed, the decremented address register contains the address of the last operand stored. For the MC68020, MC68030, MC68040, and CPU32, if the addressing register is also moved to memory, the value written is the initial register value decremented by the size of the operation. The MC68000 and MC68010 write the initial register value (not decremented).

If the effective address is specified by the postincrement mode, only a memory-to-register operation is allowed. The registers are loaded starting at the specified address; the address is incremented by the operand length (2 or 4) following each transfer. The order of loading is the same as that of control mode addressing. When the instruction has completed, the incremented address register contains the address of the last operand loaded plus the operand length. If the addressing register is also loaded from memory, the memory value is ignored and the register is written with the postincremented effective address.

MOVEM   Move Multiple Registers   MOVEM
(M68000 Family)

Condition Codes:
Not affected.

Instruction Format:

15	14	13	12	11	10	9	8	7	6	5	4	3	2	1	0
0	1	0	0	1	dr	0	0	1	SIZE		MODE	EFFECTIVE ADDRESS		REGISTER	
REGISTER LIST MASK															

Instruction Fields:

dr field—Specifies the direction of the transfer.
> 0—Register to memory.
> 1—Memory to register.

Size field—Specifies the size of the registers being transferred.
> 0—Word transfer
> 1—Long transfer

Effective Address field—Specifies the memory address for the operation. For register-to-memory transfers, only control alterable addressing modes or the predecrement addressing mode can be used as listed in the following tables:

Addressing Mode	Mode	Register	Addressing Mode	Mode	Register
Dn	—	—	(xxx).W	111	000
An	—	—	(xxx).L	111	001
(An)	010	reg. number:An	#<data>	—	—
(An) +	—	—			
− (An)	100	reg. number:An			
(d$_{16}$,An)	101	reg. number:An	(d$_{16}$,PC)	—	—
(d$_8$,An,Xn)	110	reg. number:An	(d$_8$,PC,Xn)	—	—

MC68020, MC68030, and MC68040 only

Addressing Mode	Mode	Register	Addressing Mode	Mode	Register
(bd,An,Xn)*	110	reg. number:An	(bd,PC,Xn)*	—	—
([bd,An,Xn],od)	110	reg. number:An	([bd,PC,Xn],od)	—	—
([bd,An],Xn,od)	110	reg. number:An	([bd,PC],Xn,od)	—	—

*Can be used with CPU32.

For memory-to-register transfers, only control addressing modes or the postincrement addressing mode can be used as listed in the following tables:

Addressing Mode	Mode	Register
Dn	—	—
An	—	—
(An)	010	reg. number:An
(An) +	011	reg. number:An
– (An)	—	—
(d$_{16}$,An)	101	reg. number:An
(d$_8$,An,Xn)	110	reg. number:An

Addressing Mode	Mode	Register
(xxx).W	111	000
(xxx).L	111	001
#<data>	—	—
(d$_{16}$,PC)	111	010
(d$_8$,PC,Xn)	111	011

MC68020, MC68030, and MC68040 only

(bd,An,Xn)*	110	reg. number:An	(bd,PC,Xn)*	111	011
([bd,An,Xn],od)	110	reg. number:An	([bd,PC,Xn],od)	111	011
([bd,An],Xn,od)	110	reg. number:An	([bd,PC],Xn,od)	111	011

*Can be used with CPU32.

Register List Mask field—Specifies the registers to be transferred. The low-order bit corresponds to the first register to be transferred; the high-order bit corresponds to the last register to be transferred. Thus, for both control modes and postincrement mode addresses, the mask correspondence is:

15	14	13	12	11	10	9	8	7	6	5	4	3	2	1	0
A7	A6	A5	A4	A3	A2	A1	A0	D7	D6	D5	D4	D3	D2	D1	D0

For the predecrement mode addresses, the mask correspondence is reversed:

15	14	13	12	11	10	9	8	7	6	5	4	3	2	1	0
D0	D1	D2	D3	D4	D5	D6	D7	A0	A1	A2	A3	A4	A5	A6	A7

MOVEP

Move Peripheral Data
(M68000 Family)

MOVEP

Operation: Source ♦ Destination

Assembler   MOVEP Dx,(d_{16},Ay)
Syntax: MOVEP (d_{16},Ay),Dx

Attributes: Size = (Word, Long)

Description: Moves data between a data register and alternate bytes within the address space starting at the location specified and incrementing by two. The high-order byte of the data register is transferred first, and the low-order byte is transferred last. The memory address is specified in the address register indirect plus 16-bit displacement addressing mode. This instruction was originally designed for interfacing 8-bit peripherals on a 16-bit data bus, such as the MC68000 bus. Although supported by the MC68020, MC68030, and MC68040, this instruction is not useful for those processors with an external 32-bit bus.

Example: Long transfer to/from an even address.

Byte Organization in Register

31 24	23 16	15 8	7 0
HIGH ORDER	MID UPPER	MID LOWER	LOW ORDER

Byte Organization in 16-Bit Memory (Low Address at Top)

15 8	7 0
HIGH ORDER	
MID UPPER	
MID LOWER	
LOW ORDER	

Byte Organization in 32-Bit Memory

31　　24	23　　16	15　　　8	7　　　0
HIGH ORDER		MID UPPER	
MID LOWER		LOW ORDER	

or

31　　24	23　　16	15　　　8	7　　　0
		HIGH ORDER	
MID UPPER		MID LOWER	
LOW ORDER			

Example: Word transfer to/from (odd address).

Byte Organization in Register

31　　24	23　　16	15　　　8	7　　　0
		HIGH ORDER	LOW ORDER

Byte Organization in
16-Bit Memory
(Low Address at Top)

15　　　8	7　　　0
	HIGH ORDER
	LOW ORDER

Byte Organization in 32-Bit Memory

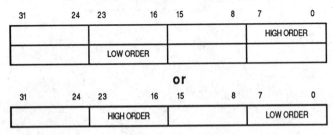

31　　24	23　　16	15　　　8	7　　　0
			HIGH ORDER
	LOW ORDER		

or

31　　24	23　　16	15　　　8	7　　　0
	HIGH ORDER		LOW ORDER

Condition Codes:
Not affected.

Instruction Format:

15	14	13	12	11	10	9	8	7	6	5	4	3	2	1	0
0	0	0	0	DATA REGISTER			OPMODE			0	0	1	ADDRESS REGISTER		
16-BIT DISPLACEMENT															

Instruction Fields:

Data Register field—Specifies the data register for the instruction.

Opmode field—Specifies the direction and size of the operation.
    100—Transfer word from memory to register.
    101—Transfer long from memory to register.
    110—Transfer word from register to memory.
    111—Transfer long from register to memory.

Address Register field—Specifies the address register which is used in the address register indirect plus displacement addressing mode.

Displacement field—Specifies the displacement used in the operand address.

4

MOVEQ

Move Quick
(M68000 Family)

MOVEQ

Operation: Immediate Data ♦ Destination

Assembler
Syntax: MOVEQ #<data>,Dn

Attributes: Size = (Long)

Description: Moves a byte of immediate data to a 32-bit data register. The data in an 8-bit field within the operation word is sign-extended to a long operand in the data register as it is transferred.

Condition Codes:

X	N	Z	V	C
—	*	*	0	0

X—Not affected.
N—Set if the result is negative; cleared otherwise.
Z—Set if the result is zero; cleared otherwise.
V—Always cleared.
C—Always cleared.

Instruction Format:

15	14	13	12	11	10	9	8	7	6	5	4	3	2	1	0
0	1	1	1	REGISTER			0	DATA							

Instruction Fields:

Register field—Specifies the data register to be loaded.

Data field—Eight bits of data, which are sign-extended to a long operand.

MULS

Operation: Source x Destination ✦ Destination

Assembler   MULS.W <ea>,Dn   16 x 16 ✦ 32
Syntax: *MULS.L <ea>,Dl   32 x 32 ✦ 32
        *MULS.L <ea>,Dh–Dl   32 x 32 ✦ 64

        *Applies to MC68020, MC68030, MC68040, CPU32

Attributes: Size = (Word, Long)

Description: Multiplies two signed operands yielding a signed result. This instruction has a word operand form and a long operand form.

In the word form, the multiplier and multiplicand are both word operands, and the result is a long-word operand. A register operand is the low-order word; the upper word of the register is ignored. All 32 bits of the product are saved in the destination data register.

In the long form, the multiplier and multiplicand are both long-word operands, and the result is either a long word or a quad word. The long-word result is the low-order 32 bits of the quad-word result; the high-order 32 bits of the product are discarded.

Condition Codes:

X	N	Z	V	C
—	*	*	*	0

X—Not affected.
N—Set if the result is negative; cleared otherwise.
Z—Set if the result is zero; cleared otherwise.
V—Set if overflow; cleared otherwise.
C—Always cleared.

NOTE

Overflow (V = 1) can occur only when multiplying 32-bit operands to yield a 32-bit result. Overflow occurs if the high-order 32 bits of the quad-word product are not the sign extension of the low-order 32 bits.

MULS

Signed Multiply
(M68000 Family)

Instruction Format:

Word

15	14	13	12	11	10	9	8	7	6	5	4	3	2	1	0
1	1	0	0	REGISTER			1	1	1	EFFECTIVE ADDRESS					
										MODE			REGISTER		

Instruction Fields:

Register field—Specifies a data register as the destination.

Effective Address field—Specifies the source operand. Only data alterable addressing modes can be used as listed in the following tables:

Addressing Mode	Mode	Register	Addressing Mode	Mode	Register
Dn	000	reg. number:Dn	(xxx).W	111	000
An	—	—	(xxx).L	111	001
(An)	010	reg. number:An	#<data>	111	100
(An) +	011	reg. number:An			
− (An)	100	reg. number:An			
(d_{16},An)	101	reg. number:An	(d_{16},PC)	111	010
(d_8,An,Xn)	110	reg. number:An	(d_8,PC,Xn)	111	011

MC68020, MC68030, and MC68040 only

Addressing Mode	Mode	Register	Addressing Mode	Mode	Register
(bd,An,Xn)*	110	reg. number:An	(bd,PC,Xn)*	111	011
([bd,An,Xn],od)	110	reg. number:An	([bd,PC,Xn],od)	111	011
([bd,An],Xn,od)	110	reg. number:An	([bd,PC],Xn,od)	111	011

*Can be used with CPU32.

MULS

Instruction Format:

Long

15	14	13	12	11	10	9	8	7	6	5	4	3	2	1	0
0	1	0	0	1	1	0	0	0	0	\multicolumn{6}{EFFECTIVE ADDRESS}						

15	14	13	12	11	10	9	8	7	6	5	4	3	2	1	0
0	1	0	0	1	1	0	0	0	0	MODE			REGISTER		
0	REGISTER DI			1	SIZE	0	0	0	0	0	0	0	REGISTER Dh		

Instruction Fields:

Effective Address field—Specifies the source operand. Only data addressing modes can be used as listed in the following tables:

Addressing Mode	Mode	Register	Addressing Mode	Mode	Register
Dn	000	reg. number:Dn	(xxx).W	111	000
An	—	—	(xxx).L	111	001
(An)	010	reg. number:An	#<data>	111	100
(An) +	011	reg. number:An			
– (An)	100	reg. number:An			
(d_{16},An)	101	reg. number:An	(d_{16},PC)	111	010
(d_8,An,Xn)	110	reg. number:An	(d_8,PC,Xn)	111	011

MC68020, MC68030, and MC68040 only

Addressing Mode	Mode	Register	Addressing Mode	Mode	Register
(bd,An,Xn)*	110	reg. number:An	(bd,PC,Xn)*	111	011
([bd,An,Xn],od)	110	reg. number:An	([bd,PC,Xn],od)	111	011
([bd,An],Xn,od)	110	reg. number:An	([bd,PC],Xn,od)	111	011

*Can be used with CPU32.

Register DI field—Specifies a data register for the destination operand. The 32-bit multiplicand comes from this register, and the low-order 32 bits of the product are loaded into this register.

Size field—Selects a 32- or 64-bit product.
   0—32-bit product to be returned to register DI.
   1—64-bit product to be returned to Dh–DI.

Register Dh field—If size is one, specifies the data register into which the high-order 32 bits of the product are loaded. If Dh = DI and size is one, the results of the operation are undefined. Otherwise, this field is unused.

MULU
Unsigned Multiply
(M68000 Family)

MULU

Operation: Source x Destination ♦ Destination

Assembler MULU.W \<ea\>,Dn   16 x 16 ♦ 32
Syntax: *MULU.L \<ea\>,Dl   32 x 32 ♦ 32
    *MULU.L \<ea\>,Dh–Dl   32 x 32 ♦ 64

   *Applies to MC68020, MC68030, MC68040, CPU32 only

Attributes: Size = (Word, Long)

Description: Multiplies two unsigned operands yielding an unsigned result. This instruction has a word operand form and a long operand form.

In the word form, the multiplier and multiplicand are both word operands, and the result is a long-word operand. A register operand is the low-order word; the upper word of the register is ignored. All 32 bits of the product are saved in the destination data register.

In the long form, the multiplier and multiplicand are both long-word operands, and the result is either a long word or a quad word. The long-word result is the low-order 32 bits of the quad-word result; the high-order 32 bits of the product are discarded.

Condition Codes:

X	N	Z	V	C
—	*	*	*	0

X—Not affected.
N—Set if the result is negative; cleared otherwise.
Z—Set if the result is zero; cleared otherwise.
V—Set if overflow; cleared otherwise.
C—Always cleared.

NOTE

Overflow (V = 1) can occur only when multiplying 32-bit operands to yield a 32-bit result. Overflow occurs if any of the high-order 32 bits of the quad-word product are not equal to zero.

MULU

Unsigned Multiply
(M68000 Family)

MULU

Instruction Format:

Word

15	14	13	12	11	10	9	8	7	6	5	4	3	2	1	0
1	1	0	0	\multicolumn{3}{c}{REGISTER}	0	1	1	\multicolumn{6}{c}{EFFECTIVE ADDRESS}

For the effective address row, columns 5-3 are MODE and columns 2-0 are REGISTER.

Instruction Fields:

Register field—Specifies a data register as the destination.

Effective Address field—Specifies the source operand. Only data addressing modes can be used as listed in the following tables:

Addressing Mode	Mode	Register
Dn	000	reg. number:Dn
An	—	—
(An)	010	reg. number:An
(An) +	011	reg. number:An
– (An)	100	reg. number:An
(d_{16},An)	101	reg. number:An
(d_8,An,Xn)	110	reg. number:An

Addressing Mode	Mode	Register
(xxx).W	111	000
(xxx).L	111	001
#<data>	111	100
(d_{16},PC)	111	010
(d_8,PC,Xn)	111	011

MC68020, MC68030, and MC68040 only

Addressing Mode	Mode	Register
(bd,An,Xn)*	110	reg. number:An
([bd,An,Xn],od)	110	reg. number:An
([bd,An],Xn,od)	110	reg. number:An

Addressing Mode	Mode	Register
(bd,PC,Xn)*	111	011
([bd,PC,Xn],od)	111	011
([bd,PC],Xn,od)	111	011

*Can be used with CPU32.

Instruction Format:

Long

15	14	13	12	11	10	9	8	7	6	5	4	3	2	1	0
											EFFECTIVE ADDRESS				
0	1	0	0	1	1	0	0	0	0		MODE			REGISTER	
0	REGISTER Dl			0	SIZE	0	0	0	0	0	0	0		REGISTER Dh	

Instruction Fields:

Effective Address field—Specifies the source operand. Only data addressing modes can be used as listed in the following tables:

Addressing Mode	Mode	Register
Dn	000	reg. number:Dn
An	—	—
(An)	010	reg. number:An
(An) +	011	reg. number:An
– (An)	100	reg. number:An
(d_{16},An)	101	reg. number:An
(d_8,An,Xn)	110	reg. number:An

Addressing Mode	Mode	Register
(xxx).W	111	000
(xxx).L	111	001
#<data>	111	100
(d_{16},PC)	111	010
(d_8,PC,Xn)	111	011

MC68020, MC68030, and MC68040 only

(bd,An,Xn)*	110	reg. number:An	(bd,PC,Xn)*	111	011
([bd,An,Xn],od)	110	reg. number:An	([bd,PC,Xn],od)	111	011
([bd,An],Xn,od)	110	reg. number:An	([bd,PC],Xn,od)	111	011

*Can be used with CPU32.

Register Dl field—Specifies a data register for the destination operand. The 32-bit multiplicand comes from this register, and the low-order 32 bits of the product are loaded into this register.

Size field—Selects a 32- or 64-bit product.
0—32-bit product to be returned to register Dl.
1—64-bit product to be returned to Dh–Dl.

Register Dh field—If size is one, specifies the data register into which the high-order 32 bits of the product are loaded. If Dh = Dl and size is one, the results of the operation are undefined. Otherwise, this field is unused.

Operation: $0 - \text{Destination}_{10} - X \rightarrow \text{Destination}$

Assembler
Syntax: NBCD <ea>

Attributes: Size = (Byte)

Description: Subtracts the destination operand and the extend bit from zero. The operation is performed using binary-coded decimal arithmetic. The packed binary-coded decimal result is saved in the destination location. This instruction produces the tens complement of the destination if the extend bit is zero or the nines complement if the extend bit is one. This is a byte operation only.

Condition Codes:

X	N	Z	V	C
*	U	*	U	*

X—Set the same as the carry bit.
N—Undefined.
Z—Cleared if the result is nonzero; unchanged otherwise.
V—Undefined.
C—Set if a decimal borrow occurs; cleared otherwise.

NOTE

Normally the Z condition code bit is set via programming before the start of the operation. This allows successful tests for zero results upon completion of multiple-precision operations.

Instruction Format:

15	14	13	12	11	10	9	8	7	6	5	4	3	2	1	0
0	1	0	0	1	0	0	0	0	0		EFFECTIVE ADDRESS				
											MODE			REGISTER	

Instruction Fields:

Effective Address field—Specifies the destination operand. Only data alterable addressing modes can be used as listed in the following tables:

Addressing Mode	Mode	Register	Addressing Mode	Mode	Register
Dn	000	reg. number:Dn	(xxx).W	111	000
An	—	—	(xxx).L	111	001
(An)	010	reg. number:An	#<data>	—	—
(An)+	011	reg. number:An			
–(An)	100	reg. number:An			
(d₁₆,An)	101	reg. number:An	(d₁₆,PC)	—	—
(d₈,An,Xn)	110	reg. number:An	(d₈,PC,Xn)	—	—

MC68020, MC68030, and MC68040 only

(bd,An,Xn)*	110	reg. number:An	(bd,PC,Xn)*	—	—
([bd,An,Xn],od)	110	reg. number:An	([bd,PC,Xn],od)	—	—
([bd,An],Xn,od)	110	reg. number:An	([bd,PC],Xn,od)	—	—

*Can be used with CPU32.

NEG

Negate
(M68000 Family)

NEG

Operation: 0 − Destination ♦ Destination

**Assembler
Syntax:**   NEG <ea>

Attributes: Size = (Byte, Word, Long)

Description: Subtracts the destination operand from zero and stores the result in the destination location. The size of the operation is specified as byte, word, or long.

Condition Codes:

X	N	Z	V	C
*	*	*	*	*

X—Set the same as the carry bit.
N—Set if the result is negative; cleared otherwise.
Z—Set if the result is zero; cleared otherwise.
V—Set if an overflow occurs; cleared otherwise.
C—Cleared if the result is zero; set otherwise.

Instruction Format:

15	14	13	12	11	10	9	8	7	6	5	4	3	2	1	0
0	1	0	0	0	1	0	0	SIZE		EFFECTIVE ADDRESS					
										MODE			REGISTER		

Instruction Fields:

Size field—Specifies the size of the operation.
    00—Byte operation
    01—Word operation
    10—Long operation

Effective Address field—Specifies the destination operand. Only data alterable addressing modes can be used as listed in the following tables:

Addressing Mode	Mode	Register
Dn	000	reg. number:Dn
An	—	—
(An)	010	reg. number:An
(An) +	011	reg. number:An
– (An)	100	reg. number:An
(d$_{16}$,An)	101	reg. number:An
(d$_8$,An,Xn)	110	reg. number:An

Addressing Mode	Mode	Register
(xxx).W	111	000
(xxx).L	111	001
#<data>	—	—
(d$_{16}$,PC)	—	—
(d$_8$,PC,Xn)	—	—

MC68020, MC68030, and MC68040 only

Addressing Mode	Mode	Register
(bd,An,Xn)*	110	reg. number:An
([bd,An,Xn],od)	110	reg. number:An
([bd,An],Xn,od)	110	reg. number:An

Addressing Mode	Mode	Register
(bd,PC,Xn)*	—	—
([bd,PC,Xn],od)	—	—
([bd,PC],Xn,od)	—	—

*Can be used with CPU32.

NEGX

Operation: 0 − Destination − X ◆ Destination

Assembler
Syntax: NEGX <ea>

Attributes: Size = (Byte, Word, Long)

Description: Subtracts the destination operand and the extend bit from zero. Stores the result in the destination location. The size of the operation is specified as byte, word, or long.

Condition Codes:

X	N	Z	V	C
*	*	*	*	*

X—Set the same as the carry bit.
N—Set if the result is negative; cleared otherwise.
Z—Cleared if the result is nonzero; unchanged otherwise.
V—Set if an overflow occurs; cleared otherwise.
C—Set if a borrow occurs; cleared otherwise.

NOTE

Normally the Z condition code bit is set via programming before the start of the operation. This allows successful tests for zero results upon completion of multiple-precision operations.

Instruction Format:

15	14	13	12	11	10	9	8	7	6	5	4	3	2	1	0
0	1	0	0	0	0	0	0	SIZE		EFFECTIVE ADDRESS					
										MODE			REGISTER		

Instruction Fields:

Size field—Specifies the size of the operation.
00—Byte operation
01—Word operation
10—Long operation

Effective Address field—Specifies the destination operand. Only data alterable addressing modes can be used as listed in the following tables:

Addressing Mode	Mode	Register
Dn	000	reg. number:Dn
An	—	—
(An)	010	reg. number:An
(An) +	011	reg. number:An
– (An)	100	reg. number:An
(d_{16},An)	101	reg. number:An
(d_8,An,Xn)	110	reg. number:An

Addressing Mode	Mode	Register
(xxx).W	111	000
(xxx).L	111	001
#<data>	—	—
(d_{16},PC)	—	—
(d_8,PC,Xn)	—	—

MC68020, MC68030, and MC68040 only

Addressing Mode	Mode	Register
(bd,An,Xn)*	110	reg. number:An
([bd,An,Xn],od)	110	reg. number:An
([bd,An],Xn,od)	110	reg. number:An

Addressing Mode	Mode	Register
(bd,PC,Xn)*	—	—
([bd,PC,Xn],od)	—	—
([bd,PC],Xn,od)	—	—

*Can be used with CPU32.

NOP

NOP
No Operation
(M68000 Family)

NOP

Operation: None

**Assembler
Syntax:** NOP

Attributes: Unsized

Description: Performs no operation. The processor state, other than the program counter, is unaffected. Execution continues with the instruction following the NOP instruction. The NOP instruction does not begin execution until all pending bus cycles have completed. This synchronizes the pipeline and prevents instruction overlap.

Condition Codes:
Not affected.

Instruction Format:

15	14	13	12	11	10	9	8	7	6	5	4	3	2	1	0
0	1	0	0	1	1	1	0	0	1	1	1	0	0	0	1

Operation: ~ Destination ♦ Destination

**Assembler
Syntax**:   NOT <ea>

Attributes: Size = (Byte, Word, Long)

Description: Calculates the ones complement of the destination operand and stores the result in the destination location. The size of the operation is specified as byte, word, or long.

Condition Codes:

X	N	Z	V	C
—	*	*	0	0

X—Not affected.
N—Set if the result is negative; cleared otherwise.
Z—Set if the result is zero; cleared otherwise.
V—Always cleared.
C—Always cleared.

Instruction Format:

15	14	13	12	11	10	9	8	7	6	5	4	3	2	1	0
0	1	0	0	0	1	1	0	SIZE		EFFECTIVE ADDRESS					

15	14	13	12	11	10	9	8	7	6	5	4	3	2	1	0
0	1	0	0	0	1	1	0	SIZE		MODE			REGISTER		

Instruction Fields:

Size field—Specifies the size of the operation.
   00—Byte operation
   01—Word operation
   10—Long operation

Effective Address field—Specifies the destination operand. Only data alterable addressing modes can be used as listed in the following tables:

Addressing Mode	Mode	Register	Addressing Mode	Mode	Register
Dn	000	reg. number:Dn	(xxx).W	111	000
An	—	—	(xxx).L	111	001
(An)	010	reg. number:An	#<data>	—	—
(An) +	011	reg. number:An			
– (An)	100	reg. number:An			
(d$_{16}$,An)	101	reg. number:An	(d$_{16}$,PC)	—	—
(d$_8$,An,Xn)	110	reg. number:An	(d$_8$,PC,Xn)	—	—

MC68020, MC68030, and MC68040 only

(bd,An,Xn)*	110	reg. number:An	(bd,PC,Xn)*	—	—
([bd,An,Xn],od)	110	reg. number:An	([bd,PC,Xn],od)	—	—
([bd,An],Xn,od)	110	reg. number:An	([bd,PC],Xn,od)	—	—

*Can be used with CPU32.

OR

Inclusive-OR Logical
(M68000 Family)

Operation: Source V Destination ♦ Destination

Assembler   OR <ea>,Dn
Syntax: OR Dn,<ea>

Attributes: Size = (Byte, Word, Long)

Description: Performs an inclusive-OR operation on the source operand and the destination operand and stores the result in the destination location. The size of the operation is specified as byte, word, or long. The contents of an address register may not be used as an operand.

Condition Codes:

X	N	Z	V	C
—	*	*	0	0

X—Not affected.
N—Set if the most significant bit of the result is set; cleared otherwise.
Z—Set if the result is zero; cleared otherwise.
V—Always cleared.
C—Always cleared.

Instruction Format:

15	14	13	12	11	10	9	8	7	6	5	4	3	2	1	0
1	0	0	0	REGISTER			OPMODE			EFFECTIVE ADDRESS					
										MODE			REGISTER		

Instruction Fields:

Register field—Specifies any of the eight data registers.

Opmode field

Byte	Word	Long	Operation
000	001	010	<ea> V Dn ♦ Dn
100	101	110	Dn V <ea> ♦ <ea>

Effective Address field—If the location specified is a source operand, only data addressing modes can be used as listed in the following tables:

Addressing Mode	Mode	Register	Addressing Mode	Mode	Register
Dn	000	reg. number:Dn	(xxx).W	111	000
An	—	—	(xxx).L	111	001
(An)	010	reg. number:An	#<data>	111	100
(An) +	011	reg. number:An			
– (An)	100	reg. number:An			
(d_{16},An)	101	reg. number:An	(d_{16},PC)	111	010
(d_8,An,Xn)	110	reg. number:An	(d_8,PC,Xn)	111	011

MC68020, MC68030, and MC68040 only

(bd,An,Xn)*	110	reg. number:An	(bd,PC,Xn)*	111	011
([bd,An,Xn],od)	110	reg. number:An	([bd,PC,Xn],od)	111	011
([bd,An],Xn,od)	110	reg. number:An	([bd,PC],Xn,od)	111	011

*Can be used with CPU32.

If the location specified is a destination operand, only memory alterable addressing modes can be used as listed in the following tables:

Addressing Mode	Mode	Register	Addressing Mode	Mode	Register
Dn	—	—	(xxx).W	111	000
An	—	—	(xxx).L	111	001
(An)	010	reg. number:An	#<data>	—	—
(An) +	011	reg. number:An			
– (An)	100	reg. number:An			
(d₁₆,An)	101	reg. number:An	(d₁₆,PC)	—	—
(d₈,An,Xn)	110	reg. number:An	(d₈,PC,Xn)	—	—

MC68020, MC68030, and MC68040 only

(bd,An,Xn)*	110	reg. number:An	(bd,PC,Xn)*	—	—
([bd,An,Xn],od)	110	reg. number:An	([bd,PC,Xn],od)	—	—
([bd,An],Xn,od)	110	reg. number:An	([bd,PC],Xn,od)	—	—

*Can be used with CPU32.

NOTE

If the destination is a data register, it must be specified using the destination Dn mode, not the destination <ea> mode.

Most assemblers use ORI when the source is immediate data.

ORI

Inclusive-OR
(M68000 Family)

ORI

Operation: Immediate Data V Destination ♦ Destination

Assembler
Syntax: ORI #<data>,<ea>

Attributes: Size = (Byte, Word, Long)

Description: Performs an inclusive-OR operation on the immediate data and the destination operand and stores the result in the destination location. The size of the operation is specified as byte, word, or long. The size of the immediate data matches the operation size.

Condition Codes:

X	N	Z	V	C
—	*	*	0	0

X—Not affected.
N—Set if the most significant bit of the result is set; cleared otherwise.
Z—Set if the result is zero; cleared otherwise.
V—Always cleared.
C—Always cleared.

Instruction Format:

15	14	13	12	11	10	9	8	7	6	5	4	3	2	1	0
0	0	0	0	0	0	0	0	SIZE		EFFECTIVE ADDRESS					
										MODE			REGISTER		
16-BIT WORD DATA								8-BIT BYTE DATA							
32-BIT LONG DATA															

Instruction Fields:

Size field—Specifies the size of the operation.
   00—Byte operation
   01—Word operation
   10—Long operation

Effective Address field—Specifies the destination operand. Only data alterable addressing modes can be used as listed in the following tables:

Addressing Mode	Mode	Register	Addressing Mode	Mode	Register
Dn	000	reg. number:Dn	(xxx).W	111	000
An	—	—	(xxx).L	111	001
(An)	010	reg. number:An	#<data>	—	—
(An) +	011	reg. number:An			
– (An)	100	reg. number:An			
(d$_{16}$,An)	101	reg. number:An	(d$_{16}$,PC)	—	—
(d$_8$,An,Xn)	110	reg. number:An	(d$_8$,PC,Xn)	—	—

MC68020, MC68030, and MC68040 only

(bd,An,Xn)*	110	reg. number:An	(bd,PC,Xn)*	—	—
([bd,An,Xn],od)	110	reg. number:An	([bd,PC,Xn],od)	—	—
([bd,An],Xn,od)	110	reg. number:An	([bd,PC],Xn,od)	—	—

*Can be used with CPU32.

Immediate field—Data immediately following the instruction.
   If size = 00, the data is the low-order byte of the immediate word.
   If size = 01, the data is the entire immediate word.
   If size = 10, the data is the next two immediate words.

**Inclusive-OR Immediate
to Condition Codes
(M68000 Family)**

Operation: Source V CCR → CCR

**Assembler
Syntax**:   ORI #<data>,CCR

Attributes: Size = (Byte)

Description: Performs an inclusive-OR operation on the immediate operand and the condition codes and stores the result in the condition code register (low-order byte of the status register). All implemented bits of the condition code register are affected.

Condition Codes:

X	N	Z	V	C
*	*	*	*	*

X—Set if bit 4 of immediate operand is one; unchanged otherwise.
N—Set if bit 3 of immediate operand is one; unchanged otherwise.
Z—Set if bit 2 of immediate operand is one; unchanged otherwise.
V—Set if bit 1 of immediate operand is one; unchanged otherwise.
C—Set if bit 0 of immediate operand is one; unchanged otherwise.

Instruction Format:

15	14	13	12	11	10	9	8	7	6	5	4	3	2	1	0
0	0	0	0	0	0	0	0	0	0	1	1	1	1	0	0
0	0	0	0	0	0	0	0	8-BIT BYTE DATA							

PACK

Pack
(MC68020, MC68030, MC68040)

Operation: Source (Unpacked BCD) + Adjustment ♦ Destination (Packed BCD)

Assembler
Syntax:
PACK –(Ax),–(Ay),#<adjustment>
PACK Dx,Dy,#<adjustment>

Attributes: Unsized

Description: Adjusts and packs the lower four bits of each of two bytes into a single byte.

When both operands are data registers, the adjustment is added to the value contained in the source register. Bits 11–8 and 3–0 of the intermediate result are concatenated and placed in bits 7–0 of the destination register. The remainder of the destination register is unaffected.

Source:

15	14	13	12	11	10	9	8	7	6	5	4	3	2	1	0
x	x	x	x	a	b	c	d	x	x	x	x	e	f	g	h
							Dx								

Add Adjustment Word:

15		0
	16-BIT EXTENSION	

Resulting in:

15	14	13	12	11	10	9	8	7	6	5	4	3	2	1	0
x'	x'	x'	x'	a'	b'	c'	d'	x'	x'	x'	x'	e'	f'	g'	h'

Destination:

15	14	13	12	11	10	9	8	7	6	5	4	3	2	1	0
u	u	u	u	u	u	u	u	a'	b'	c'	d'	e'	f'	g'	h'
							Dy								

When the predecrement addressing mode is specified, two bytes from the source are fetched and concatenated. The adjustment word is added to the concatenated bytes. Bits 3–0 of each byte are extracted. These eight bits are concatenated to form a new byte which is then written to the destination. ♦

PACK

Pack
(MC68020, MC68030, MC68040)

PACK

Source:

7	6	5	4	3	2	1	0
x	x	x	x	a	b	c	d
x	x	x	x	e	f	g	h
Ax								

Concatenated Word:

15	14	13	12	11	10	9	8	7	6	5	4	3	2	1	0
x	x	x	x	a	b	c	d	x	x	x	x	e	f	g	h

Add Adjustment Word:

15	0
16-BIT EXTENSION	

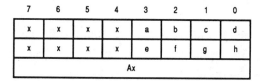

Destination:

7	6	5	4	3	2	1	0
a'	b'	c'	d'	e'	f'	g'	h'
Ay								

Condition Codes:
Not affected.

Instruction Format:

15	14	13	12	11	10	9	8	7	6	5	4	3	2	1	0
1	0	0	0	REGISTER Dy/Ay			1	0	1	0	0	R/M	REGISTER Dx/Ax		
16-BIT ADJUSTMENT EXTENSION:															

Instruction Fields:

Register Dy/Ay field—Specifies the destination register.
   If R/M = 0, specifies a data register.
   If R/M = 1, specifies an address register in the predecrement addressing mode.

R/M field—Specifies the operand addressing mode.
   0—The operation is data register to data register.
   1—The operation is memory to memory.

Register Dx/Ax field—Specifies the source register.
   If R/M = 0, specifies a data register.
   If R/M = 1, specifies an address register in the predecrement addressing mode.

Adjustment field—Immediate data word that is added to the source operand. This word is zero to pack ASCII or EBCDIC codes. Other values can be used for other codes.

4

Operation: SP − 4 → SP; <ea> → (SP)

Assembler
Syntax: PEA <ea>

Attributes: Size = (Long)

Description: Computes the effective address and pushes it onto the stack. The effective address is a long address.

Condition Codes:
Not affected.

Instruction Format:

15	14	13	12	11	10	9	8	7	6	5	4	3	2	1	0
0	1	0	0	1	0	0	0	0	1	EFFECTIVE ADDRESS					

EFFECTIVE ADDRESS	
MODE	REGISTER

Instruction Field:

Effective Address field—Specifies the address to be pushed onto the stack. Only control addressing modes can be used as listed in the following tables:

Addressing Mode	Mode	Register
Dn	—	—
An	—	—
(An)	010	reg. number:An
(An) +	—	—
− (An)	—	—
(d_{16},An)	101	reg. number:An
(d_8,An,Xn)	110	reg. number:An

Addressing Mode	Mode	Register
(xxx).W	111	000
(xxx).L	111	001
#<data>	—	—
(d_{16},PC)	111	010
(d_8,PC,Xn)	111	011

MC68020, MC68030, and MC68040 only

	Mode	Register		Mode	Register
(bd,An,Xn)*	110	reg. number:An	(bd,PC,Xn)*	111	011
([bd,An,Xn],od)	110	reg. number:An	([bd,PC,Xn],od)	111	011
([bd,An],Xn,od)	110	reg. number:An	([bd,PC],Xn,od)	111	011

*Can be used with CPU32.

Operation: Destination Rotated By <count> ♦ Destination

Assembler ROd Dx,Dy
Syntax: ROd #<data>,Dy
ROd <ea>
where d is direction, L or R

Attributes: Size = (Byte, Word, Long)

Description: Rotates the bits of the operand in the direction specified (L or R). The extend bit is not included in the rotation. The rotate count for the rotation of a register is specified in either of two ways:

1. Immediate—The rotate count (1–8) is specified in the instruction.
2. Register—The rotate count is the value in the data register specified in the instruction, modulo 64.

The size of the operation for register destinations is specified as byte, word, or long. The contents of memory, (ROd <ea>), can be rotated one bit only, and operand size is restricted to a word.

The ROL instruction rotates the bits of the operand to the left; the rotate count determines the number of bit positions rotated. Bits rotated out of the high-order bit go to the carry bit and also back into the low-order bit.

ROL:

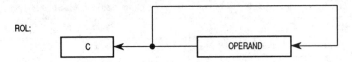

The ROR instruction rotates the bits of the operand to the right; the rotate count determines the number of bit positions rotated. Bits rotated out of the low-order bit go to the carry bit and also back into the high-order bit.

ROR:

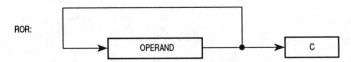

ROL, ROR

ROL, ROR

Condition Codes:

X	N	Z	V	C
—	*	*	0	*

X—Not affected.
N—Set if the most significant bit of the result is set; cleared otherwise.
Z—Set if the result is zero; cleared otherwise.
V—Always cleared.
C—Set according to the last bit rotated out of the operand; cleared when the rotate count is zero.

Instruction Format:

Register Rotate

15	14	13	12	11	10	9	8	7	6	5	4	3	2	1	0
1	1	1	0	COUNT/REGISTER			dr	SIZE		i/r	1	1	REGISTER		

Instruction Fields:

Count/Register field:

If i/r = 0, this field contains the rotate count. The values 1–7 represent counts of 1–7, and zero specifies a count of eight.

If i/r = 1, this field specifies a data register that contains the rotate count (modulo 64).

dr field—Specifies the direction of the rotate.
0—Rotate right
1—Rotate left

Size field—Specifies the size of the operation.
00—Byte operation
01—Word operation
10—Long operation

i/r field—Specifies the rotate count location.
If i/r = 0, immediate rotate count.
If i/r = 1, register rotate count.

Register field—Specifies a data register to be rotated.

ROL, ROR   Rotate (Without Extend)   ROL, ROR
(M68000 Family)

Instruction Format:

Memory Rotate

15	14	13	12	11	10	9	8	7	6	5	4	3	2	1	0
1	1	1	0	0	1	1	dr	1	1	EFFECTIVE ADDRESS					

EFFECTIVE ADDRESS — MODE (bits 5-3), REGISTER (bits 2-0)

Instruction Fields:

dr field—Specifies the direction of the rotate.
   0—Rotate right
   1—Rotate left

Effective Address field—Specifies the operand to be rotated. Only memory alterable addressing modes can be used as listed in the following tables:

Addressing Mode	Mode	Register
Dn	—	—
An	—	—
(An)	010	reg. number:An
(An) +	011	reg. number:An
− (An)	100	reg. number:An
(d$_{16}$,An)	101	reg. number:An
(d$_8$,An,Xn)	110	reg. number:An

Addressing Mode	Mode	Register
(xxx).W	111	000
(xxx).L	111	001
#<data>	—	—
(d$_{16}$,PC)	—	—
(d$_8$,PC,Xn)	—	—

MC68020, MC68030, and MC68040 only

Addressing Mode	Mode	Register
(bd,An,Xn)*	110	reg. number:An
([bd,An,Xn],od)	110	reg. number:An
([bd,An],Xn,od)	110	reg. number:An

Addressing Mode	Mode	Register
(bd,PC,Xn)*	—	—
([bd,PC,Xn],od)	—	—
([bd,PC],Xn,od)	—	—

*Can be used with CPU32.

ROXL, ROXR Rotate with Extend ROXL, ROXR
(M68000 Family)

Operation: Destination Rotated With X By Count ♦ Destination

Assembler   ROXd Dx,Dy
Syntax: ROXd #<data>,Dy
                ROXd <ea>
                where d is direction, L or R

Attributes: Size = (Byte, Word, Long)

Description: Rotates the bits of the operand in the direction specified (L or R). The extend bit is included in the rotation. The rotate count for the rotation of a register is specified in either of two ways:

1. Immediate—The rotate count (1–8) is specified in the instruction.
2. Register—The rotate count is the value in the data register specified in the instruction, modulo 64.

The size of the operation for register destinations is specified as byte, word, or long. The contents of memory, <ea>, can be rotated one bit only, and operand size is restricted to a word.

The ROXL instruction rotates the bits of the operand to the left; the rotate count determines the number of bit positions rotated. Bits rotated out of the high-order bit go to the carry bit and the extend bit; the previous value of the extend bit rotates into the low-order bit.

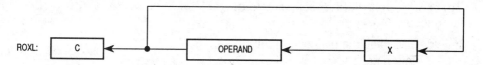

The ROXR instruction rotates the bits of the operand to the right; the rotate count determines the number of bit positions rotated. Bits rotated out of the low-order bit go to the carry bit and the extend bit; the previous value of the extend bit rotates into the high-order bit.

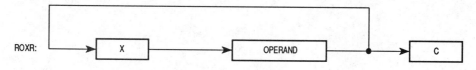

ROXL, ROXR Rotate with Extend ROXL, ROXR
(M68000 Family)

Condition Codes:

X	N	Z	V	C
*	*	*	0	*

X—Set to the value of the last bit rotated out of the operand; unaffected when the rotate count is zero.

N—Set if the most significant bit of the result is set; cleared otherwise.

Z—Set if the result is zero; cleared otherwise.

V—Always cleared.

C—Set according to the last bit rotated out of the operand; when the rotate count is zero, set to the value of the extend bit.

Instruction Format:

Register Rotate

15	14	13	12	11	10	9	8	7	6	5	4	3	2	1	0
1	1	1	0	COUNT/ REGISTER			dr	SIZE		i/r	1	0	REGISTER		

Instruction Fields:

Count/Register field:

If i/r = 0, this field contains the rotate count. The values 1–7 represent counts of 1–7, and zero specifies a count of eight.

If i/r = 1, this field specifies a data register that contains the rotate count (modulo 64).

dr field—Specifies the direction of the rotate.

0—Rotate right
1—Rotate left

Size field—Specifies the size of the operation.
    00—Byte operation
    01—Word operation
    10—Long operation

i/r field—Specifies the rotate count location.
    If i/r = 0, immediate rotate count.
    If i/r = 1, register rotate count.

Register field—Specifies a data register to be rotated.

Instruction Format:

Memory Rotate

15	14	13	12	11	10	9	8	7	6	5	4	3	2	1	0
1	1	1	0	0	1	0	dr	1	1	EFFECTIVE ADDRESS					

EFFECTIVE ADDRESS: MODE (bits 5-3), REGISTER (bits 2-0)

Instruction Fields:

dr field—Specifies the direction of the rotate.
    0—Rotate right
    1—Rotate left

Effective Address field—Specifies the operand to be rotated. Only memory alterable addressing modes can be used as listed in the following tables:

Addressing Mode	Mode	Register	Addressing Mode	Mode	Register
Dn	—	—	(xxx).W	111	000
An	—	—	(xxx).L	111	001
(An)	010	reg. number:An	#<data>	—	—
(An) +	011	reg. number:An			
– (An)	100	reg. number:An			
(d16,An)	101	reg. number:An	(d16,PC)	—	—
(d8,An,Xn)	110	reg. number:An	(d8,PC,Xn)	—	—

MC68020, MC68030, and MC68040 only

Addressing Mode	Mode	Register	Addressing Mode	Mode	Register
(bd,An,Xn)*	110	reg. number:An	(bd,PC,Xn)*	—	—
([bd,An,Xn],od)	110	reg. number:An	([bd,PC,Xn],od)	—	—
([bd,An],Xn,od)	110	reg. number:An	([bd,PC],Xn,od)	—	—

*Can be used with CPU32.

Operation: $(SP) \to PC; SP + 4 + d_n \to SP$

**Assembler
Syntax:**   RTD #<displacement>

Attributes: Unsized

Description: Pulls the program counter value from the stack and adds the sign-extended 16-bit displacement value to the stack pointer. The previous program counter value is lost.

Condition Codes:
Not affected.

Instruction Format:

15	14	13	12	11	10	9	8	7	6	5	4	3	2	1	0
0	1	0	0	1	1	1	0	0	1	1	1	0	1	0	0
16-BIT DISPLACEMENT															

Instruction Field:

Displacement field—Specifies the twos complement integer to be sign-extended and added to the stack pointer.

Operation: Reload Saved Module State from Stack

Assembler
Syntax: RTM Rn

Attributes: Unsized

Description: A previously saved module state is reloaded from the top of stack. After the module state is retrieved from the top of the stack, the caller's stack pointer is incremented by the argument count value in the module state.

Condition Codes:

Set according to the content of the word on the stack.

Instruction Format:

15	14	13	12	11	10	9	8	7	6	5	4	3	2	1	0
0	0	0	0	0	1	1	0	1	1	0	0	D/A	REGISTER		

Instruction Fields:

D/A field—Specifies whether the module data pointer is in a data or an address register.
   0—the register is a data register
   1—the register is an address register

Register field—Specifies the register number for the module data area pointer to be restored from the saved module state. If the register specified is A7 (SP), the updated value of the register reflects the stack pointer operations, and the saved module data area pointer is lost.

Return and Restore Condition Codes
(M68000 Family)

Operation: (SP) ♦ CCR; SP + 2 ♦ SP; (SP) ♦ PC; SP + 4 ♦ SP

Assembler
Syntax: RTR

Attributes: Unsized

Description: Pulls the condition code and program counter values from the stack. The previous condition code and program counter values are lost. The supervisor portion of the status register is unaffected.

Condition Codes:
Set to the condition codes from the stack.

Instruction Format:

15	14	13	12	11	10	9	8	7	6	5	4	3	2	1	0
0	1	0	0	1	1	1	0	0	1	1	1	0	1	1	1

RTS

Operation: (SP) ♦ PC; SP + 4 ♦ SP

**Assembler
Syntax:**   RTS

Attributes: Unsized

Description: Pulls the program counter value from the stack. The previous program counter value is lost.

Condition Codes:
Not affected.

Instruction Format:

15	14	13	12	11	10	9	8	7	6	5	4	3	2	1	0
0	1	0	0	1	1	1	0	0	1	1	1	0	1	0	1

SBCD

Subtract Decimal with Extend
(M68000 Family)

SBCD

Operation: $Destination_{10} - Source_{10} - X \rightarrow Destination$

Assembler
Syntax: SBCD Dx,Dy
SBCD –(Ax),–(Ay)

Attributes: Size = (Byte)

Description: Subtracts the source operand and the extend bit from the destination operand and stores the result in the destination location. The subtraction is performed using binary-coded decimal arithmetic; the operands are packed binary-coded decimal numbers. The instruction has two modes:

1. Data register to data register—the data registers specified in the instruction contain the operands.

2. Memory to memory—the address registers specified in the instruction access the operands from memory using the predecrement addressing mode.

This operation is a byte operation only.

Condition Codes:

X	N	Z	V	C
*	U	*	U	*

X—Set the same as the carry bit.
N—Undefined.
Z—Cleared if the result is nonzero; unchanged otherwise.
V—Undefined.
C—Set if a borrow (decimal) is generated; cleared otherwise.

NOTE

Normally the Z condition code bit is set via programming before the start of an operation. This allows successful tests for zero results upon completion of multiple-precision operations.

SBCD

Instruction Format:

15	14	13	12	11	10	9	8	7	6	5	4	3	2	1	0
1	0	0	0	REGISTER Dy/Ay			1	0	0	0	0	R/M	REGISTER Dx/Ax		

Instruction Fields:

Register Dy/Ay field—Specifies the destination register.
  If R/M = 0, specifies a data register.
  If R/M = 1, specifies an address register for the predecrement addressing mode.

R/M field—Specifies the operand addressing mode.
  0—The operation is data register to data register.
  1—The operation is memory to memory.

Register Dx/Ax field—Specifies the source register.
  If R/M = 0, specifies a data register.
  If R/M = 1, specifies an address register for the predecrement addressing mode.

4

Set According to Condition
(M68000 Family)

Operation: If Condition True
      Then 1s ✦ Destination
      Else 0s ✦ Destination

**Assembler
Syntax:** Scc <ea>

Attributes: Size = (Byte)

Description: Tests the specified condition code; if the condition is true, sets the byte specified by the effective address to TRUE (all ones). Otherwise, sets that byte to FALSE (all zeros). Condition code cc specifies one of the following conditional tests (refer to Table 3-19 for more information on these conditional tests):

Mnemonic	Condition	Mnemonic	Condition
CC(HI)	Carry Clear	LS	Low or Same
CS(LO)	Carry Set	LT	Less Than
EQ	Equal	MI	Minus
F	False	NE	Not Equal
GE	Greater or Equal	PL	Plus
GT	Greater Than	T	True
HI	High	VC	Overflow Clear
LE	Less or Equal	VS	Overflow Set

Condition Codes:
  Not affected.

Instruction Format:

15	14	13	12	11	10	9	8	7	6	5	4	3	2	1	0
0	1	0	1		CONDITION			1	1		EFFECTIVE ADDRESS MODE			REGISTER	

Instruction Fields:

Condition field—The binary code for one of the conditions listed in the table.

Effective Address field—Specifies the location in which the TRUE/FALSE byte is to be stored. Only data alterable addressing modes can be used as listed in the following tables:

Addressing Mode	Mode	Register	Addressing Mode	Mode	Register
Dn	000	reg. number:Dn	(xxx).W	111	000
An	—	—	(xxx).L	111	001
(An)	010	reg. number:An	#<data>	—	—
(An)+	011	reg. number:An			
−(An)	100	reg. number:An			
(d$_{16}$,An)	101	reg. number:An	(d$_{16}$,PC)	—	—
(d$_8$,An,Xn)	110	reg. number:An	(d$_8$,PC,Xn)	—	—

MC68020, MC68030, and MC68040 only

(bd,An,Xn)*	110	reg. number:An	(bd,PC,Xn)*	—	—
([bd,An,Xn],od)	110	reg. number:An	([bd,PC,Xn],od)	—	—
([bd,An],Xn,od)	110	reg. number:An	([bd,PC],Xn,od)	—	—

*Can be used with CPU32.

NOTE

A subsequent NEG.B instruction with the same effective address can be used to change the Scc result from TRUE or FALSE to the equivalent arithmetic value (TRUE = 1, FALSE = 0). In the MC68000 and MC68008, a memory destination is read before it is written.

SUB

Subtract
(M68000 Family)

SUB

Operation: Destination − Source ♦ Destination

Assembler SUB <ea>,Dn
Syntax: SUB Dn,<ea>

Attributes: Size = (Byte, Word, Long)

Description: Subtracts the source operand from the destination operand and stores the result in the destination. The size of the operation is specified as byte, word, or long. The mode of the instruction indicates which operand is the source, which is the destination, and which is the operand size.

Condition Codes:

X	N	Z	V	C
*	*	*	*	*

X—Set to the value of the carry bit.
N—Set if the result is negative; cleared otherwise.
Z—Set if the result is zero; cleared otherwise.
V—Set if an overflow is generated; cleared otherwise.
C—Set if a borrow is generated; cleared otherwise.

Instruction Format:

15	14	13	12	11	10	9	8	7	6	5	4	3	2	1	0
1	0	0	1	REGISTER			OPMODE			EFFECTIVE ADDRESS					
										MODE			REGISTER		

Instruction Fields:

Register field—Specifies any of the eight data registers.

Opmode field

Byte	Word	Long	Operation
000	001	010	Dn – <ea> ◆ Dn
100	101	110	<ea> – Dn ◆ <ea>

Effective Address field—Determines the addressing mode. If the location specified is a source operand, all addressing modes can be used as listed in the following tables:

Addressing Mode	Mode	Register		Addressing Mode	Mode	Register
Dn	000	reg. number:Dn		(xxx).W	111	000
An*	001	reg. number:An		(xxx).L	111	001
(An)	010	reg. number:An		#<data>	111	100
(An) +	011	reg. number:An				
– (An)	100	reg. number:An				
(d$_{16}$,An)	101	reg. number:An		(d$_{16}$,PC)	111	010
(d$_8$,An,Xn)	110	reg. number:An		(d$_8$,PC,Xn)	111	011

MC68020, MC68030, and MC68040 only

(bd,An,Xn)**	110	reg. number:An		(bd,PC,Xn)**	111	011
([bd,An,Xn],od)	110	reg. number:An		([bd,PC,Xn],od)	111	011
([bd,An],Xn,od)	110	reg. number:An		([bd,PC],Xn,od)	111	011

*For byte-sized operation, address register direct is not allowed.
**Can be used with CPU32.

If the location specified is a destination operand, only memory alterable addressing modes can be used as listed in the following tables:

Addressing Mode	Mode	Register
Dn	—	—
An	—	—
(An)	010	reg. number:An
(An) +	011	reg. number:An
– (An)	100	reg. number:An
(d$_{16}$,An)	101	reg. number:An
(d$_8$,An,Xn)	110	reg. number:An

Addressing Mode	Mode	Register
(xxx).W	111	000
(xxx).L	111	001
#<data>	—	—
(d$_{16}$,PC)	—	—
(d$_8$,PC,Xn)	—	—

MC68020, MC68030, and MC68040 only

(bd,An,Xn)*	110	reg. number:An	(bd,PC,Xn)*	—	—
([bd,An,Xn],od)	110	reg. number:An	([bd,PC,Xn],od)	—	—
([bd,An],Xn,od)	110	reg. number:An	([bd,PC],Xn,od)	—	—

*Can be used with CPU32.

NOTE

If the destination is a data register, it must be specified as a destination Dn address, not as a destination <ea> address.

Most assemblers use SUBA when the destination is an address register and SUBI or SUBQ when the source is immediate data.

SUBA

Operation: Destination – Source ♦ Destination

Assembler
Syntax: SUBA <ea>,An

Attributes: Size = (Word, Long)

Description: Subtracts the source operand from the destination address register and stores the result in the address register. The size of the operation is specified as word or long. Word-sized source operands are sign-extended to 32-bit quantities prior to the subtraction.

Condition Codes:
Not affected.

Instruction Format:

15	14	13	12	11	10	9	8	7	6	5	4	3	2	1	0
1	0	0	1	REGISTER			OPMODE			EFFECTIVE ADDRESS					
										MODE			REGISTER		

Instruction Fields:

Register field—Specifies the destination, any of the eight address registers.

Opmode field—Specifies the size of the operation.
  011—Word operation. The source operand is sign-extended to a long operand and the operation is performed on the address register using all 32 bits.
  111—Long operation.

Effective Address field—Specifies the source operand. All addressing modes can be used as listed in the following tables:

Addressing Mode	Mode	Register
Dn	000	reg. number:Dn
An	001	reg. number:An
(An)	010	reg. number:An
(An) +	011	reg. number:An
– (An)	100	reg. number:An
(d$_{16}$,An)	101	reg. number:An
(d$_8$,An,Xn)	110	reg. number:An

Addressing Mode	Mode	Register
(xxx).W	111	000
(xxx).L	111	001
#<data>	111	100
(d$_{16}$,PC)	111	010
(d$_8$,PC,Xn)	111	011

MC68020, MC68030, and MC68040 only

(bd,An,Xn)*	110	reg. number:An
([bd,An,Xn],od)	110	reg. number:An
([bd,An],Xn,od)	110	reg. number:An

(bd,PC,Xn)*	111	011
([bd,PC,Xn],od)	111	011
([bd,PC],Xn,od)	111	011

*Can be used with CPU32.

SUBI

Operation: Destination − Immediate Data ◆ Destination

**Assembler
Syntax:** SUBI #<data>,<ea>

Attributes: Size = (Byte, Word, Long)

Description: Subtracts the immediate data from the destination operand and stores the result in the destination location. The size of the operation is specified as byte, word, or long. The size of the immediate data matches the operation size.

Condition Codes:

X	N	Z	V	C
*	*	*	*	*

X—Set to the value of the carry bit.
N—Set if the result is negative; cleared otherwise.
Z—Set if the result is zero; cleared otherwise.
V—Set if an overflow occurs; cleared otherwise.
C—Set if a borrow occurs; cleared otherwise.

Instruction Format:

15	14	13	12	11	10	9	8	7	6	5	4	3	2	1	0
0	0	0	0	0	1	0	0	SIZE			EFFECTIVE ADDRESS				
											MODE			REGISTER	
16-BIT WORD DATA								8-BIT BYTE DATA							
32-BIT LONG DATA															

Instruction Fields:

Size field—Specifies the size of the operation.
00—Byte operation
01—Word operation
10—Long operation

Effective Address field—Specifies the destination operand. Only data alterable addressing modes can be used as listed in the following tables:

Addressing Mode	Mode	Register	Addressing Mode	Mode	Register
Dn	000	reg. number:Dn	(xxx).W	111	000
An	—	—	(xxx).L	111	001
(An)	010	reg. number:An	#<data>	—	—
(An) +	011	reg. number:An			
– (An)	100	reg. number:An			
(d_{16},An)	101	reg. number:An	(d_{16},PC)	—	—
(d_8,An,Xn)	110	reg. number:An	(d_8,PC,Xn)	—	—

MC68020, MC68030, and MC68040 only

(bd,An,Xn)*	110	reg. number:An	(bd,PC,Xn)*	—	—
([bd,An,Xn],od)	110	reg. number:An	([bd,PC,Xn],od)	—	—
([bd,An],Xn,od)	110	reg. number:An	([bd,PC],Xn,od)	—	—

*Can be used with CPU32.

Immediate field—Data immediately following the instruction.
If size = 00, the data is the low-order byte of the immediate word.
If size = 01, the data is the entire immediate word.
If size = 10, the data is the next two immediate words.

4

SUBQ

SUBQ

Operation: Destination − Immediate Data ♦ Destination

**Assembler
Syntax:** SUBQ #<data>,<ea>

Attributes: Size = (Byte, Word, Long)

Description: Subtracts the immediate data (1–8) from the destination operand. The size of the operation is specified as byte, word, or long. Only word and long operations can be used with address registers, and the condition codes are not affected. When subtracting from address registers, the entire destination address register is used, despite the operation size.

Condition Codes:

X	N	Z	V	C
*	*	*	*	*

X—Set to the value of the carry bit.
N—Set if the result is negative; cleared otherwise.
Z—Set if the result is zero; cleared otherwise.
V—Set if an overflow occurs; cleared otherwise.
C—Set if a borrow occurs; cleared otherwise.

Instruction Format:

15	14	13	12	11	10	9	8	7	6	5	4	3	2	1	0
0	1	0	1		DATA		1		SIZE		EFFECTIVE ADDRESS				
											MODE			REGISTER	

SUBQ

Subtract Quick
(M68000 Family)

SUBQ

Instruction Fields:

Data field—Three bits of immediate data; 1–7 represent immediate values of 1–7, and zero represents eight.

Size field—Specifies the size of the operation.
  00—Byte operation
  01—Word operation
  10—Long operation

Effective Address field—Specifies the destination location. Only alterable addressing modes can be used as listed in the following tables:

Addressing Mode	Mode	Register	Addressing Mode	Mode	Register
Dn	000	reg. number:Dn	(xxx).W	111	000
An*	001	reg. number:An	(xxx).L	111	001
(An)	010	reg. number:An	#<data>	—	—
(An) +	011	reg. number:An			
– (An)	100	reg. number:An			
(d_{16},An)	101	reg. number:An	(d_{16},PC)	—	—
(d_8,An,Xn)	110	reg. number:An	(d_8,PC,Xn)	—	—

MC68020, MC68030, and MC68040 only

(bd,An,Xn)**	110	reg. number:An	(bd,PC,Xn)**	—	—
([bd,An,Xn],od)	110	reg. number:An	([bd,PC,Xn],od)	—	—
([bd,An],Xn,od)	110	reg. number:An	([bd,PC],Xn,od)	—	—

*Word and long only.

**Can be used with CPU32.

SUBX

SUBX

Operation: Destination − Source − X ♦ Destination

Assembler   SUBX Dx,Dy
Syntax: SUBX −(Ax),−(Ay)

Attributes: Size = (Byte, Word, Long)

Description: Subtracts the source operand and the extend bit from the destination operand and stores the result in the destination location. The instruction has two modes:

1. Data register to data register—the data registers specified in the instruction contain the operands.
2. Memory to memory—the address registers specified in the instruction access the operands from memory using the predecrement addressing mode.

The size of the operand is specified as byte, word, or long.

Condition Codes:

X	N	Z	V	C
*	*	*	*	*

X—Set to the value of the carry bit.
N—Set if the result is negative; cleared otherwise.
Z—Cleared if the result is nonzero; unchanged otherwise.
V—Set if an overflow occurs; cleared otherwise.
C—Set if a borrow occurs; cleared otherwise.

NOTE

Normally the Z condition code bit is set via programming before the start of an operation. This allows successful tests for zero results upon completion of multiple-precision operations.

SUBX

Subtract with Extend
(M68000 Family)

SUBX

Instruction Format:

15	14	13	12	11	10	9	8	7	6	5	4	3	2	1	0
1	0	0	1	REGISTER Dy/Ay			1	SIZE		0	0	R/M	REGISTER Dx/Ax		

Instruction Fields:

Register Dy/Ay field—Specifies the destination register.
   If R/M = 0, specifies a data register.
   If R/M = 1, specifies an address register for the predecrement addressing mode.

Size field—Specifies the size of the operation.
   00—Byte operation
   01—Word operation
   10—Long operation

R/M field—Specifies the operand addressing mode.
   0—The operation is data register to data register.
   1—The operation is memory to memory.

Register Dx/Ax field—Specifies the source register:
   If R/M = 0, specifies a data register.
   If R/M = 1, specifies an address register for the predecrement addressing mode.

SWAP

Swap Register Halves
(M68000 Family)

SWAP

Operation: Register 31–16 ◆◆ Register 15–0

Assembler
Syntax: SWAP Dn

Attributes: Size = (Word)

Description: Exchange the 16-bit words (halves) of a data register.

Condition Codes:

X	N	Z	V	C
—	*	*	0	0

X—Not affected.
N—Set if the most significant bit of the 32-bit result is set; cleared otherwise.
Z—Set if the 32-bit result is zero; cleared otherwise.
V—Always cleared.
C—Always cleared.

Instruction Format:

15	14	13	12	11	10	9	8	7	6	5	4	3	2	1	0
0	1	0	0	1	0	0	0	0	1	0	0	0	REGISTER		

Instruction Field:

Register field—Specifies the data register to swap.

Operation: Destination Tested ⬧ Condition Codes; 1 ⬧ Bit 7 of Destination

**Assembler
Syntax:** TAS <ea>

Attributes: Size = (Byte)

Description: Tests and sets the byte operand addressed by the effective address field. The instruction tests the current value of the operand and sets the N and Z condition bits appropriately. TAS also sets the high-order bit of the operand. The operation uses a locked or read-modify-write transfer sequence. This instruction supports use of a flag or semaphore to coordinate several processors.

Condition Codes:

X	N	Z	V	C
—	*	*	0	0

X—Not affected.
N—Set if the most significant bit of the operand is currently set; cleared otherwise.
Z—Set if the operand was zero; cleared otherwise.
V—Always cleared.
C—Always cleared.

Instruction Format:

15	14	13	12	11	10	9	8	7	6	5	4	3	2	1	0
0	1	0	0	1	0	1	0	1	1	EFFECTIVE ADDRESS					
										MODE			REGISTER		

Instruction Fields:

Effective Address field—Specifies the location of the tested operand. Only data alterable addressing modes can be used as listed in the following tables:

Addressing Mode	Mode	Register	Addressing Mode	Mode	Register
Dn	000	reg. number:Dn	(xxx).W	111	000
An	—	—	(xxx).L	111	001
(An)	010	reg. number:An	#<data>	—	—
(An) +	011	reg. number:An			
– (An)	100	reg. number:An			
(d$_{16}$,An)	101	reg. number:An	(d$_{16}$,PC)	—	—
(d$_8$,An,Xn)	110	reg. number:An	(d$_8$,PC,Xn)	—	—

MC68020, MC68030, and MC68040 only

(bd,An,Xn)*	110	reg. number:An	(bd,PC,Xn)*	—	—
([bd,An,Xn],od)	110	reg. number:An	([bd,PC,Xn],od)	—	—
([bd,An],Xn,od)	110	reg. number:An	([bd,PC],Xn,od)	—	—

*Can be used with CPU32.

4

TRAP

TRAP

TRAP

Operation: 1 → S-Bit of SR
*SSP − 2 → SSP; Format/Offset → (SSP);
SSP − 4 → SSP; PC → (SSP); SSP − 2 → SSP;
SR → (SSP); Vector Address → PC

*The MC68000 and MC68008 do not write vector offset or format code to the system stack.

Assembler
Syntax: TRAP #<vector>

Attributes: Unsized

Description: Causes a TRAP #<vector> exception. The instruction adds the immediate operand (vector) of the instruction to 32 to obtain the vector number. The range of vector values is 0–15, which provides 16 vectors.

Condition Codes:
Not affected.

Instruction Format:

15	14	13	12	11	10	9	8	7	6	5	4	3	2	1	0
0	1	0	0	1	1	1	0	0	1	0	0		VECTOR		

Instruction Fields:

Vector field—Specifies the trap vector to be taken.

TRAPcc

Trap on Condition
(MC68020, MC68030, MC68040, CPU32)

TRAPcc

Operation: If cc
    Then TRAP

Assembler   TRAPcc
Syntax: TRAPcc.W #<data>
           TRAPcc.L #<data>

Attributes: Unsized or Size = (Word, Long)

Description: If the specified condition is true, causes a TRAPcc exception with a vector number 7. The processor pushes the address of the next instruction word (currently in the program counter) onto the stack. If the condition is not true, the processor performs no operation, and execution continues with the next instruction. The immediate data operand should be placed in the next word(s) following the operation word and is available to the trap handler. Condition code cc specifies one of the following conditional tests (refer to Table 3-19 for more information on these conditional tests):

Mnemonic	Condition	Mnemonic	Condition
CC(HI)	Carry Clear	LS	Low or Same
CS(LO)	Carry Set	LT	Less Than
EQ	Equal	MI	Minus
F	False	NE	Not Equal
GE	Greater or Equal	PL	Plus
GT	Greater Than	T	True
HI	High	VC	Overflow Clear
LE	Less or Equal	VS	Overflow Set

Condition Codes:
Not affected.

Instruction Format:

15	14	13	12	11	10	9	8	7	6	5	4	3	2	1	0
0	1	0	1		CONDITION			1	1	1	1	1		OPMODE	
OPTIONAL WORD															
OR LONG WORD															

Instruction Fields:

Condition field—The binary code for one of the conditions listed in the table.

Opmode field—Selects the instruction form.
    010—Instruction is followed by word-sized operand.
    011—Instruction is followed by long-word-sized operand.
    100—Instruction has no operand.

TRAPV

Trap on Overflow
(M68000 Family)

TRAPV

Operation: If V
   Then TRAP

Assembler
Syntax: TRAPV

Attributes: Unsized

Description: If the overflow condition is set, causes a TRAPV exception with a vector number 7. If the overflow condition is not set, the processor performs no operation and execution continues with the next instruction.

Condition Codes:
   Not affected.

Instruction Format:

15	14	13	12	11	10	9	8	7	6	5	4	3	2	1	0
0	1	0	0	1	1	1	0	0	1	1	1	0	1	1	0

TST

Test an Operand
(M68000 Family)

TST

Operation: Destination Tested → Condition Codes

**Assembler
Syntax:** TST <ea>

Attributes: Size = (Byte, Word, Long)

Description: Compares the operand with zero and sets the condition codes according to the results of the test. The size of the operation is specified as byte, word, or long.

Condition Codes:

X	N	Z	V	C
—	*	*	0	0

X—Not affected.
N—Set if the operand is negative; cleared otherwise.
Z—Set if the operand is zero; cleared otherwise.
V—Always cleared.
C—Always cleared.

Instruction Format:

15	14	13	12	11	10	9	8	7	6	5	4	3	2	1	0
0	1	0	0	1	0	1	0	SIZE		EFFECTIVE ADDRESS					
										MODE			REGISTER		

Instruction Fields:

Size field—Specifies the size of the operation.
   00—Byte operation
   01—Word operation
   10—Long operation

Effective Address field—Specifies the addressing mode for the destination operand as listed in the following tables:

Addressing Mode	Mode	Register
Dn	000	reg. number:Dn
An*	001	reg. number:An
(An)	010	reg. number:An
(An) +	011	reg. number:An
− (An)	100	reg. number:An
(d_{16},An)	101	reg. number:An
(d_8,An,Xn)	110	reg. number:An

Addressing Mode	Mode	Register
(xxx).W	111	000
(xxx).L	111	001
#<data>*	111	100
(d_{16},PC)**	111	010
(d_8,PC,Xn)**	111	011

MC68020, MC68030, and MC68040 only

(bd,An,Xn)***	110	reg. number:An
([bd,An,Xn],od)	110	reg. number:An
([bd,An],Xn,od)	110	reg. number:An

(bd,PC,Xn)***	111	011
([bd,PC,Xn],od)	111	011
([bd,PC],Xn,od)	111	011

*MC68020, MC68030, MC68040, and CPU32. Address register direct allowed only for word and long.

**PC relative addressing modes do not apply to MC68000, MC680008, or MC68010.

***Can be used with CPU32.

UNLK

Unlink
(M68000 Family)

Operation: An ◆ SP; (SP) ◆ An; SP + 4 ◆ SP

**Assembler
Syntax:** UNLK An

Attributes: Unsized

Description: Loads the stack pointer from the specified address register, then loads the address register with the long word pulled from the top of the stack.

Condition Codes:
Not affected.

Instruction Format:

15	14	13	12	11	10	9	8	7	6	5	4	3	2	1	0
0	1	0	0	1	1	1	0	0	1	0	1	1	REGISTER		

Instruction Field:

Register field—Specifies the address register for the instruction.

Unpack BCD
(MC68020, MC68030, MC68040)

Operation: Source (Packed BCD) + Adjustment ♦ Destination (Unpacked BCD)

Assembler UNPACK −(Ax),−(Ay),#<adjustment>
Syntax: UNPK Dx,Dy,#<adjustment>

Attributes: Unsized

Description: Places the two binary-coded decimal digits in the source operand byte into the lower four bits of two bytes and places zero bits in the upper four bits of both bytes. Adds the adjustment value to this unpacked value. Condition codes are not altered.

When both operands are data registers, the instruction unpacks the source register contents, adds the extension word, and places the result in the destination register. The high word of the destination register is unaffected.

Source:

15	14	13	12	11	10	9	8	7	6	5	4	3	2	1	0
u	u	u	u	u	u	u	u	a	b	c	d	e	f	g	h
Dx																

Intermediate Expansion:

15	14	13	12	11	10	9	8	7	6	5	4	3	2	1	0
0	0	0	0	a	b	c	d	0	0	0	0	e	f	g	h

Add Adjustment Word:

15	14	13	12	11	10	9	8	7	6	5	4	3	2	1	0
16-BIT EXTENSION															

Destination:

15	14	13	12	11	10	9	8	7	6	5	4	3	2	1	0
v	v	v	v	a'	b'	c'	d'	w	w	w	w	e'	f'	g'	h'
Dy																

When the specified addressing mode is predecrement, the instruction extracts two binary-coded decimal digits from a byte at the source address. After unpacking the digits and adding the adjustment word, the instruction writes the two bytes to the destination address.

Source:

7	6	5	4	3	2	1	0
a	b	c	d	e	f	g	h
Ax							

Intermediate Expansion:

15	14	13	12	11	10	9	8	7	6	5	4	3	2	1	0
0	0	0	0	a	b	c	d	0	0	0	0	e	f	g	h

Add Adjustment Word:

15	0
16-BIT EXTENSION	

Destination:

7	6	5	4	3	2	1	0
v	v	v	v	a'	b'	c'	d'
w	w	w	w	e'	f'	g'	h'
Ay							

Condition Codes:
Not affected.

Instruction Format:

15	14	13	12	11	10	9	8	7	6	5	4	3	2	1	0
1	0	0	0	REGISTER Dy/Ay			1	1	0	0	0	R/M	REGISTER Dx/Ax		
16-BIT EXTENSION: ADJUSTMENT															

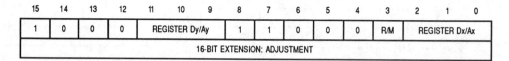

Instruction Fields:

Register Dy/Ay field—Specifies the destination register.

If R/M = 0, specifies a data register.

If R/M = 1, specifies an address register in the predecrement addressing mode.

R/M field—Specifies the operand addressing mode.

0—The operation is data register to data register.

1—The operation is memory to memory.

Register Dx/Ax field—Specifies the data register.

If R/M = 0, specifies a data register.

If R/M = 1, specifies an address register in the predecrement addressing mode.

Adjustment field—Immediate data word that is added to the source operand. Appropriate constants can be used as the adjustment to translate from binary-coded decimal to the desired code. The constant used for ASCII is $3030; for EBCDIC, $F0F0.

4

SECTION 5
FLOATING-POINT INSTRUCTIONS

This section contains information about the floating-point instructions for the MC68881, MC68882, and MC68040. In this section, all references to the MC68040 do not include the MC68LC040 and MC68EC040. Each instruction is described in detail, and the instruction descriptions are arranged in alphabetical order by instruction mnemonic.

All floating-point instructions apply to the MC68881 and MC68882 processors. The MC68040 directly supports part of the floating-point instructions through hardware. It indirectly supports the remainder by providing special traps and/or stack frames for the unimplemented instructions and data types. The following identification is noted under the instruction title for the MC68040:

Directly Supported—(MC6888X, MC68040)

Software Supported—(MC6888X, MC68040FPSW)

For all MC68040 floating-point instructions, the coprocessor ID field must be 001.

Table 5-1 lists the floating-point instructions directly supported by the MC68040, and Table 5-2 lists the floating-point instructions indirectly supported.

5

Table 5-1. Directly Supported Floating-Point Instructions

Mnemonic	Description
FABS	Floating-Point Absolute Value
FADD	Floating-Point Add
FBcc	Floating-Point Branch Conditionally
FCMP	Floating-Point Compare
FDBcc	Floating-Point Test Condition, Decrement, and Branch
FDIV	Floating-Point Divide
FMOVE	Move Floating-Point Data Register
FMOVE	Move Floating-Point System Control Register
FMOVEM	Move Multiple Floating-Point System Data Register
FMOVEM	Move Multiple Floating-Point Control Data Register
FMUL	Floating-Point Multiply
FNEG	Floating-Point Negate
FNOP	No Operation
FRESTORE*	Restore Internal Floating-Point State*
FSAVE*	Save Internal Floating-Point State*
FScc	Set According to Floating-Point Condition
FSORT	Floating-Point Square Root
FSUB	Floating-Point Subtract
FSGLDIV	Floating-Point Single-Precision Divide
FSFLMUL	Floating-Point Single-Precision Multiply
FTRAPcc	Trap on Floating-Point Condition
FTST	Test Floating-Point Operand

*These are privileged instructions; refer to **Section 6 Supervisor (Privileged) Instructions** for detailed information.

Table 5-2. Indirectly Supported Floating-Point Instructions

Mnemonic	Description
FACOS	Floating-Point Arc Cosine
FASIN	Floating-Point Arc Sine
FATAN	Floating-Point Arc Tangent
FATANH	Floating-Point Hyperbolic Arc Tangent
FCOS	Floating-Point Cosine
FCOSH	Floating-Point Hyperbolic Cosine
FETOX	Floating-Point e^x
FETOXM1	Floating-Point $e^x - 1$
FGETEXP	Floating-Point Get Exponent
FGETMAN	Floating-Point Get Mantissa
FINT	Floating-Point Integer Part
FINTRZ	Floating-Point Integer Part, Round-to-Zero
FLOG10	Floating-Point Log_{10}
FLOG2	Floating-Point Log_2
FLOGN	Floating-Point Log_e
FLOGNP1	Floating-Point $\text{Log}_e (x + 1)$
FMOD	Floating-Point Modulo Remainder
FMOVECR	Floating-Point Move Constant ROM
FREM	Floating-Point IEEE Remainder
FSCALE	Floating-Point Scale Exponent
FSIN	Floating-Point Sine
FSINCOS	Floating-Point Simultaneous Sine and Cosine
FSINH	Floating-Point Hyperbolic Sine
FTAN	Floating-Point Tangent
FTANH	Floating-Point Hyperbolic Tangent
FTENTOX	Floating-Point 10^x
FTWOTOX	Floating-Point 2^x

5

Floating-Point Absolute Value
(MC6888X, MC68040)

Operation: Absolute Value of Source ♦ FPn

Assembler
Syntax: FABS.<fmt>   <ea>,FPn
FABS.X   FPm,FPn
FABS.X   FPn
*FrABS.<fmt> <ea>,FPn
*FrABS.X   FPm,FPn
*FrABS.X   FPn
where r is rounding precision, S or D

*Supported by MC68040 only.

Attributes: Format = (Byte, Word, Long, Single, Quad, Extended, Packed)

Description: Converts the source operand to extended precision (if necessary) and
stores the absolute value of that number in the destination floating-point data
register.

FABS will round the result to the precision selected in the floating-point control
register. FSABS and FDABS will round the result to single or double precision,
respectively, regardless of the rounding precision selected in the floating-point
control register.

Operation Table:

DESTINATION	SOURCE					
	+	In Range	−	+	Zero	−	+	Infinity	−
Result	Absolute Value		Absolute Value		Absolute Value	

NOTE: If the source operand is a NAN, refer to **1.6.5 NANs** for more information.

FABS

Floating-Point Absolute Value
(MC6888X, MC68040)

FABS

Floating-Point Status Register:

Condition Codes:	Affected as described in **3.6.2 Conditional Testing.**
Quotient Byte:	Not affected.
Exception Byte:	BSUN Cleared
	SNAN Refer to **1.6.5 NANs**
	OPERR Cleared
	OVFL Cleared
	UNFL If the source is an extended-precision denormalized number, refer to exception processing in the appropriate user's manual; cleared otherwise.
	DZ Cleared
	INEX2 Cleared
	INEX1 If <fmt> is packed, refer to exception processing in the appropriate user's manual; cleared otherwise.
Accrued Exception Byte:	Affected as described in exception processing; refer to the appropriate user's manual.

Instruction Format:

15	14	13	12	11	10	9	8	7	6	5	4	3	2	1	0
1	1	1	1	COPROCESSOR ID			0	0	0	EFFECTIVE ADDRESS					
										MODE			REGISTER		
0	R/M	0	SOURCE SPECIFIER			DESTINATION REGISTER			OPMODE						

Instruction Fields:

Effective Address field—Determines the addressing mode for external operands.

If R/M = 0, this field is unused and should be all zeros.

If R/M = 1, this field specifies the location of the source operand. Only data addressing modes can be used as listed in the following table:

Addressing Mode	Mode	Register	Addressing Mode	Mode	Register
Dn*	000	reg. number:Dn	(xxx).W	111	000
An	—	—	(xxx).L	111	001
(An)	010	reg. number:An	#<data>	111	100
(An) +	011	reg. number:An			
– (An)	100	reg. number:An			
(d$_{16}$,An)	101	reg. number:An	(d$_{16}$,PC)	111	010
(d$_8$,An,Xn)	110	reg. number:An	(d$_8$,PC,Xn)	111	011
(bd,An,Xn)	110	reg. number:An	(bd,PC,Xn)	111	011
([bd,An,Xn],od)	110	reg. number:An	([bd,PC,Xn],od)	111	011
([bd,An],Xn,od)	110	reg. number:An	([bd,PC],Xn,od)	111	011

*Only if <fmt> is byte, word, long, or single.

R/M field—Specifies the source operand address mode.

0—The operation is register to register.

1—The operation is <ea> to register.

Source Specifier field—Specifies the source register or data format.

    If R/M = 0, specifies the source floating-point data register.

    If R/M = 1, specifies the source data format:

        000—Long-Word Integer (L)

        001—Single-Precision Real (S)

        010—Extended-Precision Real (X)

        011—Packed-Decimal Real (P)*

        100—Word Integer (W)

        101—Double-Precision Real (D)

        110—Byte Integer (B)

        *This encoding will cause an unimplemented data type
        exception in the MC68040 to allow emulation in software.

Destination Register field—Specifies the destination floating-point data register.

Opmode field—Specifies the instruction and rounding precision.

0011000	FABS	Rounding precision specified by the floating-point control register.
1011000	FSABS	Single-precision rounding specified.
1011100	FDABS	Double-precision rounding specified.

5

Operation: Arc Cosine of Source ♦ FPn

Assembler   FACOS.<fmt> <ea>,FPn
Syntax: FACOS.X   FPm,FPn
                  FACOS.X   FPn

Attributes: Format = (Byte, Word, Long, Single, Double, Extended, Packed)

Description: Converts the source operand to extended precision (if necessary) and calculates the arc cosine of that number. Stores the result in the destination floating-point data register. This function is not defined for source operands outside of the range [−1...+1]; if the source is not in the correct range, a NAN is returned as the result and the OPERR bit is set in the floating-point status register. If the source is in the correct range, the result is in the range of [0...π].

Operation Table:

DESTINATION	SOURCE[1]					
	+	In Range	−	+	Zero	−	+	Infinity	−
Result		Arc Cosine			$+\pi/2$			NAN[2]	

NOTES:
1. If the source operand is a NAN, refer to **1.6.5 NANs** for more information.
2. Sets the OPERR bit in the floating-point status register exception byte.

Floating-Point Status Register:

Condition Codes: Affected as described in **3.6.2 Conditional Testing**.

Quotient Byte: Not affected.
Exception Byte: BSUN   Cleared
                    SNAN   Refer to **1.6.5 NANs**.
                    OPERR   Set if the source is infinity, > +1 or < −1; cleared otherwise.
                    OVFL   Cleared
                    UNFL   Cleared
                    DZ   Cleared
                    INEX2   Refer to inexact result in the appropriate user's manual.
                    INEX1   If <fmt> is packed, refer to inexact result on decimal input in the appropriate user's manual; cleared otherwise.
Accrued Exception Byte: Affected as described in IEEE exception and trap compatibility in the appropriate user's manual.

FACOS

Instruction Format:

15	14	13	12	11	10	9	8	7	6	5	4	3	2	1	0
1	1	1	1	COPROCESSOR ID			0	0	0	EFFECTIVE ADDRESS MODE			REGISTER		
0	R/M	0	SOURCE SPECIFIER			DESTINATION REGISTER			0	0	1	1	1	0	0

Instruction Fields:

Coprocessor ID field—Specifies which coprocessor in the system is to execute this instruction. Motorola assemblers default to ID = 1 for the floating-point coprocessor.

Effective Address field—Determines the addressing mode for external operands.

If R/M = 0, this field is unused and should be all zeros.

If R/M = 1, this field is encoded with an M68000 family addressing mode as listed in the following table:

Addressing Mode	Mode	Register	Addressing Mode	Mode	Register
Dn*	000	reg. number:Dn	(xxx).W	111	000
An	—	—	(xxx).L	111	001
(An)	010	reg. number:An	#<data>	111	100
(An) +	011	reg. number:An			
– (An)	100	reg. number:An			
(d16,An)	101	reg. number:An	(d16,PC)	111	010
(d8,An,Xn)	110	reg. number:An	(d8,PC,Xn)	111	011
(bd,An,Xn)	110	reg. number:An	(bd,PC,Xn)	111	011
([bd,An,Xn],od)	110	reg. number:An	([bd,PC,Xn],od)	111	011
([bd,An],Xn,od)	110	reg. number:An	([bd,PC],Xn,od)	111	011

*Only if <fmt> is byte, word, long, or single.

R/M field—Specifies the source operand address mode.

0—The operation is register to register.

1—The operation is <ea> to register.

Source Specifier field—Specifies the source register or data format.
If R/M = 0, specifies the source floating-point data register.
If R/M = 1, specifies the source data format:

  000—Long-Word Integer (L)
  001—Single-Precision Real (S)
  010—Extended-Precision Real (X)
  011—Packed-Decimal Real (P)
  100—Word Integer (W)
  101—Double-Precision Real (D)
  110—Byte Integer (B)

Destination Register field—Specifies the destination floating-point data register. If R/M = 0 and the source and destination fields are equal, then the input operand is taken from the specified floating-point data register, and the result is then written into the same register. If the single register syntax is used, Motorola assemblers set the source and destination fields to the same value.

5

FADD

Floating-Point Add
(MC6888X, MC68040)

FADD

Operation: Source + FPn ♦ FPn

Assembler   FADD.<fmt>   <ea>,FPn
Syntax: FADD.X   FPm,FPn
                     *FrADD.<fmt> <ea>,FPn
                     *FrADD.X   FPm,FPn
                     where r is rounding precision, S or D

                     *Supported by MC68040 only.

Attributes   Format = (Byte, Word, Long, Single, Double, Extended, Packed)

Description: Converts the source operand to extended precision (if necessary) and adds that number to the number contained in the destination floating-point data register. Stores the result in the destination floating-point data register.

FADD will round the result to the precision selected in the floating-point control register. FSADD and FDADD will round the result to single or double-precision, respectively, regardless of the rounding precision selected in the floating-point control register.

Operation Table:

DESTINATION		SOURCE[1]						
		+	In Range	−	+	Zero	−	+	Infinity	−
In Range	+ −		Add			Add		+inf	−inf
Zero	+ −		Add		+0.0 0.0[2]		0.0[2] −0.0	+inf	−inf
Infinity	+ −		+inf −inf			+inf −inf		+inf NAN[3]	NAN[3] −inf

NOTES:
1. If either operand is a NAN, refer to **1.6.5 NANs** for more information.
2. Returns +0.0 in rounding modes RN, RZ, and RP; returns −0.0 in RM.
3. Sets the OPERR bit in the floating-point status register exception byte.

FADD

Floating-Point Add
(MC6888X, MC68040)

FADD

Floating-Point Status Register:

Condition Codes:	Affected as described in **3.6.2 Conditional Testing**.
Quotient Byte:	Not affected.

Exception Byte:

BSUN	Cleared
SNAN	Refer to **1.6.5 NANs**.
OPERR	Set if the source and the destination are opposite-signed infinities; cleared otherwise.
OVFL	Refer to exception processing in the appropriate user's manual.
UNFL	Refer to exception processing in the appropriate user's manual.
DZ	Cleared
INEX2	Refer to exception processing in the appropriate user's manual.
INEX1	If <fmt> is packed, refer to exception processing in the appropriate user's manual; cleared otherwise.

Accrued Exception Byte: Affected as described in exception processing in the appropriate user's manual.

Instruction Format:

15	14	13	12	11	10	9	8	7	6	5	4	3	2	1	0
1	1	1	1	COPROCESSOR ID			0	0	0	EFFECTIVE ADDRESS MODE			REGISTER		
0	R/M	0	SOURCE SPECIFIER		DESTINATION REGISTER			OPMODE							

Instruction Fields:

Effective Address field—Determines the addressing mode for external operands.
If R/M = 0, this field is unused and should be all zeros.

FADD

Floating-Point Add
(MC6888X, MC68040)

FADD

If R/M = 1, specifies the location of the source operand location. Only data addressing modes can be used as listed in the following table:

Addressing Mode	Mode	Register	Addressing Mode	Mode	Register
Dn*	000	reg. number:Dn	(xxx).W	111	000
An	—	—	(xxx).L	111	001
(An)	010	reg. number:An	#<data>	111	100
(An) +	011	reg. number:An			
– (An)	100	reg. number:An			
(d_{16},An)	101	reg. number:An	(d_{16},PC)	111	010
(d_8,An,Xn)	110	reg. number:An	(d_8,PC,Xn)	111	011
(bd,An,Xn)	110	reg. number:An	(bd,PC,Xn)	111	011
([bd,An,Xn],od)	110	reg. number:An	([bd,PC,Xn],od)	111	011
([bd,An],Xn,od)	110	reg. number:An	([bd,PC],Xn,od)	111	011

*Only if <ea> is byte, word, long, or single.

R/M field—Specifies the source operand address mode.
   0—The operation is register to register.
   1—The operation is <ea> to register.

Source Specifier field—Specifies the source register or data format.
   If R/M = 0, specifies the source floating-point data register.
   If R/M = 1, specifies the source data format:
      000—Long-Word Integer (L)
      001—Single-Precision Real (S)
      010—Extended-Precision Real (X)
      011—Packed-Decimal Real (P)*
      100—Word Integer (W)
      101—Double-Precision Real (D)
      110—Byte Integer (B)

   *This encoding will cause an unimplemented data type
   exception to allow emulation in software.

Destination Register field—Specifies the destination floating-point data register.

Opmode field—Specifies the instruction and rounding precision.
   0100010   FADD   Rounding precision specified by the floating-point control register.
   1100010   FSADD   Single-precision rounding specified.
   1100110   FDADD   Double-precision rounding specified.

FASIN

Arc Sine

(MC6888X, M68040FPSP)

FASIN

Operation: Arc Sine of the Source ⬧ FPn

Assembler   FASIN.<fmt>   <ea>,FPn
Syntax: FASIN.X   FPm,FPn
             FASIN.X   FPn

Attributes: Format = (Byte, Word, Long, Single, Double, Extended, Packed)

Description: Converts the source operand to extended precision (if necessary) and calculates the arc sine of the number. Stores the result in the destination floating-point data register. This function is not defined for source operands outside of the range [−1…+1]; if the source is not in the correct range, a NAN is returned as the result and the OPERR bit is set in the floating-point status register. If the source is in the correct range, the result is in the range of [−π/2…+π/2].

Operation Table:

DESTINATION	SOURCE[1]					
	+	In Range	−	+	Zero	−	+	Infinity	−
Result		Arc Sine		+0.0		−0.0		NAN[2]	

NOTES:
1. If the source operand is a NAN, refer to **1.6.5 NANs** for more information.
2. Sets the OPERR bit in the floating-point status register exception byte.

FASIN

Arc Sine
(MC6888X, M68040FPSP)

FASIN

Floating-Point Status Register:

Condition Codes: Affected as described in **3.6.2 Conditional Testing**.

Quotient Byte: Not affected.

Exception Byte:

BSUN	Cleared
SNAN	Refer to **1.6.5 NANs**.
OPERR	Set if the source is infinity, > +1 or < −1; cleared otherwise
OVFL	Cleared
UNFL	Can be set for an underflow condition.
DZ	Cleared
INEX2	Refer to inexact result in the appropriate user's manual.
INEX1	If <fmt> is packed, refer to inexact result on decimal input in the appropriate user's manual; cleared otherwise.

Accrued Exception Byte: Affected as described in IEEE exception and trap compatibility in the appropriate user's manual.

Instruction Format:

15	14	13	12	11	10	9	8	7	6	5	4	3	2	1	0
1	1	1	1	COPROCESSOR ID			0	0	0	EFFECTIVE ADDRESS					
										MODE			REGISTER		
0	R/M	0	SOURCE SPECIFIER			DESTINATION REGISTER			0	0	0	1	1	0	0

Instruction Fields:

Coprocessor ID field—Specifies which coprocessor in the system is to execute this instruction. Motorola assemblers default to ID = 1 for the floating-point coprocessor.

FASIN

Arc Sine
(MC6888X, M68040FPSP)

FASIN

Effective Address field—Determines the addressing mode for external operands.
If R/M = 0, this field is unused and should be all zeros.
If R/M = 1, this field is encoded with an M68000 family addressing mode as listed
in the following table:

Addressing Mode	Mode	Register	Addressing Mode	Mode	Register
Dn*	000	reg. number:Dn	(xxx).W	111	000
An	—	—	(xxx).L	111	001
(An)	010	reg. number:An	#<data>	111	100
(An) +	011	reg. number:An			
– (An)	100	reg. number:An			
(d$_{16}$,An)	101	reg. number:An	(d$_{16}$,PC)	111	010
(d$_8$,An,Xn)	110	reg. number:An	(d$_8$,PC,Xn)	111	011
(bd,An,Xn)	110	reg. number:An	(bd,PC,Xn)	111	011
([bd,An,Xn],od)	110	reg. number:An	([bd,PC,Xn],od)	111	011
([bd,An],Xn,od)	110	reg. number:An	([bd,PC],Xn,od)	111	011

*Only if <fmt> is byte, word, long, or single.

R/M field—Specifies the source operand address mode.
    0—The operation is register to register.
    1—The operation is <ea> to register.

Source Specifier field—Specifies the source register or data format.
If R/M = 0, specifies the source floating-point data register.
If R/M = 1, specifies the source data format:
    000—Long-Word Integer (L)
    001—Single-Precision Real (S)
    010—Extended-Precision Real (X)
    011—Packed-Decimal Real (P)
    100—Word Integer (W)
    101—Double-Precision Real (D)
    110—Byte Integer (B)

Destination Register field—Specifies the destination floating-point data register. If
R/M = 0 and the source and destination fields are equal, then the input operand is
taken from the specified floating-point data register, and the result is then written
into the same register. If the single register syntax is used, Motorola assemblers
set the source and destination fields to the same value.

FATAN

Arc Tangent
(MC6888X, M68040FPSP)

FATAN

Operation: Arc Tangent of Source ♦ FPn

Assembler FATAN.<fmt>   <ea>,FPn
Syntax: FATAN.X   FPm,FPn
             FATAN.X   FPm,FPnz

Attributes: Format = (Byte, Word, Long, Single, Double, Extended, Packed)

Description: Converts the source operand to extended precision (if necessary) and calculates the arc tangent of that number. Stores the result in the destination floating-point data register. The result is in the range of $[-\pi/2...+\pi/2]$.

Operation Table:

DESTINATION	SOURCE					
	+	In Range	–	+	Zero	–	+	Infinity	–
Result		Arc Tangent		+0.0		–0.0	$+\pi/2$		$-\pi/2$

NOTE: If the source operand is a NAN, refer to **1.6.5 NANs** for more information.

Floating-Point Status Register:

Condition Codes: Affected as described in **3.6.2 Conditional Testing**.

Quotient Byte: Not affected.

Exception Byte: BSUN   Cleared
                        SNAN   Refer to **1.6.5 NANs**.
                        OPERR   Cleared
                        OVFL   Cleared
                        UNFL   Refer to underflow in the appropriate user's manual.
                        DZ   Cleared
                        INEX2   Refer to inexact result in the appropriate user's manual.
                        INEX1   If <fmt> is packed, refer to inexact result on decimal input in the appropriate user's manual; cleared otherwise.

Accrued Exception Byte: Affected as described in IEEE exception and trap compatibility in the appropriate user's manual.

FATAN

Arc Tangent
(MC6888X, M68040FPSP)

FATAN

Instruction Format:

15	14	13	12	11	10	9	8	7	6	5	4	3	2	1	0
1	1	1	1	COPROCESSOR ID			0	0	0	EFFECTIVE ADDRESS					
										MODE			REGISTER		
0	R/M	0	SOURCE SPECIFIER			DESTINATION REGISTER			0	0	0	1	0	1	0

Instruction Fields:

Coprocessor ID field—Specifies which coprocessor in the system is to execute this instruction. Motorola assemblers default to ID = 1 for the floating-point coprocessor.

Effective Address field—Determines the addressing mode for external operands.

If R/M = 0, this field is unused and should be all zeros.

If R/M = 1, this field is encoded with an M68000 family addressing mode as listed in the following table:

Addressing Mode	Mode	Register		Addressing Mode	Mode	Register
Dn*	000	reg. number:Dn		(xxx).W	111	000
An	—	—		(xxx).L	111	001
(An)	010	reg. number:An		#<data>	111	100
(An) +	011	reg. number:An				
– (An)	100	reg. number:An				
(d$_{16}$,An)	101	reg. number:An		(d$_{16}$,PC)	111	010
(d$_8$,An,Xn)	110	reg. number:An		(d$_8$,PC,Xn)	111	011
(bd,An,Xn)	110	reg. number:An		(bd,PC,Xn)	111	011
([bd,An,Xn],od)	110	reg. number:An		([bd,PC,Xn],od)	111	011
([bd,An],Xn,od)	110	reg. number:An		([bd,PC],Xn,od)	111	011

*Only if <fmt> is byte, word, long, or single.

R/M field—Specifies the source operand address mode.

0—The operation is register to register.

1—The operation is <ea> to register.

FATAN

Arc Tangent
(MC6888X, M68040FPSP)

FATAN

Source Specifier field—Specifies the source register or data format.
If R/M = 0, specifies the source floating-point data register.
If R/M = 1, specifies the source data format:
   000—Long-Word Integer (L)
   001—Single-Precision Real (S)
   010—Extended-Precision Real (X)
   011—Packed-Decimal Real (P)
   100—Word Integer (W)
   101—Double-Precision Real (D)
   110—Byte Integer (B)

Destination Register field—Specifies the destination floating-point data register. If R/M = 0 and the source and destination fields are equal, then the input operand is taken from the specified floating-point data register, and the result is then written into the same register. If the single register syntax is used, Motorola assemblers set the source and destination fields to the same value.

5

FATANH

Hyperbolic Arc Tangent
(MC6888X, M68040FPSP)

FATANH

Operation: Hyperbolic Arc Tangent of Source ⬩ FPn

Assembler   FATANH.<fmt>   <ea>,FPn
Syntax: FATANH.X   FPm,FPn
  FATANH.X   FPn

Attributes: Format = (Byte, Word, Long, Single, Double, Extended, Packed)

Description: Converts the source operand to extended precision (if necessary) and calculates the hyperbolic arc tangent of that value. Stores the result in the destination floating-point data register. This function is not defined for source operands outside of the range (−1...+1); and the result is equal to −infinity or +infinity if the source is equal to +1 or −1, respectively. If the source is outside of the range [−1...+1], a NAN is returned as the result, and the OPERR bit is set in the floating-point status register.

Operation Table:

DESTINATION	SOURCE[1]					
	+ In Range −		+ Zero −		+ Infinity −	
Result	Hyperbolic Arc Tangent	+0.0		−0.0	NAN[2]	

NOTE:
1. If the source operand is a NAN, refer to **1.6.5 NANs** for more information.
2. Sets the OPERR bit in the floating-point status register exception byte.

Floating-Point Status Register:

Condition Codes: Affected as described in **3.6.2 Conditional Testing**.

Quotient Byte: Not affected.

FATANH

Hyperbolic Arc Tangent
(MC6888X, M68040FPSP)

FATANH

Exception Byte:

BSUN	Cleared
SNAN	Refer to **1.6.5 NANs**.
OPERR	Set if the source is > +1 or < −1; cleared otherwise.
OVFL	Cleared
UNFL	Refer to underflow in the appropriate user's manual.
DZ	Set if the source is equal to +1 or −1; cleared otherwise.
INEX2	Refer to inexact result in the appropriate user's manual.
INEX1	If <fmt> is packed, refer to inexact result on decimal input in the appropriate user's manual; cleared otherwise.

Accrued Exception Byte: Affected as described in IEEE exception and trap compatibility in the appropriate user's manual.

5

Instruction Format:

15	14	13	12	11	10	9	8	7	6	5	4	3	2	1	0
1	1	1	1	COPROCESSOR ID			0	0	0	EFFECTIVE ADDRESS MODE			REGISTER		
0	R/M	0	SOURCE SPECIFIER		DESTINATION REGISTER			0	0	0	1	1	0	1

Instruction Fields:

Coprocessor ID field—Specifies which coprocessor in the system is to execute this instruction. Motorola assemblers default to ID = 1 for the floating-point coprocessor.

Effective Address field—Determines the addressing mode for external operands.
If R/M = 0, this field is unused and should be all zeros.
If R/M = 1, this field is encoded with an M68000 family addressing mode as listed
in the following table:

Addressing Mode	Mode	Register
Dn*	000	reg. number:Dn
An	—	—
(An)	010	reg. number:An
(An) +	011	reg. number:An
– (An)	100	reg. number:An
(d_{16},An)	101	reg. number:An
(d_8,An,Xn)	110	reg. number:An
(bd,An,Xn)	110	reg. number:An
([bd,An,Xn],od)	110	reg. number:An
([bd,An],Xn,od)	110	reg. number:An

Addressing Mode	Mode	Register
(xxx).W	111	000
(xxx).L	111	001
#<data>	111	100
(d_{16},PC)	111	010
(d_8,PC,Xn)	111	011
(bd,PC,Xn)	111	011
([bd,PC,Xn],od)	111	011
([bd,PC],Xn,od)	111	011

*Only if <fmt> is byte, word, long, or single.

R/M field—Specifies the source operand address mode.
   0—The operation is register to register.
   1—The operation is <ea> to register.

Source Specifier field—Specifies the source register or data format.
  If R/M = 0, specifies the source floating-point data register.
  If R/M = 1, specifies the source data format:
     000—Long-Word Integer (L)
     001—Single-Precision Real (S)
     010—Extended-Precision Real (X)
     011—Packed-Decimal Real (P)
     100—Word Integer (W)
     101—Double-Precision Real (D)
     110—Byte Integer (B)

Destination Register field—Specifies the destination floating-point data register. If
R/M = 0 and the source and destination fields are equal, then the input operand is
taken from the specified floating-point data register, and the result is then written
into the same register. If the single register syntax is used, Motorola assemblers
set the source and destination fields to the same value.

Operation: If Condition True
        Then PC + d_n ⇒ PC

Assembler:
Syntax: FBcc.<size>,<label>

Attributes: Size = (Word, Long)

Description: If the specified floating-point condition is met, program execution continues at the location (PC) + displacement. The displacement is a twos-complement integer that counts the relative distance in bytes. The value of the program counter used to calculate the destination address is the address of the branch instruction plus two. If the displacement size is word, then a 16-bit displacement is stored in the word immediately following the instruction operation word. If the displacement size is long word, then a 32-bit displacement is stored in the two words immediately following the instruction operation word.

The conditional specifier cc selects any one of the 32 floating-point conditional tests as described in **3.6.2 Conditional Testing**.

5

Floating-Point Status Register:

Condition Codes: Not affected.

Quotient Byte: Not affected.

Exception Byte: BSUN   Set if the NAN condition code is set and the condition selected is an IEEE nonaware test.
             SNAN   Not Affected.
             OPERR Not Affected.
             OVF   Not Affected.
             UNFL   Not Affected.
             DZ   Not Affected.
             INEX2 Not Affected.
             INEX1 Not Affected.

Accrued Exception Byte: The IOP bit is set if the BSUN bit is set in the exception byte. No other bit is affected.

FBcc

Floating-Point Branch Conditionally
(MC6888X, MC68040)

FBcc

Instruction Format:

15	14	13	12	11	10	9	8	7	6	5	4	3	2	1	0
1	1	1	1	COPROCESSOR ID			0	1	SIZE	CONDITIONAL PREDICATE					
16-BIT DISPLACEMENT OR MOST SIGNIFICANT WORD OF 32-BIT DISPLACEMENT															
LEAST SIGNIFICANT WORD OF 32-BIT DISPLACEMENT (IF NEEDED)															

Instruction Fields:

Size field—Specifies the size of the signed displacement.
If Format = 0, then the displacement is 16 bits and is sign-extended before use.
If Format = 1, then the displacement is 32 bits.

Conditional Predicate field—Specifies one of 32 conditional tests as defined in
1.3.2 Conditional Test Definitions.

NOTE

When a BSUN exception occurs, the main processor takes a preinstruction exception. If the exception handler returns without modifying the image of the program counter on the stack frame (to point to the instruction following the FBcc), then it must clear the cause of the exception (by clearing the NAN bit or disabling the BSUN trap), or the exception will occur again immediately upon return to the routine that caused the exception.

FCMP

Operation: FPn – Source

Assembler   FCMP.<fmt> <ea>,FPn
Syntax: FCMP.X FPm,FPn

Attributes: Format = (Byte, Word, Long, Single, Double, Extended, Packed)

Description: Converts the source operand to extended precision (if necessary) and subtracts the operand from the destination floating-point data register. The result of the subtraction is not retained, but it is used to set the floating-point condition codes as described in **3.6.2 Conditional Testing**.

Operation Table: The entries in this operation table differ from those of the tables describing most of the floating-point instructions. For each combination of input operand types, the condition code bits that may be set are indicated. If the name of a condition code bit is given and is not enclosed in brackets, then it is always set. If the name of a condition code bit is enclosed in brackets, then that bit is either set or cleared, as appropriate. If the name of a condition code bit is not given, then that bit is always cleared by the operation. The infinity bit is always cleared by the FCMP instruction since it is not used by any of the conditional predicate equations. Note that the NAN bit is not shown since NANs are always handled in the same manner (as described in **1.6.5 NANs**).

DESTINATION		+ In Range −		+ Zero −		+ Infinity −	
		SOURCE					
In Range	+	{NZ}	none	none	none	N	none
	−	N	{NZ}	N	N	N	none
Zero	+	N	none	Z	Z	N	none
	−	N	none	NZ	NZ	N	none
Infinity	+	none	none	none	none	Z	none
	−	N	N	N	N	N	NZ

NOTE: If either operand is a NAN, refer to **1.6.5 NANs** for more information.

Floating-Point Status Register:

Condition Codes: Affected as described in the preceding operation table.

Quotient Byte: Not affected.

Exception Byte:

BSUN	Cleared
SNAN	Refer to **1.6.5 NANs**.
OPERR	Cleared
OVFL	Cleared
UNFL	Cleared
DZ	Cleared
INEX2	Cleared
INEX1	If <fmt> is packed, refer to exception processing in the appropriate user's manual; cleared otherwise.

Accrued Exception Byte: Affected as described in exception processing in the appropriate user's manual.

Instruction Format:

15	14	13	12	11	10	9	8	7	6	5	4	3	2	1	0
1	1	1	1	COPROCESSOR ID			0	0	0	EFFECTIVE ADDRESS					
										MODE			REGISTER		
0	R/M	0	SOURCE SPECIFIER			DESTINATION REGISTER			0	1	1	1	0	0	0

FCMP

Instruction Fields:

Effective Address field—Determines the addressing mode for external operands.

If R/M = 0, this field is unused and should be all zeros.

If R/M = 1, specifies the location of the source operand location. Only data addressing modes can be used as listed in the following table:

Addressing Mode	Mode	Register	Addressing Mode	Mode	Register
Dn*	000	reg. number:Dn	(xxx).W	111	000
An	—	—	(xxx).L	111	001
(An)	010	reg. number:An	#<data>	111	100
(An) +	011	reg. number:An			
– (An)	100	reg. number:An			
(d16,An)	101	reg. number:An	(d16,PC)	111	010
(d8,An,Xn)	110	reg. number:An	(d8,PC,Xn)	111	011
(bd,An,Xn)	110	reg. number:An	(bd,PC,Xn)	111	011
([bd,An,Xn],od)	110	reg. number:An	([bd,PC,Xn],od)	111	011
([bd,An],Xn,od)	110	reg. number:An	([bd,PC],Xn,od)	111	011

*Only if <fmt> is byte, word, long, or single.

R/M field—Specifies the source operand address mode.

0—The operation is register to register.

1—The operation is <ea> to register.

Source Specifier field—Specifies the source register or data format.

If R/M = 0, specifies the source floating-point data register.

If R/M = 1, specifies the source data format:

000—Long-Word Integer (L)

001—Single-Precision Real (S)

010—Extended-Precision Real (X)

011—Packed-Decimal Real (P)*

100—Word Integer (W)

101—Double-Precision Real (D)

110—Byte Integer (B)

*This encoding in the MC68040 will cause an unimplemented data type exception to allow emulation in software.

Destination Register field—Specifies the destination floating-point data register.

Operation: Cosine of Source $\rightarrow$ FPn

Assembler   FCOS.<fmt> <ea>,FPn
Syntax: FCOS.X FPm,FPn
                  FCOS.X FPn

Attributes: Format = (Byte, Word, Long, Single, Double, Extended, Packed)

Description: Converts the source operand to extended precision (if necessary) and calculates the cosine of that number. Stores the result in the destination floating-point data register. This function is not defined for source operands of ±infinity. If the source operand is not in the range of $[-2\pi...+2\pi]$, then the argument is reduced to within that range before the cosine is calculated. However, large arguments may lose accuracy during reduction, and very large arguments (greater than approximately 10^{20}) lose all accuracy. The result is in the range of $[-1...+1]$.

Operation Table:

DESTINATION	SOURCE[1]					
	+	In Range	−	+	Zero	−	+	Infinity	−
Result		Cosine			+1.0			NAN[2]	

NOTE:
1. If the source operand is a NAN, refer to **1.6.5 NANs** for more information.
2. Sets the OPERR bit in the floating-point status register exception byte.

FCOS

Cosine

(MC6888X, M68040FPSP)

FCOS

Floating-Point Status Register:

Condition Codes: Affected as described in **3.6.2 Conditional Testing.**

Quotient Byte: Not affected

Exception Byte:

BSUN	Cleared
SNAN	Refer to **1.6.5 NANs.**
OPERR	Set if the source operand is ±infinity; cleared otherwise.
OVFL	Cleared
UNFL	Cleared
DZ	Cleared
INEX2	Refer to inexact result in the appropriate user's manual.
INEX1	If <fmt> is packed, refer to inexact result on decimal input in the appropriate user's manual; cleared otherwise.

Accrued Exception Byte: Affected as described in IEEE exception and trap compatibility in the appropriate user's manual.

Instruction Format:

15	14	13	12	11	10	9	8	7	6	5	4	3	2	1	0
1	1	1	1	COPROCESSOR ID			0	0	0	EFFECTIVE ADDRESS					
										MODE			REGISTER		
0	R/M	0	SOURCE SPECIFIER			DESTINATION REGISTER			0	0	1	1	1	0	1

Instruction Fields:

Coprocessor ID field—Specifies which coprocessor in the system is to execute this instruction. Motorola assemblers default to ID = 1 for the floating-point coprocessor.

FCOS

Cosine
(MC6888X, M68040FPSP)

FCOS

Effective Address field—Determines the addressing mode for external operands.
If R/M = 0, this field is unused and should contain zeros.
If R/M = 1, this field is encoded with an M68000 family addressing mode as listed in the following table:

Addressing Mode	Mode	Register	Addressing Mode	Mode	Register
Dn*	000	reg. number:Dn	(xxx).W	111	000
An	—	—	(xxx).L	111	001
(An)	010	reg. number:An	#<data>	111	100
(An) +	011	reg. number:An			
– (An)	100	reg. number:An			
(d$_{16}$,An)	101	reg. number:An	(d$_{16}$,PC)	111	010
(d$_8$,An,Xn)	110	reg. number:An	(d$_8$,PC,Xn)	111	011
(bd,An,Xn)	110	reg. number:An	(bd,PC,Xn)	111	011
([bd,An,Xn],od)	110	reg. number:An	([bd,PC,Xn],od)	111	011
([bd,An],Xn,od)	110	reg. number:An	([bd,PC],Xn,od)	111	011

*Only if <fmt> is byte, word, long, or single.

R/M field—Specifies the source operand address mode.
    0—The operation is register to register.
    1—The operation is <ea> to register.

Source Specifier field—Specifies the source register or data format.
    If R/M = 0, specifies the source floating-point data register.
    If R/M = 1, specifies the source data format:
        000—Long-Word Integer (L)
        001—Single-Precision Real (S)
        010—Extended-Precision Real (X)
        011—Packed-Decimal Real (P)
        100—Word Integer (W)
        101—Double-Precision Real (D)
        110—Byte Integer (B)

Destination Register field—Specifies the destination floating-point data register. If R/M = 0 and the source and destination fields are equal, then the input operand is taken from the specified floating-point data register, and the result is written into the same register. If the single register syntax is used, Motorola assemblers set the source and destination fields to the same value.

Hyperbolic Cosine
(MC6888X, M68040FPSP)

Operation: Hyperbolic Cosine of Source ♦ FPn

Assembler FCOSH.<fmt> <ea>,FPn
Syntax: FCOSH.X FPm,FPn
FCOSH.X FPn

Attributes: Format = (Byte, Word, Long, Single, Double, Extended, Packed)

Description: Converts the source operand to extended precision (if necessary) and calculates the hyperbolic cosine of that number. Stores the result in the destination floating-point data register.

Operation Table:

DESTINATION	SOURCE					
	+	In Range	−	+ Zero −	+	Infinity −
Result	Hyperbolic Cosine			+1.0	+inf	

NOTE: If the source operand is a NAN, refer to **1.6.5 NANs** for more information.

Floating-Point Status Register:

Condition Codes: Affected as described in **3.6.2 Conditional Testing**.

Quotient Byte: Not affected.

Exception Byte:
BSUN Cleared
SNAN Refer to **1.6.5 NANs**.
OPERR Cleared
OVFL Refer to overflow in the appropriate user's manual.
UNFL Cleared
DZ Cleared
INEX2 Refer to inexact result in the appropriate user's manual.
INEX1 If <fmt> is packed, refer to inexact result on decimal input in the appropriate user's manual; cleared otherwise.

Accrued Exception Byte: Affected as described in IEEE exception and trap compatibility in the appropriate user's manual.

5

FCOSH

Hyperbolic Cosine
(MC6888X, M68040FPSP)

FCOSH

Instruction Format:

15	14	13	12	11	10	9	8	7	6	5	4	3	2	1	0
1	1	1	1	COPROCESSOR ID		0	0	0		EFFECTIVE ADDRESS					
										MODE			REGISTER		
0	R/M	0	SOURCE SPECIFIER		DESTINATION REGISTER			0	0	1	1	0	0	1	

Instruction Fields:

Coprocessor ID field—Specifies which coprocessor in the system is to execute this instruction. Motorola assemblers default to ID = 1 for the floating-point coprocessor.

Effective Address field—Determines the addressing mode for external operands.

If R/M = 0, this field is unused and should be all zeros.

If R/M = 1, this field is encoded with an M68000 family addressing mode as listed in the following table:

Addressing Mode	Mode	Register	Addressing Mode	Mode	Register
Dn*	000	reg. number:Dn	(xxx).W	111	000
An	—	—	(xxx).L	111	001
(An)	010	reg. number:An	#<data>	111	100
(An)+	011	reg. number:An			
−(An)	100	reg. number:An			
(d$_{16}$,An)	101	reg. number:An	(d$_{16}$,PC)	111	010
(d$_8$,An,Xn)	110	reg. number:An	(d$_8$,PC,Xn)	111	011
(bd,An,Xn)	110	reg. number:An	(bd,PC,Xn)	111	011
([bd,An,Xn],od)	110	reg. number:An	([bd,PC,Xn],od)	111	011
([bd,An],Xn,od)	110	reg. number:An	([bd,PC],Xn,od)	111	011

*Only if <fmt> is byte, word, long, or single.

R/M field—Specifies the source operand address mode.
  0—The operation is register to register.
  1—The operation is <ea> to register.

Source Specifier field—Specifies the source register or data format.
  If R/M = 0, specifies the source floating-point data register.
  If R/M = 1, specifies the source data format:
    000—Long-Word Integer (L)
    001—Single-Precision Real (S)
    010—Extended-Precision Real (X)
    011—Packed-Decimal Real (P)
    100—Word Integer (W)
    101—Double-Precision Real (D)
    110—Byte Integer (B)

Destination Register field—Specifies the destination floating-point data register. If R/M = 0 and the source and destination fields are equal, then the input operand is taken from the specified floating-point data register, and the result is written into the same register. If the single register syntax is used, Motorola assemblers set the source and destination fields to the same value.

5

Operation: If Condition True
                        Then No Operation
                   Else Dn − 1 ♦ Dn
                        If Dn ≠ −1
                             Then PC + d_n ♦ PC
                        Else Execute Next Instruction

**Assembler
Syntax:**   FDBcc Dn,<label>

Attributes: Unsized

Description: This instruction is a looping primitive of three parameters: a floating-point condition, a counter (data register), and a 16-bit displacement. The instruction first tests the condition to determine if the termination condition for the loop has been met, and if so, execution continues with the next instruction in the instruction stream. If the termination condition is not true, the low-order 16 bits of the counter register are decremented by one. If the result is −1, the count is exhausted, and execution continues with the next instruction. If the result is not equal to −1, execution continues at the location specified by the current value of the program counter plus the sign-extended 16-bit displacement. The value of the program counter used in the branch address calculation is the address of the displacement word.

The conditional specifier cc selects any one of the 32 floating-point conditional tests as described in **3.6.2 Conditional Testing**.

Floating-Point Status Register:

Condition Codes:	Not affected.
Quotient Byte:	Not affected.

Exception Byte:	BSUN	Set if the NAN condition code is set and the condition selected is an IEEE nonaware test.
	SNAN	Not Affected.
	OPERR	Not Affected.
	OVFL	Not Affected.
	UNFL	Not Affected.
	DZ	Not Affected.
	NEX2	Not Affected.
	INEX1	Not Affected.

Accrued Exception Byte: The IOP bit is set if the BSUN bit is set in the exception byte. No other bit is affected.

FDBcc

Floating-Point Test Condition, Decrement, and Branch
(MC6888X, MC68040)

FDBcc

Instruction Format:

15	14	13	12	11	10	9	8	7	6	5	4	3	2	1	0
1	1	1	1	COPROCESSOR ID			0	0	1	0	0	1	COUNT REGISTER		
0	0	0	0	0	0	0	0	0	0	CONDITIONAL PREDICATE					
16-BIT DISPLACEMENT															

Instruction Fields:

Count Register field—Specifies data register that is used as the counter.

Conditional Predicate field—Specifies one of the 32 floating-point conditional tests as described in **3.6.2 Conditional Testing**.

Displacement field—Specifies the branch distance (from the address of the instruction plus two) to the destination in bytes.

NOTE

The terminating condition is like that defined by the UNTIL loop constructs of high-level languages. For example: FDBOLT can be stated as "decrement and branch until ordered less than".

There are two basic ways of entering a loop: at the beginning or by branching to the trailing FDBcc instruction. If a loop structure terminated with FDBcc is entered at the beginning, the control counter must be one less than the number of loop executions desired. This count is useful for indexed addressing modes and dynamically specified bit operations. However, when entering a loop by branching directly to the trailing FDBcc instruction, the count should equal the loop execution count. In this case, if the counter is zero when the loop is entered, the FDBcc instruction does not branch, causing a complete bypass of the main loop.

When a BSUN exception occurs, a preinstruction exception is taken by the main processor. If the exception handler returns without modifying the image of the program counter on the stack frame (to point to the instruction following the FDBcc), then it must clear the cause of the exception (by clearing the NAN bit or disabling the BSUN trap), or the exception will occur again immediately upon return to the routine that caused the exception.

FDIV

Operation: FPn ÷ Source ◆ FPn

Assembler   FDIV.<fmt> <ea>,FPn
Syntax: FDIV.X FPm,FPn
            *FrDIV.<fmt> <ea>,FPn
            *FrDIV.X FPm,FPn
            where r is rounding precision, S or D

            *Supported by MC68040 only

Attributes: Format = (Byte, Word, Long, Single, Double, Extended, Packed)

Description: Converts the source operand to extended precision (if necessary) and divides that number into the number in the destination floating-point data register. Stores the result in the destination floating-point data register.

FDIV will round the result to the precision selected in the floating-point control register. FSDIV and FDDIV will round the result to single or double precision, respectively, regardless of the rounding precision selected in the floating-point control register.

Operation Table:

DESTINATION		+ In Range –		+ Zero –		+ Infinity –	
In Range	+	Divide		+inf[2]	–inf[2]	+0.0	–0.0
	–			–inf[2]	+inf[2]	–0.0	+0.0
Zero	+	+0.0	+0.0	NAN[3]		+0.0	–0.0
	–	–0.0	+0.0			–0.0	+0.0
Infinity	+	+inf	–inf	+inf	–inf	NAN[3]	
	–	–inf	+inf	–inf	+inf		

Header spanning SOURCE[1]

NOTES:
1. If either operand is a NAN, refer to **1.6.5 NANs** for more information.
2. Sets the DZ bit in the floating-point status register exception byte.
3. Sets the OPERR bit in the floating-point status register exception byte.

Floating-Point Status Register:

Condition Codes:	Affected as described in **3.6.2 Conditional Testing**.
Quotient Byte:	Not affected.

Exception Byte:

BSUN	Cleared
SNAN	Refer to **1.6.5 NANs**.
OPERR	Set for 0 ÷ 0 or infinity ÷ infinity; cleared otherwise.
OVFL	Refer to exception processing in the appropriate user's manual.
UNFL	Refer to exception processing in the appropriate user's manual.
DZ	Set if the source is zero and the destination is in range; cleared otherwise.
INEX2	Refer to exception processing in the appropriate user's manual.
INEX1	If <fmt> is packed, refer to exception processing in the appropriate user's manual; cleared otherwise.

Accrued Exception Byte: Affected as described in exception processing in the appropriate user's manual.

Instruction Format:

15	14	13	12	11	10	9	8	7	6	5	4	3	2	1	0
1	1	1	1	COPROCESSOR ID			0	0	0	EFFECTIVE ADDRESS					
										MODE			REGISTER		
0	R/M	0	SOURCE SPECIFIER			DESTINATION REGISTER			OPMODE						

Floating-Point Divide
(MC6888X, MC68040)

Instruction Fields:

Effective Address field—Determines the addressing mode for external operands.

If R/M = 0, this field is unused and should be all zeros.

If R/M = 1, specifies the location of the source operand location. Only data addressing modes can be used as listed in the following table:

Addressing Mode	Mode	Register	Addressing Mode	Mode	Register
Dn*	000	reg. number:Dn	(xxx).W	111	000
An	—	—	(xxx).L	111	001
(An)	010	reg. number:An	#<data>	111	100
(An) +	011	reg. number:An			
– (An)	100	reg. number:An			
(d$_{16}$,An)	101	reg. number:An	(d$_{16}$,PC)	111	010
(d$_8$,An,Xn)	110	reg. number:An	(d$_8$,PC,Xn)	111	011
(bd,An,Xn)	110	reg. number:An	(bd,PC,Xn)	111	011
([bd,An,Xn],od)	110	reg. number:An	([bd,PC,Xn],od)	111	011
([bd,An],Xn,od)	110	reg. number:An	([bd,PC],Xn,od)	111	011

*Only if <fmt> is byte, word, long, or single.

R/M field—Specifies the source operand address mode.

   0—The operation is register to register.

   1—The operation is <ea> to register.

Source Specifier field—Specifies the source register or data format.

If R/M = 0, specifies the source floating-point data register.

If R/M = 1, specifies the source data format:

   000—Long-Word Integer (L)

   001—Single-Precision Real (S)

   010—Extended-Precision Real (X)

   011—Packed-Decimal Real (P)*

   100—Word Integer (W)

   101—Double-Precision Real (D)

   110—Byte Integer (B)

*This encoding in the MC68040 will cause an unimplemented data type exception to allow emulation in software.

Destination Register field—Specifies the destination floating-point data register.

Opmode field—Specifies the instruction and rounding precision.

0100000	FDIV	Rounding precision specified by the floating-point control register.
1100000	FSDIV	Single-precision rounding specified.
1100100	FDDIV	Double-precision rounding specified.

5

FETOX

e^x

(MC6888X, M68040FPSP)

FETOX

Operation: $e^{Source} \rightarrow FPn$

Assembler Syntax:
FETOX.<fmt> <ea>,FPn
FETOX.X FPm,FPn
FETOX.X FPn

Attributes: Format = (Byte, Word, Long, Single, Double, Extended, Packed)

Description: Converts the source operand to extended precision (if necessary) and calculates e to the power of that number. Stores the result in the destination floating-point data register.

Operation Table:

DESTINATION	SOURCE					
	+	In Range	−	+ Zero −	+ Infinity	−
Result		e^x		+1.0	+inf	+0.0

NOTE: If the source operand is a NAN, refer to **1.6.5 NANs** for more information.

Floating-Point Status Register:

Condition Codes: Affected as described in **3.6.2 Conditional Testing**.

Quotient Byte: Not affected.

Exception Byte:
BSUN   Cleared
SNAN   Refer to **1.6.5 NANs**.
OPERR   Cleared
OVFL   Refer to overflow in the appropriate user's manual.
UNFL   Refer to underflow in the appropriate user's manual.
DZ   Cleared
INEX2   Refer to inexact result in the appropriate user's manual.
INEX1   If <fmt> is packed, refer to inexact result on decimal input in the appropriate user's manual; cleared otherwise.

Accrued Exception Byte: Affected as described in IEEE exception and trap compatibility in the appropriate user's manual.

Instruction Format:

15	14	13	12	11	10	9	8	7	6	5	4	3	2	1	0
1	1	1	1	COPROCESSOR ID			0	0	0	EFFECTIVE ADDRESS					
										MODE			REGISTER		
0	R/M	0		SOURCE SPECIFIER		DESTINATION REGISTER			0	0	1	0	0	0	0

Instruction Fields:

Coprocessor ID field—Specifies which coprocessor in the system is to execute this instruction. Motorola assemblers default to ID = 1 for the floating-point coprocessor.

Effective Address field—Determines the addressing mode for external operands.

If R/M = 0, this field is unused and should be all zeros.

If R/M = 1, this field is encoded with an M68000 family addressing mode as listed in the following table:

Addressing Mode	Mode	Register	Addressing Mode	Mode	Register
Dn*	000	reg. number:Dn	(xxx).W	111	000
An	—	—	(xxx).L	111	001
(An)	010	reg. number:An	#<data>	111	100
(An) +	011	reg. number:An			
– (An)	100	reg. number:An			
(d$_{16}$,An)	101	reg. number:An	(d$_{16}$,PC)	111	010
(d$_8$,An,Xn)	110	reg. number:An	(d$_8$,PC,Xn)	111	011
(bd,An,Xn)	110	reg. number:An	(bd,PC,Xn)	111	011
([bd,An,Xn],od)	110	reg. number:An	([bd,PC,Xn],od)	111	011
([bd,An],Xn,od)	110	reg. number:An	([bd,PC],Xn,od)	111	011

*Only if <fmt> is byte, word, long, or single.

5

R/M field—Specifies the source operand address mode.
   0—The operation is register to register.
   1—The operation is <ea> to register.

Source Specifier Field—Specifies the source register or data format.
   If R/M = 0, specifies the source floating-point data register.
   If R/M = 1, specifies the source data format:
      000—Long-Word Integer (L)
      001—Single-Precision Real (S)
      010—Extended-Precision Real (X)
      011—Packed-Decimal Real (P)*
      100—Word Integer (W)
      101—Double-Precision Real (D)
      110—Byte Integer (B)

Destination Register field—Specifies the destination floating-point data register. If R/M = 0 and the source and destination fields are equal, then the input operand is taken from the specified floating-point data register, and the result is written into the same register. If the single register syntax is used, Motorola assemblers set the source and destination fields to the same value.

Operation: $e^{Source} - 1 \rightarrow FPn$

Assembler   FETOXM1.<fmt> <ea>,FPn
Syntax: FETOXM1.X FPm,FPn
      FETOXM1.X FPn

Attributes: Format = (Byte, Word, Long, Single, Double, Extended, Packed)

Description: Converts the source operand to extended precision (if necessary) and calculates e to the power of that number. Subtracts one from the value and stores the result in the destination floating-point data register.

Operation Table:

DESTINATION	+ In Range −	+ Zero −	+ Infinity −
Result	$e^x - 1$	+0.0 −0.0	+inf −1.0

NOTE: If the source operand is a NAN, refer to **1.6.5 NANs** for more information.

Floating-Point Status Register:

Condition Codes: Affected as described in **3.6.2 Conditional Testing**.

Quotient Byte: Not affected.

Exception Byte: BSUN   Cleared
                     SNAN   Refer to **1.6.5 NANs**.
                     OPERR   Cleared
                     OVFL   Refer to overflow in the appropriate user's manual.
                     UNFL   Refer to underflow in the appropriate user's manual.
                     DZ   Cleared
                     INEX2   Refer to inexact result in the appropriate user's manual.
                     INEX1   If <fmt> is packed, refer to inexact result on decimal input in the appropriate user's manual; cleared otherwise.

Accrued Exception Byte: Affected as described in IEEE exception and trap compatibility in the appropriate user's manual.

$e^x - 1$

(MC6888X, M68040FPSP)

Instruction Format:

15	14	13	12	11	10	9	8	7	6	5	4	3	2	1	0
1	1	1	1	COPROCESSOR ID			0	0	0	EFFECTIVE ADDRESS MODE				REGISTER	
0	R/M	0	SOURCE SPECIFIER			DESTINATION REGISTER			0	0	0	1	0	0	0

Instruction Fields:

Coprocessor ID field—Specifies which coprocessor in the system is to execute this instruction. Motorola assemblers default to ID = 1 for the floating-point coprocessor.

Effective Address field—Determines the addressing mode for external operands.
If R/M = 0, this field is unused and should be all zeros.
If R/M = 1, this field is encoded with an M68000 family addressing mode as listed in the following table:

Addressing Mode	Mode	Register	Addressing Mode	Mode	Register
Dn*	000	reg. number:Dn	(xxx).W	111	000
An	—	—	(xxx).L	111	001
(An)	010	reg. number:An	#<data>	111	100
(An) +	011	reg. number:An			
– (An)	100	reg. number:An			
(d_{16},An)	101	reg. number:An	(d_{16},PC)	111	010
(d_8,An,Xn)	110	reg. number:An	(d_8,PC,Xn)	111	011
(bd,An,Xn)	110	reg. number:An	(bd,PC,Xn)	111	011
([bd,An,Xn],od)	110	reg. number:An	([bd,PC,Xn],od)	111	011
([bd,An],Xn,od)	110	reg. number:An	([bd,PC],Xn,od)	111	011

*Only if <fmt> is byte, word, long, or single.

R/M field—Specifies the source operand address mode.
  0—The operation is register to register.
  1—The operation is <ea> to register.

Source Specifier Field—Specifies the source register or data format.
  If R/M = 0, specifies the source floating-point data register.
  If R/M = 1, specifies the source data format:
    000—Long-Word Integer (L)
    001—Single-Precision Real (S)
    010—Extended-Precision Real (X)
    011—Packed-Decimal Real (P)
    100—Word Integer (W)
    101—Double-Precision Real (D)
    110—Byte Integer (B)

Destination Register field—Specifies the destination floating-point data register. If R/M = 0 and the source and destination fields are equal, then the input operand is taken from the specified floating-point data register, and the result is written into the same register. If the single register syntax is used, Motorola assemblers set the source and destination fields to the same value.

5

FGETEXP

FGETEXP   Get Exponent   **FGETEXP**

(MC6888X, M68040FPSP)

Operation: Exponent of Source ♦ FPn

Assembler   FGETEXP.<fmt> <ea>,FPn
Syntax: FGETEXP.X FPm,FPn
                 FGETEXP.X FPn

Attributes: Format = (Byte, Word, Long, Single, Double, Extended, Packed)

Description: Converts the source operand to extended precision (if necessary) and extracts the binary exponent. Removes the exponent bias, converts the exponent to an extended-precision floating-point number, and stores the result in the destination floating-point data register.

Operation Table:

DESTINATION	SOURCE[1]							
	+	In Range	–	+	Zero	–	+	Infinity –
Result		Exponent		+0.0		–0.0		NAN[2]

NOTES:
1. If the source operand is a NAN, refer to **1.6.5 NANs** for more information.
2. Sets the OPERR bit in the floating-point status register exception byte.

Floating-Point Status Register:

Condition Codes: Affected as described in **3.6.2 Conditional Testing**.

Quotient Byte: Not affected.

Exception Byte: BSUN   Cleared
                   SNAN   Refer to **1.6.5 NANs**.
                   OPERR Set if the source is ±infinity; cleared otherwise.
                   OVFL   Cleared
                   UNFL   Cleared
                   DZ   Cleared
                   INEX2 Cleared
                   INEX1 If <fmt> is packed, refer to inexact result on decimal input in the appropriate user's manual; cleared otherwise.

Accrued Exception Byte: Affected as described in IEEE exception and trap compatibility in the appropriate user's manual.

FGETEXP

Get Exponent
(MC6888X, M68040FPSP)

FGETEXP

Instruction Format:

15	14	13	12	11	10	9	8	7	6	5	4	3	2	1	0
1	1	1	1	COPROCESSOR ID			0	0	0	EFFECTIVE ADDRESS MODE			REGISTER		
0	R/M	0	SOURCE SPECIFIER			DESTINATION REGISTER			0	0	1	1	1	1	0

Instruction Fields:

Coprocessor ID field—Specifies which coprocessor in the system is to execute this instruction. Motorola assemblers default to ID = 1 for the floating-point coprocessor.

Effective Address field—Determines the addressing mode for external operands.

If R/M = 0, this field is unused and should be all zeros.

If R/M = 1, this field is encoded with an M68000 family addressing mode as listed in the following table:

Addressing Mode	Mode	Register	Addressing Mode	Mode	Register
Dn*	000	reg. number:Dn	(xxx).W	111	000
An	—	—	(xxx).L	111	001
(An)	010	reg. number:An	#<data>	111	100
(An) +	011	reg. number:An			
– (An)	100	reg. number:An			
(d$_{16}$,An)	101	reg. number:An	(d$_{16}$,PC)	111	010
(d$_8$,An,Xn)	110	reg. number:An	(d$_8$,PC,Xn)	111	011
(bd,An,Xn)	110	reg. number:An	(bd,PC,Xn)	111	011
([bd,An,Xn],od)	110	reg. number:An	([bd,PC,Xn],od)	111	011
([bd,An],Xn,od)	110	reg. number:An	([bd,PC],Xn,od)	111	011

*Only if <fmt> is byte, word, long, or single.

R/M field—Specifies the source operand address mode.

0—The operation is register to register.

1—The operation is <ea> to register.

Source Specifier field—Specifies the source register or data format.
If R/M = 0, specifies the source floating-point data register.
If R/M = 1, specifies the source data format:

    000—Long-Word Integer (L)

    001—Single-Precision Real (S)

    010—Extended-Precision Real (X)

    011—Packed-Decimal Real (P)

    100—Word Integer (W)

    101—Double-Precision Real (D)

    110—Byte Integer (B)

Destination Register field—Specifies the destination floating-point data register. If R/M = 0 and the source and destination fields are equal, then the input operand is taken from the specified floating-point data register, and the result is written into the same register. If the single register syntax is used, Motorola assemblers set the source and destination fields to the same value.

5

FGETMAN

Get Mantissa
(MC6888X, M68040FPSP)

FGETMAN

Operation: Mantissa of Source ♦ FPn

Assembler FGETMAN.<fmt> <ea>,FPn
Syntax: FGETMAN.X FPm,FPn
FGETMAN.X FPn

Attributes: Format = (Byte, Word, Long, Single, Double, Extended, Packed)

Description: Converts the source operand to extended precision (if necessary) and extracts the mantissa. Converts the mantissa to an extended-precision value and stores the result in the destination floating-point data register. The result is in the range [1.0...2.0] with the sign of the source mantissa, zero, or a NAN.

Operation Table:

DESTINATION	SOURCE[1]								
	+	In Range	–	+	Zero	–	+	Infinity	–
Result		Mantissa		+0.0		–0.0		NAN[2]	

NOTES:
1. If the source operand is a NAN, refer to **1.6.5 NANs** for more information.
2. Sets the OPERR bit in the floating-point status register exception byte.

Floating-Point Status Register:

Condition Codes: Affected as described in **3.6.2 Conditional Testing**.

Quotient Byte: Not affected.

Exception Byte:
     BSUN   Cleared
     SNAN   Refer to **1.6.5 NANs**.
     OPERR   Set if the source is ±infinity; cleared otherwise.
     OVFL   Cleared
     UNFL   Cleared
     DZ   Cleared
     INEX2   Cleared
     INEX1   If <fmt> is packed, refer to inexact result on decimal input in the appropriate user's manual; cleared otherwise.

Accrued Exception Byte: Affected as described in IEEE exception and trap compatibility in the appropriate user's manual.

FGETMAN

Get Mantissa
(MC6888X, M68040FPSP)

FGETMAN

Instruction Format:

15	14	13	12	11	10	9	8	7	6	5	4	3	2	1	0
1	1	1	1	COPROCESSOR ID			0	0	0	EFFECTIVE ADDRESS MODE			REGISTER		
0	R/M	0	SOURCE SPECIFIER			DESTINATION REGISTER			0	0	1	1	1	1	1

Instruction Fields:

Coprocessor ID field—Specifies which coprocessor in the system is to execute this instruction. Motorola assemblers default to ID = 1 for the floating-point coprocessor.

Effective Address field—Determines the addressing mode for external operands.

If R/M = 0, this field is unused and should be all zeros.

If R/M = 1, this field is encoded with an M68000 family addressing mode as listed in the following table:

Addressing Mode	Mode	Register
Dn*	000	reg. number:Dn
An	—	—
(An)	010	reg. number:An
(An) +	011	reg. number:An
– (An)	100	reg. number:An
(d_{16},An)	101	reg. number:An
(d_8,An,Xn)	110	reg. number:An
(bd,An,Xn)	110	reg. number:An
([bd,An,Xn],od)	110	reg. number:An
([bd,An],Xn,od)	110	reg. number:An

Addressing Mode	Mode	Register
(xxx).W	111	000
(xxx).L	111	001
#<data>	111	100
(d_{16},PC)	111	010
(d_8,PC,Xn)	111	011
(bd,PC,Xn)	111	011
([bd,PC,Xn],od)	111	011
([bd,PC],Xn,od)	111	011

*Only if <fmt> is byte, word, long, or single.

R/M field—Specifies the source operand address mode.

0—The operation is register to register.

1—The operation is <ea> to register.

Source Specifier field—Specifies the source register or data format.

If R/M = 0, specifies the source floating-point data register.

If R/M = 1, specifies the source data format:

   000—Long-Word Integer (L)

   001—Single-Precision Real (S)

   010—Extended-Precision Real (X)

   011—Packed-Decimal Real (P)

   100—Word Integer (W)

   101—Double-Precision Real (D)

   110—Byte Integer (B)

Destination Register field—Specifies the destination floating-point data register. If R/M = 0 and the source and destination fields are equal, then the input operand is taken from the specified floating-point data register, and the result is written into the same register. If the single register syntax is used, Motorola assemblers set the source and destination fields to the same value.

5

Operation: Integer Part of Source ♦ FPn

Assembler   FINT.<fmt> <ea>,FPn
Syntax: FINT.X FPm,FPn
                  FINT.X FPn

Attributes: Format = (Byte, Word, Long, Single, Double, Extended, Packed)

Description: Converts the source operand to extended precision (if necessary), extracts the integer part, and converts it to an extended-precision floating-point number. Stores the result in the destination floating-point data register. The integer part is extracted by rounding the extended-precision number to an integer using the current rounding mode selected in the floating-point control register mode control byte. Thus, the integer part returned is the number that is to the left of the radix point when the exponent is zero, after rounding. For example, the integer part of 137.57 is 137.0 for the round-to-zero and round-to-negative infinity modes and 138.0 for the round-to-nearest and round-to-positive infinity modes. Note that the result of this operation is a floating-point number.

Operation Table:

DESTINATION	SOURCE					
	+	In Range	–	+	Zero	–	+	Infinity	–
Result		Integer		+0.0		–0.0	+inf		–inf

NOTE: If the source operand is a NAN, refer to **1.6.5 NANs** for more information.

Floating-Point Status Register:

Condition Codes: Affected as described in **3.6.2 Conditional Testing**.

Quotient Byte: Not affected.

Exception Byte:

BSUN	Cleared
SNAN	Refer to **1.6.5 NANs**.
OPERR	Cleared
OVFL	Cleared
UNFL	Cleared
DZ	Cleared
INEX2	Refer to inexact result in the appropriate user's manual.
INEX1	If <fmt> is packed, refer to inexact result on decimal input in the appropriate user's manual; cleared otherwise.

Accrued Exception Byte: Affected as described in IEEE exception and trap compatibility in the appropriate user's manual.

Instruction Format:

15	14	13	12	11	10	9	8	7	6	5	4	3	2	1	0
1	1	1	1	COPROCESSOR ID			0	0	0	EFFECTIVE ADDRESS MODE			REGISTER		
0	R/M	0	SOURCE SPECIFIER			DESTINATION REGISTER			0	0	0	0	0	0	1

Instruction Fields:

Coprocessor ID field—Specifies which coprocessor in the system is to execute this instruction. Motorola assemblers default to ID = 1 for the floating-point coprocessor.

Effective Address field—Determines the addressing mode for external operands.
  If R/M = 0, this field is unused and should be all zeros.
  If R/M = 1, this field is encoded with an M68000 family addressing mode as listed
  in the following table:

Addressing Mode	Mode	Register	Addressing Mode	Mode	Register
Dn*	000	reg. number:Dn	(xxx).W	111	000
An	—	—	(xxx).L	111	001
(An)	010	reg. number:An	#<data>	111	100
(An) +	011	reg. number:An			
– (An)	100	reg. number:An			
(d$_{16}$,An)	101	reg. number:An	(d$_{16}$,PC)	111	010
(d$_8$,An,Xn)	110	reg. number:An	(d$_8$,PC,Xn)	111	011
(bd,An,Xn)	110	reg. number:An	(bd,PC,Xn)	111	011
([bd,An,Xn],od)	110	reg. number:An	([bd,PC,Xn],od)	111	011
([bd,An],Xn,od)	110	reg. number:An	([bd,PC],Xn,od)	111	011

*Only if <fmt> is byte, word, long, or single.

R/M field—Specifies the source operand address mode.
  0—The operation is register to register.
  1—The operation is <ea> to register.

Source Specifier field—Specifies the source register or data format.
  If R/M = 0, specifies the source floating-point data register.
  If R/M = 1, specifies the source data format:
    000—Long-Word Integer (L)
    001—Single-Precision Real (S)
    010—Extended-Precision Real (X)
    011—Packed-Decimal Real (P)
    100—Word Integer (W)
    101—Double-Precision Real (D)
    110—Byte Integer (B)

Destination Register field—Specifies the destination floating-point data register. If
  R/M = 0 and the source and destination fields are equal, then the input operand is
  taken from the specified floating-point data register, and the result is written into
  the same register. If the single register syntax is used, Motorola assemblers set
  the source and destination fields to the same value.

FINTRZ

FINTRZ

Operation: Integer Part of Source → FPn

Assembler   FINTRZ.<fmt> <ea>,FPn
Syntax: FINTRZ.X FPm,FPn
      FINTRZ.X FPn

Attributes: Format = (Byte, Word, Long, Single, Double, Extended, Packed)

Description: Converts the source operand to extended precision (if necessary) and extracts the integer part and converts it to an extended-precision floating-point number. Stores the result in the destination floating-point data register. The integer part is extracted by rounding the extended-precision number to an integer using the round-to-zero mode, regardless of the rounding mode selected in the floating-point control register mode control byte (making it useful for FORTRAN assignments). Thus, the integer part returned is the number that is to the left of the radix point when the exponent is zero. For example, the integer part of 137.57 is 137.0; the integer part of 0.1245×10^2 is 12.0. Note that the result of this operation is a floating-point number.

Operation Table:

| | SOURCE | | | | | |
DESTINATION	+ In Range –	+	Zero	–	+ Infinity –	
Result	Integer, Forced Round-to-Zero	+0.0		–0.0	+inf	–inf

NOTE: If the source operand is a NAN, refer to **1.6.5 NANs** for more information.

FINTRZ

Integer Part, Round-to-Zero
(MC6888X, M68040FPSP)

FINTRZ

Floating-Point Status Register:

Condition Codes:	Affected as described in **3.6.2 Conditional Testing**.
Quotient Byte:	Not affected.

Exception Byte:

BSUN	Cleared
SNAN	Refer to **1.6.5 NANs**.
OPERR	Cleared
OVFL	Cleared
UNFL	Cleared
DZ	Cleared
INEX2	Refer to inexact result in the appropriate user's manual.
INEX1	If <fmt> is packed, refer to inexact result on decimal input in the appropriate user's manual; cleared otherwise.

Accrued Exception Byte: Affected as described in IEEE exception and trap compatibility in the appropriate user's manual.

Instruction Format:

15	14	13	12	11	10	9	8	7	6	5	4	3	2	1	0
1	1	1	1	COPROCESSOR ID			0	0	0	EFFECTIVE ADDRESS					
										MODE			REGISTER		
0	R/M	0	SOURCE SPECIFIER			DESTINATION REGISTER			0	0	0	0	0	1	1

Instruction Fields:

Coprocessor ID field—Specifies which coprocessor in the system is to execute this instruction. Motorola assemblers default to ID = 1 for the floating-point coprocessor.

Effective Address field—Determines the addressing mode for external operands.
If R/M = 0, this field is unused and should be all zeros.
If R/M = 1, this field is encoded with an M68000 family addressing mode as listed
in the following table:

Addressing Mode	Mode	Register	Addressing Mode	Mode	Register
Dn*	000	reg. number:Dn	(xxx).W	111	000
An	—	—	(xxx).L	111	001
(An)	010	reg. number:An	#<data>	111	100
(An) +	011	reg. number:An			
– (An)	100	reg. number:An			
(d$_{16}$,An)	101	reg. number:An	(d$_{16}$,PC)	111	010
(d$_8$,An,Xn)	110	reg. number:An	(d$_8$,PC,Xn)	111	011
(bd,An,Xn)	110	reg. number:An	(bd,PC,Xn)	111	011
([bd,An,Xn],od)	110	reg. number:An	([bd,PC,Xn],od)	111	011
([bd,An],Xn,od)	110	reg. number:An	([bd,PC],Xn,od)	111	011

*Only if <fmt> is byte, word, long, or single.

R/M field—Specifies the source operand address mode.
   0—The operation is register to register.
   1—The operation is <ea> to register.

Source Specifier field—Specifies the source register or data format.
   If R/M = 0, specifies the source floating-point data register.
   If RM=1, specifies the source data format:
      000—Long-Word Integer (L)
      001—Single-Precision Real (S)
      010—Extended-Precision Real (X)
      011—Packed-Decimal Real (P)
      100—Word Integer (W)
      101—Double-Precision Real (D)
      110—Byte Integer (B)

Destination Register field—Specifies the destination floating-point data register. If
   R/M = 0 and the source and destination fields are equal, then the input operand is
   taken from the specified floating-point data register, and the result is written into
   the same register. If the single register syntax is used, Motorola assemblers set
   the source and destination fields to the same value.

Operation: Log$_{10}$ of Source $\rightarrow$ FPn

Assembler Syntax:
FLOG10.<fmt> <ea>,FPn
FLOG10.X FPm,FPn
FLOG10.X FPn

Attributes: Format = (Byte, Word, Long, Single, Double, Extended, Packed)

Description: Convert the source operand to extended precision (if necessary) and calculates the logarithm of that number using base 10 arithmetic. Stores the result in the destination floating-point data register. This function is not defined for input values less than zero.

Operation Table:

DESTINATION	SOURCE[1]					
	+ In Range –		+ Zero –		+ Infinity –	
Result	Log$_{10}$	NAN[2]	–inf[3]		+inf	NAN[2]

NOTES:
1. If the source operand is a NAN, refer to **1.6.5 NANs** for more information.
2. Sets the OPERR bit in the floating-point status register exception byte.
3. Sets the DZ bit in the floating-point status register exception byte.

Floating-Point Status Register:

Condition Codes: Affected as described in **3.6.2 Conditional Testing**.

Quotient Byte: Not affected.

Exception Byte:
BSUN	Cleared
SNAN	Refer to **1.6.5 NANs**.
OPERR	Set if the source operand is <0; cleared otherwise.
OVFL	Cleared
UNFL	Cleared
DZ	Set if the source is ±0; cleared otherwise
INEX2	Refer to inexact result in the appropriate user's manual.
INEX1	If <fmt> is packed, refer to inexact result on decimal input in the appropriate user's manual; cleared otherwise.

Accrued Exception Byte: Affected as described in IEEE exception and trap compatibility in the appropriate user's manual.

Instruction Format:

15	14	13	12	11	10	9	8	7	6	5	4	3	2	1	0
1	1	1	1	COPROCESSOR ID			0	0	0	EFFECTIVE ADDRESS MODE			REGISTER		
0	R/M	0	SOURCE SPECIFIER			DESTINATION REGISTER			0	0	1	0	1	0	1

Instruction Fields:

Coprocessor ID field—Specifies which coprocessor in the system is to execute this instruction. Motorola assemblers default to ID = 1 for the floating-point coprocessor.

Effective Address field—Determines the addressing mode for external operands.

If R/M = 0, this field is unused and should be all zeros.

If R/M = 1, this field is encoded with an M68000 family addressing mode as listed in the following table:

Addressing Mode	Mode	Register	Addressing Mode	Mode	Register
Dn*	000	reg. number:Dn	(xxx).W	111	000
An	—	—	(xxx).L	111	001
(An)	010	reg. number:An	#<data>	111	100
(An) +	011	reg. number:An			
– (An)	100	reg. number:An			
(d$_{16}$,An)	101	reg. number:An	(d$_{16}$,PC)	111	010
(d$_8$,An,Xn)	110	reg. number:An	(d$_8$,PC,Xn)	111	011
(bd,An,Xn)	110	reg. number:An	(bd,PC,Xn)	111	011
([bd,An,Xn],od)	110	reg. number:An	([bd,PC,Xn],od)	111	011
([bd,An],Xn,od)	110	reg. number:An	([bd,PC],Xn,od)	111	011

*Only if <fmt> is byte, word, long, or single.

R/M field—Specifies the source operand address mode.

  0—The operation is register to register.

  1—The operation is <ea> to register.

Source Specifier field—Specifies the source register or data format.

  If R/M = 0, specifies the source floating-point data register.

  If R/M = 1, specifies the source data format:

    000—Long-Word Integer (L)

    001—Single-Precision Real (S)

    010—Extended-Precision Real (X)

    011—Packed-Decimal Real (P)

    100—Word Integer (W)

    101—Double-Precision Real (D)

    110—Byte Integer (B)

Destination Register field—Specifies the destination floating-point data register. If R/M = 0 and the source and destination fields are equal, then the input operand is taken from the specified floating-point data register, and the result is written into the same register. If the single register syntax is used, Motorola assemblers set the source and destination fields to the same value.

Operation: Log$_2$ of Source $\rightarrow$ FPn

Assembler
Syntax:
FLOG2.<fmt> <ea>,FPn
FLOG2.X FPm,FPn
FLOG2.X FPn

Attributes: Format = (Byte, Word, Long, Single, Double, Extended, Packed)

Description: Converts the source operand to extended precision (if necessary) and calculates the logarithm of that number using base two arithmetic. Stores the result in the destination floating-point data register. This function is not defined for input values less than zero.

Operation Table:

DESTINATION	SOURCE[1]					
	+	In Range	−	+ Zero −	+	Infinity −
Result	Log$_2$		NAN[2]	−inf[3]	+inf	NAN[2]

NOTES:
1. If the source operand is a NAN, refer to **1.6.5 NANs** for more information.
2. Sets the OPERR bit in the floating-point status register exception byte.
3. Sets the DZ bit in the floating-point status register exception byte.

Floating-Point Status Register:

Condition Codes: Affected as described in **3.6.2 Conditional Testing**.

Quotient Byte: Not affected.

Exception Byte:
BSUN	Cleared
SNAN	Refer to **1.6.5 NANs**.
OPERR	Set if the source is < 0; cleared otherwise
OVFL	Cleared
UNFL	Cleared
DZ	Set if the source is ±0; cleared otherwise
INEX2	Refer to inexact result in the appropriate user's manual.
INEX1	If <fmt> is packed, refer to inexact result on decimal input in the appropriate user's manual; cleared otherwise.

Accrued Exception Byte: Affected as described in IEEE exception and trap compatibility in the appropriate user's manual.

Instruction Format:

15	14	13	12	11	10	9	8	7	6	5	4	3	2	1	0
1	1	1	1	\multicolumn{3}{COPROCESSOR ID}			0	0	0	\multicolumn{2}{EFFECTIVE ADDRESS — MODE}		\multicolumn{3}{REGISTER}	
0	R/M	0	\multicolumn{3}{SOURCE SPECIFIER}			\multicolumn{2}{DESTINATION REGISTER}		0	0	1	0	1	1	0

Instruction Fields:

Coprocessor ID field—Specifies which coprocessor in the system is to execute this instruction. Motorola assemblers default to ID = 1 for the floating-point coprocessor.

Effective Address field—Determines the addressing mode for external operands.
If R/M = 0, this field is unused and should be all zeros.
If R/M = 1, this field is encoded with an M68000 family addressing mode as listed in the following table:

Addressing Mode	Mode	Register
Dn*	000	reg. number:Dn
An	—	—.
(An)	010	reg. number:An
(An) +	011	reg. number:An
– (An)	100	reg. number:An
(d$_{16}$,An)	101	reg. number:An
(d$_8$,An,Xn)	110	reg. number:An
(bd,An,Xn)	110	reg. number:An
([bd,An,Xn],od)	110	reg. number:An
([bd,An],Xn,od)	110	reg. number:An

Addressing Mode	Mode	Register
(xxx).W	111	000
(xxx).L	111	001
#<data>	111	100
(d$_{16}$,PC)	111	010
(d$_8$,PC,Xn)	111	011
(bd,PC,Xn)	111	011
([bd,PC,Xn],od)	111	011
([bd,PC],Xn,od)	111	011

*Only if <fmt> is byte, word, long, or single.

R/M field—Specifies the source operand address mode.
   0—The operation is register to register.
   1—The operation is <ea> to register.

Source Specifier field—Specifies the source register or data format.
   If R/M = 0, specifies the source floating-point data register.
   If R/M = 1, specifies the source data format:
      000—Long-Word Integer (L)
      001—Single-Precision Real (S)
      010—Extended-Precision Real (X)
      011—Packed-Decimal Real (P)
      100—Word Integer (W)
      101—Double-Precision Real (D)
      110—Byte Integer (B)

Destination Register field—Specifies the destination floating-point data register. If R/M = 0 and the source and destination fields are equal, then the input operand is taken from the specified floating-point data register, and the result is written into the same register. If the single register syntax is used, Motorola assemblers set the source and destination fields to the same value.

5

Operation: Log$_e$ of Source ♦ FPn

Assembler FLOGN.<fmt> <ea>,FPn
Syntax: FLOGN.X FPm,FPn
FLOGN.X FPn

Attributes: Format = (Byte, Word, Long, Single, Double, Extended, Packed)

Description: Converts the source operand to extended precision (if necessary) and calculates the natural logarithm of that number. Stores the result in the destination floating-point data register. This function is not defined for input values less than zero.

Operation Table:

DESTINATION	+ In Range	–	+ Zero	–	+ Infinity	–
	SOURCE[1]					
Result	ln(x)	NAN[2]	–inf[3]		+inf	NAN[2]

NOTES:
1. If the source operand is a NAN, refer to **1.6.5 NANs** for more information.
2. Sets the OPERR bit in the floating-point status register exception byte.
3. Sets the DZ bit in the floating-point status register exception byte.

Floating-Point Status Register:

Condition Codes: Affected as described in **3.6.2 Conditional Testing**.

Quotient Byte: Not affected.

Exception Byte:
BSUN Cleared
SNAN Refer to **1.6.5 NANs**.
OPERR Set if the source operand is < 0; cleared otherwise.
OVFL Cleared
UNFL Cleared
DZ Set if the source is ±0; cleared otherwise
INEX2 Refer to inexact result in the appropriate user's manual.
INEX1 If <fmt> is packed, refer to inexact result on decimal input in the appropriate user's manual; cleared otherwise.

Accrued Exception Byte: Affected as described in IEEE exception and trap compatibility in the appropriate user's manual.

FLOGN

(MC6888X, M68040FPSP)

FLOGN

Instruction Format:

15	14	13	12	11	10	9	8	7	6	5	4	3	2	1	0
1	1	1	1	COPROCESSOR ID			0	0	0	EFFECTIVE ADDRESS MODE			REGISTER		
0	R/M	0	SOURCE SPECIFIER			DESTINATION REGISTER			0	0	1	0	1	0	0

Instruction Fields:

Coprocessor ID field—Specifies which coprocessor in the system is to execute this instruction. Motorola assemblers default to ID = 1 for the floating-point coprocessor.

Effective Address field—Determines the addressing mode for external operands.

If R/M = 0, this field is unused and should be all zeros.

If R/M = 1, this field is encoded with an M68000 family addressing mode as listed in the following table:

Addressing Mode	Mode	Register	Addressing Mode	Mode	Register
Dn*	000	reg. number:Dn	(xxx).W	111	000
An	—	—	(xxx).L	111	001
(An)	010	reg. number:An	#<data>	111	100
(An) +	011	reg. number:An			
– (An)	100	reg. number:An			
(d$_{16}$,An)	101	reg. number:An	(d$_{16}$,PC)	111	010
(d$_8$,An,Xn)	110	reg. number:An	(d$_8$,PC,Xn)	111	011
(bd,An,Xn)	110	reg. number:An	(bd,PC,Xn)	111	011
([bd,An,Xn],od)	110	reg. number:An	([bd,PC,Xn],od)	111	011
([bd,An],Xn,od)	110	reg. number:An	([bd,PC],Xn,od)	111	011

*Only if <fmt> is byte, word, long, or single.

R/M field—Specifies the source operand address mode.
0—The operation is register to register.
1—The operation is <ea> to register.

Source Specifier field—Specifies the source register or data format.
If R/M = 0, specifies the source floating-point data register.
If R/M = 1, specifies the source data format:
000—Long-Word Integer (L)
001—Single-Precision Real (S)
010—Extended-Precision Real (X)
011—Packed-Decimal Real (P)
100—Word Integer (W)
101—Double-Precision Real (D)
110—Byte Integer (B)

Destination Register field—Specifies the destination floating-point data register. If R/M = 0 and the source and destination fields are equal, then the input operand is taken from the specified floating-point data register, and the result is written into the same register. If the single register syntax is used, Motorola assemblers set the source and destination fields to the same value.

5

Operation: Log$_e$ of (Source + 1) $\rightarrow$ FPn

Assembler Syntax:
FLOGNP1.\<fmt> \<ea>,FPn
FLOGNP1.X FPm,FPn
FLOGNP1.X FPn

Attributes: Format = (Byte, Word, Long, Single, Double, Extended, Packed)

Description: Converts the source operand to extended precision (if necessary), adds one to that value, and calculates the natural logarithm of that intermediate result. Stores the result in the destination floating-point data register. This function is not defined for input values less than −1.

Operation Table:

DESTINATION	SOURCE[1]					
	+ In Range −		+ Zero −		+ Infinity −	
Result	ln(x+1)	ln(x+1)[2]	+0.0	−0.0	+inf	NAN[3]

NOTES:
1. If the source operand is a NAN, refer to **1.6.5 NANs** for more information.
2. If the source is −1, sets the DZ bit in the floating-point status register exception byte and returns a NAN. If the source is < −1, sets the OPERR bit in the floating-point status register exception byte and returns a NAN.
3. Sets the OPERR bit in the floating-point status register exception byte.

Floating-Point Status Register:

Condition Codes: Affected as described in **3.6.2 Conditional Testing**.

Quotient Byte: Not affected.

Exception Byte:

BSUN	Cleared
SNAN	Refer to **1.6.5 NANs**.
OPERR	Set if the source operand is < -1; cleared otherwise.
OVFL	Cleared
UNFL	Refer to underflow in the appropriate user's manual.
DZ	Set if the source operand is -1; cleared otherwise
INEX2	Refer to inexact result in the appropriate user's manual.
INEX1	If <fmt> is packed, refer to inexact result on decimal input in the appropriate user's manual; cleared otherwise.

Accrued Exception Byte: Affected as described in IEEE exception and trap compatibility in the appropriate user's manual.

Instruction Format:

15	14	13	12	11	10	9	8	7	6	5	4	3	2	1	0
1	1	1	1	COPROCESSOR ID			0	0	0	EFFECTIVE ADDRESS					
										MODE			REGISTER		
0	R/M	0	SOURCE SPECIFIER			DESTINATION REGISTER			0	0	0	0	1	1	0

Instruction Fields:

Coprocessor ID field—Specifies which coprocessor in the system is to execute this instruction. Motorola assemblers default to ID = 1 for the floating-point coprocessor.

Effective Address field—Determines the addressing mode for external operands.
If R/M = 0, this field is unused and should be all zeros.
If R/M = 1, this field is encoded with an M68000 family addressing mode as listed in the following table:

Addressing Mode	Mode	Register	Addressing Mode	Mode	Register
Dn*	000	reg. number:Dn	(xxx).W	111	000
An	—	—	(xxx).L	111	001
(An)	010	reg. number:An	#<data>	111	100
(An) +	011	reg. number:An			
− (An)	100	reg. number:An			
(d$_{16}$,An)	101	reg. number:An	(d$_{16}$,PC)	111	010
(d$_8$,An,Xn)	110	reg. number:An	(d$_8$,PC,Xn)	111	011
(bd,An,Xn)	110	reg. number:An	(bd,PC,Xn)	111	011
([bd,An,Xn],od)	110	reg. number:An	([bd,PC,Xn],od)	111	011
([bd,An],Xn,od)	110	reg. number:An	([bd,PC],Xn,od)	111	011

*Only if <fmt> is byte, word, long, or single.

R/M field—Specifies the source operand address mode.
  0—The operation is register to register.
  1—The operation is <ea> to register.

Source Specifier field—Specifies the source register or data format.
  If R/M = 0, specifies the source floating-point data register.
  If R/M = 1, specifies the source data format:
    000—Long-Word Integer (L)
    001—Single-Precision Real (S)
    010—Extended-Precision Real (X)
    011—Packed-Decimal Real (P)
    100—Word Integer (W)
    101—Double-Precision Real (D)
    110—Byte Integer (B)

Destination Register field—Specifies the destination floating-point data register. If R/M = 0 and the source and destination fields are equal, then the input operand is taken from the specified floating-point data register, and the result is written into the same register. If the single register syntax is used, Motorola assemblers set the source and destination fields to the same value.

FMOD

Modulo Remainder
(MC6888X, M68040FPSP)

FMOD

Operation: Modulo Remainder of (FPn ÷ Source) ♦ FPn

Assembler FMOD.<fmt> <ea>,FPn
Syntax: FMOD.X FPm,FPn

Attributes: Format = (Byte, Word, Long, Single, Double, Extended, Packed)

Description: Converts the source operand to extended precision (if necessary) and calculates the modulo remainder of the number in the destination floating-point data register, using the source operand as the modulus. Stores the result in the destination floating-point data register and stores the sign and seven least significant bits of the quotient in the floating-point status register quotient byte (the quotient is the result of FPn ÷ Source). The modulo remainder function is defined as:

$$FPn - (Source \times N)$$

where N = INT(FPn ÷ Source) in the round-to-zero mode.

The FMOD function is not defined for a source operand equal to zero or for a destination operand equal to infinity. Note that this function is not the same as the FREM instruction, which uses the round-to-nearest mode and thus returns the remainder that is required by the IEEE *Specification for Binary Floating-Point Arithmetic*.

Operation Table:

DESTINATION		+ In Range −	+ Zero −	+ Infinity −
In Range	+ −	Modulo Remainder	NAN[2]	FPn[3]
Zero	+ −	+0.0 −0.0	NAN[2]	+0.0 −0.0
Infinity	+ −	NAN[2]	NAN[2]	NAN[2]

(Header spanning: SOURCE[1])

NOTES:
1. If the source operand is a NAN, refer to **1.6.5 NANs** for more information.
2. Sets the OPERR bit in the floating-point status register exception byte.
3. Returns the value of FPn before the operation. However, the result is processed by the normal instruction termination procedure to round it as required. Thus, an overflow and/or inexact result may occur if the rounding precision has been changed to a smaller size since the FPn value was loaded.

FMOD

Floating-Point Status Register:

Condition Codes: Affected as described in **3.6.2 Conditional Testing**.

Quotient Byte: Loaded with the sign and least significant seven bits of the quotient (FPn ÷ Source). The sign of the quotient is the exclusive-OR of the sign bits of the source and destination operands.

Exception Byte: BSUN   Cleared

                     SNAN   Refer to **1.6.5 NANs**.

                     OPERR Set if the source is zero or the destination is infinity; cleared otherwise.

                     OVFL   Cleared

                     UNFL   Refer to underflow in the appropriate user's manual.

                     DZ   Cleared

                     INEX2 Refer to inexact result in the appropriate user's manual.

                     INEX1 If <fmt> is packed, in the appropriate user's manual for inexact result on decimal input; cleared otherwise.

Accrued Exception Byte: Affected as described in IEEE exception and trap compatibility in the appropriate user's manual.

Instruction Format:

15	14	13	12	11	10	9	8	7	6	5	4	3	2	1	0
1	1	1	1	COPROCESSOR ID			0	0	0	EFFECTIVE ADDRESS					
										MODE			REGISTER		
0	R/M	0	SOURCE SPECIFIER			DESTINATION REGISTER			0	1	0	0	0	0	1

Instruction Fields:

Coprocessor ID field—Specifies which coprocessor in the system is to execute this instruction. Motorola assemblers default to ID = 1 for the floating-point coprocessor.

Effective Address field—Determines the addressing mode for external operands.
If R/M = 0, this field is unused and should be all zeros.
If R/M = 1, this field is encoded with an M68000 family addressing mode as listed in the following table:

Addressing Mode	Mode	Register	Addressing Mode	Mode	Register
Dn*	000	reg. number:Dn	(xxx).W	111	000
An	—	—	(xxx).L	111	001
(An)	010	reg. number:An	#<data>	111	100
(An) +	011	reg. number:An			
– (An)	100	reg. number:An			
(d$_{16}$,An)	101	reg. number:An	(d$_{16}$,PC)	111	010
(d$_8$,An,Xn)	110	reg. number:An	(d$_8$,PC,Xn)	111	011
(bd,An,Xn)	110	reg. number:An	(bd,PC,Xn)	111	011
([bd,An,Xn],od)	110	reg. number:An	([bd,PC,Xn],od)	111	011
([bd,An],Xn,od)	110	reg. number:An	([bd,PC],Xn,od)	111	011

*Only if <fmt> is byte, word, long, or single.

R/M field—Specifies the source operand address mode.
  0—The operation is register to register.
  1—The operation is <ea> to register.

Source Specifier field—Specifies the source register or data format.
  If R/M = 0, specifies the source floating-point data register.
  If R/M = 1, specifies the source data format:
    000—Long-Word Integer (L)
    001—Single-Precision Real (S)
    010—Extended-Precision Real (X)
    011—Packed-Decimal Real (P)
    100—Word Integer (W)
    101—Double-Precision Real (D)
    110—Byte Integer (B)

Destination Register field—Specifies the destination floating-point data register.

FMOVE   Move Floating-Point Data Register   FMOVE
(MC6888X, MC68040)

Operation: Source ♦ Destination

Assembler   FMOVE.<fmt> <ea>,FPn
Syntax: FMOVE.<fmt> FPm,<ea>
FMOVE.P FPm,<ea>{Dn}
FMOVE.P FPm,<ea>{k}
*FrMOVE.<fmt> <ea>,FPn
where r is rounding precision, S or D

*Supported by MC68040 only

Attributes: Format = (Byte, Word, Long, Single, Double, Extended, Packed)

Description: Moves the contents of the source operand to the destination operand. Although the primary function of this instruction is data movement, it is also considered an arithmetic instruction since conversions from the source operand format to the destination operand format are performed implicitly during the move operation. Also, the source operand is rounded according to the selected rounding precision and mode.

Unlike the MOVE instruction, the FMOVE instruction does not support a memory-to-memory format. For such transfers, it is much faster to utilize the MOVE instruction to transfer the floating-point data than to use the FMOVE instruction. The FMOVE instruction only supports memory-to-register, register-to-register, and register-to-memory operations (in this context, memory may refer to an integer data register if the data format is byte, word, long, or single). The memory-to-register and register-to-register operation uses a command word encoding distinctly different from that used by the register-to-memory operation; these two operation classes are described separately.

Memory-to-Register and Register-to-Register Operation: Converts the source operand to an extended-precision floating-point number (if necessary) and stores it in the destination floating-point data register. MOVE will round the result to the precision selected in the floating-point control register. FSMOVE and FDMOVE will round the result to single or double precision, respectively, regardless of the rounding precision selected in the floating-point control register. Depending on the source data format and the rounding precision, some operations may produce an inexact result. In the following table, combinations that can produce an inexact result are marked with a dot (·), but all other combinations produce an exact result.

Rounding Precision	Source Format						
	B	W	L	S	D	X	P
Single			•		•	•	•
Double						•	•
Extended							•

Floating-Point Status Register (<ea> to Register):

Condition Codes:	Affected as described in **3.6.2 Conditional Testing**.
Quotient Byte:	Not affected.

Exception Byte:

BSUN	Cleared
SNAN	Refer to **1.6.5 NANs**.
OPERR	Cleared
OVFL	Cleared
UNFL	Refer to exception processing in the appropriate user's manual if the source is an extended-precision denormalized number; cleared otherwise.
DZ	Cleared
INEX2	Refer to exception processing in the appropriate user's manual if <fmt> is L, D, or X; cleared otherwise.
INEX1	Refer to exception processing in the appropriate user's manual if <fmt> is P; cleared otherwise.

Accrued Exception Byte: Affected as described in exception processing in the appropriate user's manual.

FMOVE   Move Floating-Point Data Register   FMOVE
(MC6888X, MC68040)

Instruction Format:

<ea> to Register

15	14	13	12	11	10	9	8	7	6	5	4	3	2	1	0
1	1	1	1	COPROCESSOR ID			0	0	0	EFFECTIVE ADDRESS MODE			REGISTER		
0	R/M	0	SOURCE SPECIFIER		DESTINATION REGISTER		OPMODE								

Instruction Fields:

Effective Address field—Determines the addressing mode for external operands.

If R/M = 0, this field is unused and should be all zeros.

If R/M = 1, specifies the location of the source operand. Only data addressing modes can be used as listed in the following table:

Addressing Mode	Mode	Register	Addressing Mode	Mode	Register
Dn*	000	reg. number:Dn	(xxx).W	111	000
An	—	—	(xxx).L	111	001
(An)	010	reg. number:An	#<data>	111	100
(An) +	011	reg. number:An			
– (An)	100	reg. number:An			
(d$_{16}$,An)	101	reg. number:An	(d$_{16}$,PC)	111	010
(d$_8$,An,Xn)	110	reg. number:An	(d$_8$,PC,Xn)	111	011
(bd,An,Xn)	110	reg. number:An	(bd,PC,Xn)	111	011
([bd,An,Xn],od)	110	reg. number:An	([bd,PC,Xn],od)	111	011
([bd,An],Xn,od)	110	reg. number:An	([bd,PC],Xn,od)	111	011

*Only if <fmt> is byte, word, long, or single.

R/M field—Specifies the source operand address mode.

0—The operation is register to register.

1—The operation is <ea> to register.

Source Specifier field—Specifies the source register or data format.
If R/M = 0, specifies the source floating-point data register.
If R/M = 1, specifies the source data format:
- 000—Long-Word Integer (L)
- 001—Single-Precision Real (S)
- 010—Extended-Precision Real (X)
- 011—Packed-Decimal Real (P)*
- 100—Word Integer (W)
- 101—Double-Precision Real (D)
- 110—Byte Integer (B)

*This encoding in the MC68040 will cause an unimplemented
data type exception to allow emulation in software.

Destination Register field—Specifies the destination floating-point data register.

Opmode field—Specifies the instruction and rounding precision.

0000000	FMOVE	Rounding precision specified by the floating-point control register.
1000000	FSMOVE	Single-precision rounding specified.
1000100	FDMOVE	Double-precision rounding specified.

Register-to-Memory Operation: Rounds the source operand to the size of the specified destination format and stores it at the destination effective address. If the format of the destination is packed decimal, a third operand is required to specify the format of the resultant string. This operand, called the k-factor, is a 7-bit signed integer (twos complement) and may be specified as an immediate value or in an integer data register. If a data register contains the k-factor, only the least significant seven bits are used, and the rest of the register is ignored.

Floating-Point Status Register (Register-to-Memory):

Condition Codes:	Not affected.	
Quotient Byte:	Not affected.	
Exception Byte:	BSUN	Cleared
<fmt> is B, W, or L	SNAN	Refer to **1.6.5 NANs**.
	OPERR	Set if the source operand is infinity or if the destination size is exceeded after conversion and rounding; cleared otherwise.
	OVFL	Cleared
	UNFL	Cleared
	DZ	Cleared
	INEX2	Refer to exception processing in the appropriate user's manual.
	INEX1	Cleared
<fmt> is S, D, or X	BSUN	Cleared
	SNAN	Refer to **1.6.5 NANs**
	OVFL	Refer to exception processing in the appropriate user's manual.
	UNFL	Refer to exception processing in the appropriate user's manual.
	DZ	Cleared
	INEX2	Refer to exception processing in the appropriate user's manual.
	INEX1	Cleared
<fmt> is P	BSUN	Cleared
	SNAN	Refer to **1.6.5 NANs**.
	OPERR	Set if the k-factor > +17 or the magnitude of the decimal exponent exceeds three digits; cleared otherwise.
	OVFL	Cleared
	UNFL	Cleared
	DZ	Cleared
	INEX2	Refer to exception processing in the appropriate user's manual.
	INEX1	Cleared
Accrued Exception Byte:	Affected as described in exception processing in the appropriate user's manual.	

5

FMOVE   Move Floating-Point Data Register   FMOVE
(MC6888X, MC68040)

Instruction Format:

Register-to-Memory

15	14	13	12	11	10	9	8	7	6	5	4	3	2	1	0
1	1	1	COPROCESSOR ID			1	0	0	0	EFFECTIVE ADDRESS MODE			REGISTER		
0	1	1	DESTINATION FORMAT			SOURCE REGISTER			K-FACTOR (IF REQUIRED)						

Instruction Fields:

Effective Address field—Specifies the destination location. Only data alterable addressing modes can be used as listed in the following table:

Addressing Mode	Mode	Register	Addressing Mode	Mode	Register
Dn*	000	reg. number:Dn	(xxx).W	111	000
An	—	—	(xxx).L	111	001
(An)	010	reg. number:An	#<data>	—	—
(An) +	011	reg. number:An			
– (An)	100	reg. number:An			
(d16,An)	101	reg. number:An	(d16,PC)	—	—
(d8,An,Xn)	110	reg. number:An	(d8,PC,Xn)	—	—
(bd,An,Xn)	110	reg. number:An	(bd,PC,Xn)	—	—
([bd,An,Xn],od)	110	reg. number:An	([bd,PC,Xn],od)	—	—
([bd,An],Xn,od)	110	reg. number:An	([bd,PC],Xn,od)	—	—

*Only if <fmt> is byte, word, long, or single.

Destination Format field—Specifies the data format of the destination operand:

000—Long-Word Integer (L)

001—Single-Precision Real (S)

010—Extended-Precision Real (X)

011—Packed-Decimal Real with Static k-Factor (P{#k})*

100—Word Integer (W)

101—Double-Precision Real (D)

110—Byte Integer (B)

111—Packed-Decimal Real with Dynamic k-Factor (P{Dn})*

*This encoding will cause an unimplemented data type exception in the MC68040 to allow emulation in software.

FMOVE   Move Floating-Point Data Register   FMOVE
(MC6888X, MC68040)

Source Register field—Specifies the source floating-point data register.

k-Factor field—If the destination format is packed decimal, used to specify the format of the decimal string. For any other destination format, this field should be set to all zeros. For a static k-factor, this field is encoded with a twos-complement integer where the value defines the format as follows:

−64 to 0—Indicates the number of significant digits to the right of the decimal point (FORTRAN "F" format).

+1 to +17—Indicates the number of significant digits in the mantissa (FORTRAN "E" format).

+18 to +63—Sets the OPERR bit in the floating-point status register exception byte and treated as +17.

The format of this field for a dynamic k-factor is:

$$r\ r\ r\ 0\ 0\ 0\ 0$$

where "rrr" is the number of the main processor data register that contains the k-factor value.

The following table gives several examples of how the k-factor value affects the format of the decimal string that is produced by the floating-point coprocessor. The format of the string that is generated is independent of the source of the k-factor (static or dynamic).

k-Factor	Source Operand Value	Destination String
−5	+12345.678765	+1.234567877E + 4
−3	+12345.678765	+1.2345679E + 4
−1	+12345.678765	+1.23457E + 4
0	+12345.678765	+1.2346E + 4
+1	+12345.678765	+1.E + 4
+3	+12345.678765	+1.23E + 4
+5	+12345.678765	+1.2346E + 4

Operation: Source ◆ Destination

Assembler   FMOVE.L <ea>,FPCR
Syntax: FMOVE.L FPCR,<ea>

Attributes: Size = (Long)

Description: Moves the contents of a floating-point system control register (floating-point control register, floating-point status register, or floating-point instruction address register) to or from an effective address. A 32-bit transfer is always performed, even though the system control register may not have 32 implemented bits. Unimplemented bits of a control register are read as zeros and are ignored during writes (must be zero for compatibility with future devices).

For the MC68881, this instruction does not cause pending exceptions (other than protocol violations) to be reported. Furthermore, a write to the floating-point control register exception enable byte or the floating-point status register exception status byte cannot generate a new exception, regardless of the value written.

Floating-Point Status Register: Changed only if the destination is the floating-point status register, in which case all bits are modified to reflect the value of the source operand.

Instruction Format:

15	14	13	12	11	10	9	8	7	6	5	4	3	2	1	0
1	1	1	1	COPROCESSOR ID			0	0	0	EFFECTIVE ADDRESS					
										MODE			REGISTER		
1	0	dr	REGISTER SELECT			0	0	0	0	0	0	0	0	0	0

Instruction Fields:

Effective Address field—(Memory-to-Register) All addressing modes can be used as listed in the following table:

Addressing Mode	Mode	Register	Addressing Mode	Mode	Register
Dn	000	reg. number:Dn	(xxx).W	111	000
An*	001	reg. number:An	(xxx).L	111	001
(An)	010	reg. number:An	#<data>	111	100
(An) +	011	reg. number:An			
– (An)	100	reg. number:An			
(d16,An)	101	reg. number:An	(d16,PC)	111	010
(d8,An,Xn)	110	reg. number:An	(d8,PC,Xn)	111	011
(bd,An,Xn)	110	reg. number:An	(bd,PC,Xn)	111	011
([bd,An,Xn],od)	110	reg. number:An	([bd,PC,Xn],od)	111	011
([bd,An],Xn,od)	110	reg. number:An	([bd,PC],Xn,od)	111	011

*Only if the source register is the floating-point instruction address register.

Effective Address field—(Register-to-Memory) Only alterable addressing modes can be used as listed in the following table:

Addressing Mode	Mode	Register	Addressing Mode	Mode	Register
Dn	000	reg. number:Dn	(xxx).W	111	000
An*	001	reg. number:An	(xxx).L	111	001
(An)	010	reg. number:An	#<data>	—	—
(An) +	011	reg. number:An			
– (An)	100	reg. number:An			
(d16,An)	101	reg. number:An	(d16,PC)	—	—
(d8,An,Xn)	110	reg. number:An	(d8,PC,Xn)	—	—
(bd,An,Xn)	110	reg. number:An	(bd,PC,Xn)	—	—
([bd,An,Xn],od)	110	reg. number:An	([bd,PC,Xn],od)	—	—
([bd,An],Xn,od)	110	reg. number:An	([bd,PC],Xn,od)	—	—

*Only if the destination register is the floating-point instruction address register.

dr field—Specifies the direction of the data transfer.

0—From <ea> to the specified system control register.

1—From the specified system control register to <ea>.

Register Select field—Specifies the system control register to be moved:

    100   Floating-Point Control Register

    010   Floating-Point Status Register

    001   Floating-Point Instruction Address Register

5

FMOVECR

Move Constant ROM
(MC6888X, M68040FPSP)

FMOVECR

Operation: ROM Constant → FPn

Assembler
Syntax: FMOVECR.X #<ccc>,FPn

Attributes: Format = (Extended)

Description: Fetches an extended-precision constant from the floating-point coprocessor on-chip ROM, rounds the mantissa to the precision specified in the floating-point control register mode control byte, and stores it in the destination floating-point data register. The constant is specified by a predefined offset into the constant ROM. The values of the constants contained in the ROM are shown in the offset table at the end of this description.

Floating-Point Status Register:

Condition Codes:	Affected as described in **3.6.2 Conditional Testing**.
Quotient Byte:	Not affected.
Exception Byte:	BSUN Cleared
	SNAN Cleared
	OPERR Cleared
	OVFL Cleared
	UNFL Cleared
	DZ Cleared
	INEX2 Refer to inexact result in the appropriate user's manual.
	INEX1 Cleared
Accrued Exception Byte:	Affected as described in IEEE exception and trap compatibility in the appropriate user's manual.

Instruction Format:

15	14	13	12	11	10	9	8	7	6	5	4	3	2	1	0
1	1	1	1	COPROCESSOR ID			0	0	0	0	0	0	0	0	0
0	1	0	1	1	1	DESTINATION REGISTER			ROM OFFSET						

Instruction Fields:

Coprocessor ID field—Specifies which coprocessor in the system is to execute this instruction. Motorola assemblers default to ID = 1 for the floating-point coprocessor.

Destination Register field—Specifies the destination floating-point data register.

ROM Offset field—Specifies the offset into the floating-point coprocessor on-chip constant ROM where the desired constant is located. The offsets for the available constants are as follows:

Offset	Constant
$00	π
$0B	$Log_{10}(2)$
$0C	e
$0D	$Log_2(e)$
$0E	$Log_{10}(e)$
$0F	0.0
$30	$1n(2)$
$31	$1n(10)$
$32	10^0
$33	10^1
$34	10^2
$35	10^4
$36	10^8
$37	10^{16}
$38	10^{32}
$39	10^{64}
$3A	10^{128}
$3B	10^{256}
$3C	10^{512}
$3D	10^{1024}
$3E	10^{2048}
$3F	10^{4096}

The on-chip ROM contains other constants useful only to the on-chip microcode routines. The values contained at offsets other than those defined above are reserved for the use of Motorola and may be different on various mask sets of the floating-point coprocessor. These undefined values yield the value 0.0 in the M68040FPSP.

FMOVEM

Move Multiple Floating-Point Data Registers **FMOVEM**

(MC6888X, MC68040)

Operation: Register List ♦ Destination
Source ♦ Register List

Assembler FMOVEM.X <list>,<ea>
Syntax: FMOVEM.X Dn,<ea>
FMOVEM.X <ea>,<list>
FMOVEM.X <ea>,Dn

Attributes: Format = (Extended)

Description: Moves one or more extended-precision numbers to or from a list of floating-point data registers. No conversion or rounding is performed during this operation, and the floating-point status register is not affected by the instruction. For the MC68881, this instruction does not cause pending exceptions (other than protocol violations) to be reported. Furthermore, a write to the floating-point control register exception enable byte or the floating-point status register exception status byte connot generate a new exception, despite the value written.

Any combination of the eight floating-point data registers can be transferred, with the selected registers specified by a user-supplied mask. This mask is an 8-bit number, where each bit corresponds to one register; if a bit is set in the mask, that register is moved. The register select mask may be specified as a static value contained in the instruction or a dynamic value in the least significant eight bits of an integer data register (the remaining bits of the register are ignored).

FMOVEM allows three types of addressing modes: the control modes, the predecrement mode, or the postincrement mode. If the effective address is one of the control addressing modes, the registers are transferred between the processor and memory starting at the specified address and up through higher addresses. The order of the transfer is from FP0–FP7.

5

FMOVEM

If the effective address is the predecrement mode, only a register-to-memory operation is allowed. The registers are stored starting at the address contained in the address register and down through lower addresses. Before each register is stored, the address register is decremented by 12 (the size of an extended-precision number in memory) and the floating-point data register is then stored at the resultant address. When the operation is complete, the address register points to the image of the last floating-point data register stored. The order of the transfer is from FP7–FP0.

If the effective address is the postincrement mode, only a memory-to-register operation is allowed. The registers are loaded starting at the specified address and up through higher addresses. After each register is stored, the address register is incremented by 12 (the size of an extended-precision number in memory). When the operation is complete, the address register points to the byte immediately following the image of the last floating-point data register loaded. The order of the transfer is the same as for the control addressing modes: FP0–FP7.

Floating-Point Status Register: Not Affected. Note that the FMOVEM instruction provides the only mechanism for moving a floating-point data item between the floating-point unit and memory without performing any data conversions or affecting the condition code and exception status bits.

Instruction Format:

15	14	13	12	11	10	9	8	7	6	5	4	3	2	1	0
1	1	1	1	COPROCESSOR ID			0	0	0	EFFECTIVE ADDRESS					
										MODE			REGISTER		
1	1	dr	MODE		0	0	0	REGISTER LIST							

FMOVEM Move Multiple Floating-Point FMOVEM
Data Registers
(MC6888X, MC68040)

Instruction Fields:

Effective Address field—(Memory-to-Register) Only control addressing modes or the postincrement addressing mode can be used as listed in the following table:

Addressing Mode	Mode	Register	Addressing Mode	Mode	Register
Dn	—	—	(xxx).W	111	000
An	—	—	(xxx).L	111	001
(An)	010	reg. number:An	#<data>	—	—
(An) +	011	reg. number:An			
– (An)	—	—			
(d16,An)	101	reg. number:An	(d16,PC)	111	010
(d8,An,Xn)	110	reg. number:An	(d8,PC,Xn)	111	011
(bd,An,Xn)	110	reg. number:An	(bd,PC,Xn)	111	011
([bd,An,Xn],od)	110	reg. number:An	([bd,PC,Xn],od)	111	011
([bd,An],Xn,od)	110	reg. number:An	([bd,PC],Xn,od)	111	011

Effective Address field—(Register-to-Memory) Only control alterable addressing modes or the predecrement addressing mode can be used as listed in the following table:

Addressing Mode	Mode	Register	Addressing Mode	Mode	Register
Dn	—	—	(xxx).W	111	000
An	—	—	(xxx).L	111	001
(An)	010	reg. number:An	#<data>	—	—
(An) +	—	—			
– (An)	100	reg. number:An			
(d16,An)	101	reg. number:An	(d16,PC)	—	—
(d8,An,Xn)	110	reg. number:An	(d8,PC,Xn)	—	—
(bd,An,Xn)	110	reg. number:An	(bd,PC,Xn)	—	—
([bd,An,Xn],od)	110	reg. number:An	([bd,PC,Xn],od)	—	—
([bd,An],Xn,od)	110	reg. number:An	([bd,PC],Xn,od)	—	—

Move Multiple Floating-Point
Data Registers
(MC6888X, MC68040)

dr field—Specifies the direction of the transfer.
   0—Move the listed registers from memory to the floating-point unit.
   1—Move the listed registers from the floating-point unit to memory.

Mode field—Specifies the type of the register list and addressing mode.
   00—Static register list, predecrement addressing mode.
   01—Dynamic register list, predecrement addressing mode.
   10—Static register list, postincrement or control addressing mode.
   11—Dynamic register list, postincrement or control addressing mode.

Register List field:

Static list—contains the register select mask. If a register is to be moved, the corresponding bit in the mask is set as shown below; otherwise it is clear.

Dynamic list—contains the integer data register number, rrr, as listed in the following table:

List Type	Register List Format							
Static, – (An)	FP7	FP6	FP5	FP4	FP3	FP2	FP1	FP0
Static, (An) +, or Control	FP0	FP1	FP2	FP3	FP4	FP5	FP6	FP7
Dynamic	0	r	r	r	0	0	0	0

The format of the dynamic list mask is the same as for the static list and is contained in the least significant eight bits of the specified main processor data register.

Programming Note: This instruction provides a very useful feature, dynamic register list specification, that can significantly enhance system performance. If the calling conventions used for procedure calls utilize the dynamic register list feature, the number of floating-point data registers saved and restored can be reduced.

To utilize the dynamic register specification feature of the FMOVEM instruction, both the calling and the called procedures must be written to communicate information about register usage. When one procedure calls another, a register mask must be passed to the called procedure to indicate which registers must not be altered upon return to the calling procedure. The called procedure then saves only those registers that are modified and are already in use. Several techniques can be used to utilize this mechanism, and an example follows.

In this example, a convention is defined by which each called procedure is passed a word mask in D7 that identifies all floating-point registers in use by the calling procedure. Bits 15–8 identify the registers in the order FP0–FP7, and bits 7–0 identify the registers in the order FP7–FP0 (the two masks are required due to the different transfer order used by the predecrement and postincrement addressing modes). The code used by the calling procedure consists of simply moving the mask (which is generated at compile time) for the floating-point data registers currently in use into D7:

Calling procedure...

MOVE.W	#ACTIVE,D7	Load the list of FP registers that are in use.
BSR	PROC_2	

The entry code for all other procedures computes two masks. The first mask identifies the registers in use by the calling procedure that are used by the called procedure (and therefore saved and restored by the called procedure). The second mask identifies the registers in use by the calling procedure that are used by the called procedure (and therefore not saved on entry). The appropriate registers are then stored along with the two masks:

Called procedure...

MOVE.W	D7,D6	Copy the list of active registers.
AND.W	#WILL_USE,D7	Generate the list of doubly-used registers.
FMOVEM	D7,–(A7)	Save those registers.
MOVE.W	D7,–(A7)	Save the register list.
EOR.W	D7,D6	Generate the list of not saved active registers.
MOVE.W	D6,–(A7)	Save it for later use.

If the second procedure calls a third procedure, a register mask is passed to the third procedure that indicates which registers must not be altered by the third procedure. This mask identifies any registers in the list from the first procedure that were not saved by the second procedure, plus any registers used by the second procedure that must not be altered by the third procedure.

An example of the calculation of this mask is as follows:

Nested calling sequence...

MOVE.W	UNSAVED (A7),D7	Load the list of active registers not saved at entry.
OR.W	#WILL_USE,D7	Combine with those active at this time.
BSR	PROC_3	

Upon return from a procedure, the restoration of the necessary registers follows the same convention, and the register mask generated during the save operation on entry is used to restore the required floating-point data registers:

Return to caller...

ADDQ.L	#2,A7	Discard the list of registers not saved.
MOVE.B	(A7)+,D7	Get the saved register list (pop word, use byte).
FMOVEM	(A7)+,D7	Restore the registers.
•		
•		
•		
RTS		Return to the calling routine.

Operation: Register List ♦ Destination
Source ♦ Register List

Assembler   FMOVEM.L <list>,<ea>
Syntax: FMOVEM.L <ea>,<list>

Attributes: Size = (Long)

Description: Moves one or more 32-bit values into or out of the specified system control registers. Any combination of the three system control registers may be specified. The registers are always moved in the same order, regardless of the addressing mode used; the floating-point control register is moved first, followed by the floating-point status register, and the floating-point instruction address register is moved last. If a register is not selected for the transfer, the relative order of the transfer of the other registers is the same. The first register is transferred between the floating-point unit and the specified address, with successive registers located up through higher addresses.

For the MC68881, this instruction does not cause pending exceptions (other than protocol violations) to be reported. Furthermore, a write to the floating-point control register exception enable byte or the floating-point status register exception status byte connot generate a new exception, despite the value written.

When more than one register is moved, the memory or memory-alterable addressing modes can be used as shown in the addressing mode tables. If the addressing mode is predecrement, the address register is first decremented by the total size of the register images to be moved (i.e., four times the number of registers), and then the registers are transferred starting at the resultant address. For the postincrement addressing mode, the selected registers are transferred to or from the specified address, and then the address register is incremented by the total size of the register images transferred. If a single system control register is selected, the data register direct addressing mode may be used; if the only register selected is the floating-point instruction address register, then the address register direct addressing mode is allowed. Note that if a single register is selected, the opcode generated is the same as for the FMOVE single system control register instruction.

FMOVEM

Move Multiple Floating-Point Control Registers
(MC6888X, MC68040)

FMOVEM

Floating-Point Status Register: Changed only if the destination list includes the floating-point status register in which case all bits are modified to reflect the value of the source register image.

Instruction Format:

15	14	13	12	11	10	9	8	7	6	5	4	3	2	1	0
1	1	1	1	COPROCESSOR ID			0	0	0	EFFECTIVE ADDRESS MODE			REGISTER		
1	0	dr	REGISTER LIST		0	0	0	0	0	0	0	0	0	0	0

Instruction Fields:

Effective Address field—Determines the addressing mode for the operation.

Memory-to-Register—Only control addressing modes or the postincrement addressing mode can be used as listed in the following table:

Addressing Mode	Mode	Register	Addressing Mode	Mode	Register
Dn*	000	reg. number:Dn	(xxx).W	111	000
An**	001	reg. number:An	(xxx).L	111	001
(An)	010	reg. number:An	#<data>	111	100
(An) +	011	reg. number:An			
– (An)	100	reg. number:An			
(d$_{16}$,An)	101	reg. number:An	(d$_{16}$,PC)	111	010
(d$_8$,An,Xn)	110	reg. number:An	(d$_8$,PC,Xn)	111	011
(bd,An,Xn)	110	reg. number:An	(bd,PC,Xn)	111	011
([bd,An,Xn],od)	110	reg. number:An	([bd,PC,Xn],od)	111	011
([bd,An],Xn,od)	110	reg. number:An	([bd,PC],Xn,od)	111	011

*Only if a single floating-point instruction address register, floating-point status register, or floating-point control register is selected.

**Only if the floating-point instruction address register is the single register selected.

FMOVEM   Move Multiple Floating-Point   FMOVEM
Control Registers
(MC6888X, MC68040)

Register-to-Memory—Only control alterable addressing modes or the predecrement addressing mode can be used as listed in the following table:

Addressing Mode	Mode	Register	Addressing Mode	Mode	Register
Dn*	000	reg. number:Dn	(xxx).W	111	000
An**	001	reg. number:An	(xxx).L	111	001
(An)	010	reg. number:An	#<data>	—	—
(An) +	011	reg. number:An			
– (An)	100	reg. number:An			
(d_{16},An)	101	reg. number:An	(d_{16},PC)	—	—
(d_8,An,Xn)	110	reg. number:An	(d_8,PC,Xn)	—	—
(bd,An,Xn)	110	reg. number:An	(bd,PC,Xn)	—	—
([bd,An,Xn],od)	110	reg. number:An	([bd,PC,Xn],od)	—	—
([bd,An],Xn,od)	110	reg. number:An	([bd,PC],Xn,od)	—	—

*Only if a single floating-point control register is selected.
**Only if the floating-point instruction address register is the single register selected.

dr field—Specifies the direction of the transfer.
   0—Move the listed registers from memory to the floating-point unit.
   1—Move the listed registers from the floating-point unit to memory.

Register List field—Contains the register select mask. If a register is to be moved, the corresponding bit in the list is set; otherwise, it is clear. At least one register must be specified.

Bit Number	Register
12	Floating-Point Control Register
11	Floating-Point Status Register
10	Floating-Point Instruction Address Register

FMUL

Floating-Point Multiply
(MC6888X, MC68040)

FMUL

Operation: Source x FPn → FPn

Assembler
Syntax:
FMUL.<fmt> <ea>,FPn
FMUL.X FPm,FPn
*FrMUL<fmt> <ea>,FPn
*FrMUL.X FPm,FPn
where r is rounding precision, S or D

*Supported by MC68040 only

Attributes: Format = (Byte, Word, Long, Single, Double, Extended, Packed)

Description: Converts the source operand to extended precision (if necessary) and multiplies that number by the number in the destination floating-point data register. Stores the result in the destination floating-point data register.

FMUL will round the result to the precision selected in the floating-point control register. FSMUL and FDMUL will round the result to single or double precision, respectively, regardless of the rounding precision selected in the floating-point control register.

Operation Table:

DESTINATION		SOURCE[1]						
		+	**In Range**	**−**	**+**	**Zero**	**−**	**+** Infinity **−**
In Range	**+**	Multiply			+0.0		−0.0	+inf −inf
	−				−0.0		+0.0	−inf +inf
Zero	**+**	+0.0		−0.0	+0.0		−0.0	NAN[2]
	−	−0.0		+0.0	−0.0		+0.0	
Infinity	**+**	+inf		−inf	NAN[2]			+inf −inf
	−	−inf		+inf				−inf +inf

NOTES:
1. If the source operand is a NAN, refer to **1.6.5 NANs** for more information.
2. Sets the OPERR bit in the floating-point status register exception byte.

Floating-Point Status Register:

Condition Codes: Affected as described in **3.6.2 Conditional Testing**.

Quotient Byte: Not affected.

Exception Byte:
BSUN	Cleared
SNAN	Refer to **1.6.5 NANs**.
OPERR	Set for 0 x infinity; cleared otherwise.
OVFL	Refer to exception processing in the appropriate user's manual.
UNFL	Refer to exception processing in the appropriate user's manual.
DZ	Cleared
INEX2	Refer to exception processing in the appropriate user's manual.
INEX1	If <fmt> is packed, refer to exception processing in the appropriate user's manual; cleared otherwise.

Accrued Exception Byte: Affected as described in exception processing in the appropriate user's manual.

Instruction Format:

15	14	13	12	11	10	9	8	7	6	5	4	3	2	1	0
1	1	1	1	COPROCESSOR ID			0	0	0	EFFECTIVE ADDRESS					
										MODE			REGISTER		
0	R/M	0	SOURCE SPECIFIER			DESTINATION REGISTER			OPMODE						

FMUL

FMUL

Instruction Fields:

Effective Address field—Determines the addressing mode for external operands.

If R/M = 0, this field is unused and should be all zeros.

If R/M = 1, specifies the location of the source operand location. Only data addressing modes can be used as listed in the following table:

Addressing Mode	Mode	Register	Addressing Mode	Mode	Register
Dn*	000	reg. number:Dn	(xxx).W	111	000
An	—	—	(xxx).L	111	001
(An)	010	reg. number:An	#<data>	111	100
(An) +	011	reg. number:An			
– (An)	100	reg. number:An			
(d$_{16}$,An)	101	reg. number:An	(d$_{16}$,PC)	111	010
(d$_8$,An,Xn)	110	reg. number:An	(d$_8$,PC,Xn)	111	011
(bd,An,Xn)	110	reg. number:An	(bd,PC,Xn)	111	011
([bd,An,Xn],od)	110	reg. number:An	([bd,PC,Xn],od)	111	011
([bd,An],Xn,od)	110	reg. number:An	([bd,PC],Xn,od)	111	011

*Only if <fmt> is byte, word, long, or single.

R/M field—Specifies the source operand address mode.

0—The operation is register to register.

1—The operation is <ea> to register.

Source Specifier field—Specifies the source register or data format.

If R/M = 0, specifies the source floating-point data register.

If R/M = 1, specifies the source data format:

000—Long-Word Integer (L)

001—Single-Precision Real (S)

010—Extended-Precision Real (X)

011—Packed-Decimal Real (P)*

100—Word Integer (W)

101—Double-Precision Real (D)

110—Byte Integer (B)

*This encoding will cause an unimplemented data type exception in the MC68040 to allow emulation in software.

Destination Register field—Specifies the destination floating-point data register.

Opmode field—Specifies the instruction and rounding precision.

0100011	FMUL	Rounding precision specified by the floating-point control register.
1100011	FSMUL	Single-precision rounding specified.
1100111	FDMUL	Double-precision rounding specified.

5

FNEG

Floating-Point Negate
(MC6888X, MC68040)

FNEG

Operation: −(Source) ♦ FPn

Assembler
Syntax:
FNEG.\<fmt\> \<ea\>,FPn
FNEG.X FPm,FPn
FNEG.X FPn
*FrNEG.\<fmt\> \<ea\>,FPn
*FrNEG.X FPm,FPn
*FrNEG.X FPn
where r is rounding precision, S or D

*Supported by MC68040 only

Attributes: Format = (Byte, Word, Long, Single, Double, Extended, Packed)

Description: Converts the source operand to extended precision (if necessary) and inverts the sign of the mantissa. Stores the result in the destination floating-point data register.

FNEG will round the result to the precision selected in the floating-point control register. FSNEG and FDNEG will round the result to single or double precision, respectively, regardless of the rounding precision selected in the floating-point control register.

Operation Table:

	SOURCE							
DESTINATION	**+**	**In Range**	**−**	**+**	**Zero**	**−**	**+**	**Infinity**	**−**
Result		Negate		−0.0		+0.0	−inf		+inf

NOTE: If the source operand is a NAN, refer to **1.6.5 NANs** for more information.

FNEG

Floating-Point Negate
(MC6888X, MC68040)

FNEG

Floating-Point Status Register:

Condition Codes: Affected as described in **3.6.2 Conditional Testing**.

Quotient Byte: Not affected.

Exception Byte:
BSUN	Cleared
SNAN	Refer to **1.6.5 NANs**.
OPERR	Cleared
OVFL	Cleared
UNFL	If source is an extended-precision denormalized number, refer to exception processing in the appropriate user's manual; cleared otherwise.
DZ	Cleared
INEX2	Cleared
INEX1	If <fmt> is packed, refer to exception processing in the appropriate user's manual; cleared otherwise.

Accrued Exception Byte: Affected as described in exception processing in the appropriate user's manual.

Instruction Format:

15	14	13	12	11	10	9	8	7	6	5	4	3	2	1	0
1	1	1	1	COPROCESSOR ID			0	0	0	EFFECTIVE ADDRESS					
										MODE			REGISTER		
0	R/M	0	SOURCE SPECIFIER			DESTINATION REGISTER			OPMODE					

Instruction Fields:

Effective Address field—Determines the addressing mode for external operands.

If R/M = 0, this field is unused and should be all zeros.

If R/M = 1, specifies the location of the source operand. Only data addressing modes can be used as listed in the following table:

Addressing Mode	Mode	Register	Addressing Mode	Mode	Register
Dn*	000	reg. number:Dn	(xxx).W	111	000
An	—	—	(xxx).L	111	001
(An)	010	reg. number:An	#<data>	111	100
(An) +	011	reg. number:An			
– (An)	100	reg. number:An			
(d$_{16}$,An)	101	reg. number:An	(d$_{16}$,PC)	111	010
(d$_8$,An,Xn)	110	reg. number:An	(d$_8$,PC,Xn)	111	011
(bd,An,Xn)	110	reg. number:An	(bd,PC,Xn)	111	011
([bd,An,Xn],od)	110	reg. number:An	([bd,PC,Xn],od)	111	011
([bd,An],Xn,od)	110	reg. number:An	([bd,PC],Xn,od)	111	011

*Only if <fmt> is byte, word, long, or single.

R/M field—Specifies the source operand address mode.

0—The operation is register to register.

1—The operation is <ea> to register.

Source Specifier field—Specifies the source register or data format.

If R/M = 0, specifies the source floating-point data register.

If R/M = 1, specifies the source data format:

000—Long-Word Integer (L)

001—Single-Precision Real (S)

010—Extended-Precision Real (X)

011—Packed-Decimal Real (P)*

100—Word Integer (W)

101—Double-Precision Real (D)

110—Byte Integer (B)

*This encoding will cause an unimplemented data type exception to allow emulation in software.

Destination Register field—Specifies the destination floating-point data register. If R/M = 0 and the source and destination fields are equal, then the input operand is taken from the specified floating-point data register and the result is written into the same register. If the single register syntax is used, Motorola assemblers set the source and destination fields to the same value.

Opmode field—Specifies the instruction and rounding precision.

0011010	FNEG	Rounding precision specified by the floating-point control register.
1011010	FSNEG	Single-precision rounding specified.
1011110	FDNEG	Double-precision rounding specified.

FNOP

Operation: None

**Assembler
Syntax:**   FNOP

Attributes: Unsized

Description: This instruction does not perform any explicit operation. However, it is useful to force synchronization of the floating-point unit with an integer unit or to force processing of pending exceptions. For most floating-point instructions, the integer unit is allowed to continue with the execution of the next instruction once the floating-point unit has any operands needed for an operation, thus supporting concurrent execution of floating-point and integer instructions. The FNOP instruction synchronizes the floating-point unit and the integer unit by causing the integer unit to wait until all previous floating-point instructions have completed. Execution of FNOP also forces any exceptions pending from the execution of a previous floating-point instruction to be processed as a preinstruction exception.

The MC68882 may not wait to begin execution of another floating-point instruction until it has completed execution of the current instruction. The FNOP instruction synchronizes the coprocessor and microprocessor unit by causing the microprocessor unit to wait until the current instruction (or both instructions) have completed.

The FNOP instruction also forces the processing of exceptions pending from the execution of previous instructions. This is also inherent in the way that the floating-point coprocessor utilizes the M68000 family coprocessor interface. Once the floating-point coprocessor has received the input operand for an arithmetic instruction, it always releases the main processor to execute the next instruction (regardless of whether or not concurrent execution is prevented for the instruction due to tracing) without reporting the exception during the execution of that instruction. Then, when the main processor attempts to initiate the execution of the next floating-point coprocessor instruction, a preinstruction exception may be reported to initiate exception processing for an exception that occurred during a previous instruction. By using the FNOP instruction, the user can force any pending exceptions to be processed without performing any other operations.

Floating-Point Status Register: Not Affected.

Instruction Format:

15	14	13	12	11	10	9	8	7	6	5	4	3	2	1	0
1	1	1	1	COPROCESSOR ID			0	1	0	0	0	0	0	0	0
0	0	0	0	0	0	0	0	0	0	0	0	0	0	0	0

Instruction Fields:

Coprocessor ID field—Specifies which coprocessor in the system is to execute this instruction. Motorola assemblers default to ID = 1 for the floating-point coprocessor.

NOTE

FNOP uses the same opcode as the FBcc.W <label> instruction, with cc = F (nontrapping false) and <label> = +2 (which results in a displacement of 0).

5

FREM

IEEE Remainder
(MC6888X, M68040FPSP)

FREM

Operation: IEEE Remainder of (FPn ÷ Source) ♦ FPn

Assembler FREM.<fmt> <ea>,FPn
Syntax: FREM.X FPm,FPn

Attributes: Format = (Byte, Word, Long, Single, Double, Extended, Packed)

Description: Converts the source operand to extended precision (if necessary) and calculates the modulo remainder of the number in the destination floating-point data register, using the source operand as the modulus. Stores the result in the destination floating-point data register and stores the sign and seven least significant bits of the quotient in the floating-point status register quotient byte (the quotient is the result of FPn ÷ Source). The IEEE remainder function is defined as:

$$FPn - (Source \times N)$$

where N = INT (FPn ÷ Source) in the round-to-nearest mode.

The FREM function is not defined for a source operand equal to zero or for a destination operand equal to infinity. Note that this function is not the same as the FMOD instruction, which uses the round-to-zero mode and thus returns a remainder that is different from the remainder required by the IEEE *Specification for Binary Floating-Point Arithmetic.*

Operation Table:

DESTINATION		+ In Range −	+ Zero −	+ Infinity −
			SOURCE[1]	
In Range	+ / −	IEEE Remainder	NAN[2]	FPn[3]
Zero	+ / −	+0.0 / −0.0	NAN[2]	+0.0 / −0.0
Infinity	+ / −	NAN[2]	NAN[2]	NAN[2]

NOTES:
1. If either operand is a NAN, refer to **1.6.5 NANs** for more information.
2. Sets the OPERR bit in the floating-point status register exception byte.
3. Returns the value of FPn before the operation. However, the result is processed by the normal instruction termination procedure to round it as required. Thus, an underflow and/or inexact result may occur if the rounding precision has been changed to a smaller size since the FPn value was loaded.

Floating-Point Status Register:

Condition Codes: Affected as described in **3.6.2 Conditional Testing.**

Quotient Byte: Loaded with the sign and least significant seven bits of the quotient (FPn ÷ Source). The sign of the quotient is the exclusive-OR of the sign bits of the source and destination operands.

Exception Byte:

BSUN	Cleared
SNAN	Refer to **1.6.5 NANs**.
OPERR	Set if the source is zero or the destination is infinity; cleared otherwise.
OVFL	Cleared
UNFL	Refer to underflow in the appropriate user's manual.
DZ	Cleared
INEX2	Cleared
INEX1	If <fmt> is packed, refer to inexact result on decimal input in the appropriate user's manual; cleared otherwise.

Accrued Exception Byte: Affected as described in IEEE exception and trap compatibility in the appropriate user's manual.

Instruction Format:

15	14	13	12	11	10	9	8	7	6	5	4	3	2	1	0
1	1	1	1	COPROCESSOR ID			0	0	0	EFFECTIVE ADDRESS					
										MODE			REGISTER		
0	R/M	0	SOURCE SPECIFIER			DESTINATION REGISTER			0	1	0	0	1	0	1

Instruction Fields:

Coprocessor ID field—Specifies which coprocessor in the system is to execute this instruction. Motorola assemblers default to ID = 1 for the floating-point coprocessor.

Effective Address field—Determines the addressing mode for external operands.
  If R/M = 0, this field is unused and should be all zeros.
  If R/M = 1, this field is encoded with an M68000 family addressing mode as listed
  in the following table:

Addressing Mode	Mode	Register
Dn*	000	reg. number:Dn
An	—	—
(An)	010	reg. number:An
(An) +	011	reg. number:An
– (An)	100	reg. number:An
(d$_{16}$,An)	101	reg. number:An
(d$_8$,An,Xn)	110	reg. number:An
(bd,An,Xn)	110	reg. number:An
([bd,An,Xn],od)	110	reg. number:An
([bd,An],Xn,od)	110	reg. number:An

Addressing Mode	Mode	Register
(xxx).W	111	000
(xxx).L	111	001
#<data>	111	100
(d$_{16}$,PC)	111	010
(d$_8$,PC,Xn)	111	011
(bd,PC,Xn)	111	011
([bd,PC,Xn],od)	111	011
([bd,PC],Xn,od)	111	011

*Only if <fmt> is byte, word, long, or single.

R/M field—Specifies the source operand address mode.
  0—The operation is register to register.
  1—The operation is <ea> to register.

Source Specifier field—Specifies the source register or data format.
  If R/M = 0, specifies the source floating-point data register.
  If R/M = 1, specifies the source data format:
    000—Long-Word Integer (L)
    001—Single-Precision Real (S)
    010—Extended-Precision Real (X)
    011—Packed-Decimal Real (P)
    100—Word Integer (W)
    101—Double-Precision Real (D)
    110—Byte Integer (B)

Destination Register field—Specifies the destination floating-point data register.

FSCALE

Scale Exponent
(MC6888X, M68040FPSP)

FSCALE

Operation $FPn \times INT(2^{Source}) \rightarrow FPn$

Assembler   FSCALE.<fmt> <ea>,FPn
Syntax: FSCALE.X FPm,FPn

Attributes: Format = (Byte, Word, Long, Single, Double, Extended, Packed)

Description: Converts the source operand to an integer (if necessary) and adds that integer to the destination exponent. Stores the result in the destination floating-point data register. This function has the effect of multiplying the destination by 2^{Source}, but is much faster than a multiply operation when the source is an integer value.

The floating-point coprocessor assumes that the scale factor is an integer value before the operation is executed. If not, the value is chopped (i.e., rounded using the round-to-zero mode) to an integer before it is added to the exponent. When the absolute value of the source operand is $\geq 2^{14}$, an overflow or underflow always results.

Operation Table:

DESTINATION		SOURCE[1]				
		+ In Range −	+	Zero −	+	Infinity −
In Range	+ −	Scale Exponent		FPn[2]		NAN[3]
Zero	+ −	+0.0 −0.0		+0.0 −0.0		NAN[3]
Infinity	+ −	+inf −inf		+inf −inf		NAN[3]

NOTES:
1. If the source operand is a NAN, refer to **1.6.5 NANs** for more information.
2. Returns the value FPn before the operation. However, the result is processed by the normal instruction termination procedure to round it as required. Thus, an underflow and/or inexact result may occur if the rounding precision has been changed to a smaller size since the FPn value was loaded.
3. Sets the OPERR bit in the floating-point status register exception byte.

FSCALE

Scale Exponent
(MC6888X, M68040FPSP)

FSCALE

Floating-Point Status Register:

Condition Codes:	Affected as described in **3.6.2 Conditional Testing**.
Quotient Byte:	Not affected
Exception Byte:	BSUN Cleared
	SNAN Refer to **1.6.5 NANs**.
	OPERR Set if the source operand is ±infinity; cleared otherwise.
	OVFL Refer to overflow in the appropriate user's manual.
	UNFL Refer to underflow in the appropriate user's manual.
	DZ Cleared
	INEX2 Cleared
	INEX1 If <fmt> is packed, refer to inexact result on decimal input in the appropriate user's manual; cleared otherwise.
Accrued Exception Byte:	Affected as described in IEEE exception and trap compatibility in the appropriate user's manual.

Instruction Format:

15	14	13	12	11	10	9	8	7	6	5	4	3	2	1	0
1	1	1	1	COPROCESSOR ID			0	0	0	EFFECTIVE ADDRESS MODE			REGISTER		
0	R/M	0	SOURCE SPECIFIER			DESTINATION REGISTER			0	1	0	0	1	1	0

Instruction Fields:

Coprocessor ID field—Specifies which coprocessor in the system is to execute this instruction. Motorola assemblers default to ID = 1 for the floating-point coprocessor.

Effective Address field—Determines the addressing mode for external operands.
If R/M = 0, this field is unused and should be all zeros.
If R/M = 1, this field is encoded with an M68000 family addressing mode as listed in the following table:

Addressing Mode	Mode	Register	Addressing Mode	Mode	Register
Dn*	000	reg. number:Dn	(xxx).W	111	000
An	—	—	(xxx).L	111	001
(An)	010	reg. number:An	#<data>	111	100
(An) +	011	reg. number:An			
– (An)	100	reg. number:An			
(d$_{16}$,An)	101	reg. number:An	(d$_{16}$,PC)	111	010
(d$_8$,An,Xn)	110	reg. number:An	(d$_8$,PC,Xn)	111	011
(bd,An,Xn)	110	reg. number:An	(bd,PC,Xn)	111	011
([bd,An,Xn],od)	110	reg. number:An	([bd,PC,Xn],od)	111	011
([bd,An],Xn,od)	110	reg. number:An	([bd,PC],Xn,od)	111	011

*Only if <fmt> is byte, word, long, or single.

R/M field—Specifies the source operand address mode.
　　0—The operation is register to register.
　　1—The operation is <ea> to register.

Source Specifier field—Specifies the source register or data format.
　　If R/M = 0, specifies the source floating-point data register.
　　If R/M = 1, specifies the source data format:
　　　　000—Long-Word Integer (L)
　　　　001—Single-Precision Real (S)
　　　　010—Extended-Precision Real (X)
　　　　011—Packed-Decimal Real (P)
　　　　100—Word Integer (W)
　　　　101—Double-Precision Real (D)
　　　　110—Byte Integer (B)

Destination Register field—Specifies the destination floating-point data register.

Operation: If (Condition True)
      Then 1s ◆ Destination
      Else 0s ◆ Destination

**Assembler
Syntax:**   FScc.<size> <ea>

Attributes: Size = (Byte)

Description: If the specified floating-point condition is true, sets the byte integer operand at the destination to TRUE (all ones); otherwise, sets the byte to FALSE (all zeros). The conditional specifier cc may select any one of the 32 floating-point conditional tests as described in **1.3.2 Conditional Test Definitions**.

Floating-Point Status Register:

Condition Codes:	Not affected.	
Quotient Byte:	Not affected.	
Exception Byte:	BSUN	Set if the NAN condition code is set and the condition selected is an IEEE nonaware test.
	SNAN	Not Affected.
	OPERR	Not Affected.
	OVFL	Not Affected.
	UNFL	Not Affected.
	DZ	Not Affected.
	INEX2	Not Affected.
	INEX1	Not Affected.

Accrued Exception Byte: The IOP bit is set if the BSUN bit is set in the exception byte. No other bit is affected.

Instruction Format:

15	14	13	12	11	10	9	8	7	6	5	4	3	2	1	0
1	1	1	1	COPROCESSOR ID			0	0	1	EFFECTIVE ADDRESS					
										MODE			REGISTER		
0	0	0	0	0	0	0	0	0	0	CONDITIONAL PREDICATE					

Instruction Fields:

Effective Address field—Specifies the addressing mode for the byte integer operand. Only data alterable addressing modes can be used as listed in the following table:

Addressing Mode	Mode	Register	Addressing Mode	Mode	Register
Dn	000	reg. number:Dn	(xxx).W	111	000
An	—	—	(xxx).L	111	001
(An)	010	reg. number:An	#<data>	—	—
(An) +	011	reg. number:An			
– (An)	100	reg. number:An			
(d$_{16}$,An)	101	reg. number:An	(d$_{16}$,PC)	—	—
(d$_8$,An,Xn)	110	reg. number:An	(d$_8$,PC,Xn)	—	—
(bd,An,Xn)	110	reg. number:An	(bd,PC,Xn)	—	—
([bd,An,Xn],od)	110	reg. number:An	([bd,PC,Xn],od)	—	—
([bd,An],Xn,od)	110	reg. number:An	([bd,PC],Xn,od)	—	—

Conditional Predicate field—Specifies one of 32 conditional tests as defined in **3.6.2 Conditional Testing**.

NOTE

When a BSUN exception occurs, a preinstruction exception is taken. If the exception handler returns without modifying the image of the program counter on the stack frame (to point to the instruction following the FScc), then it must clear the cause of the exception (by clearing the NAN bit or disabling the BSUN trap) or the exception occurs again immediately upon return to the routine that caused the exception.

FSGLDIV

Single-Precision Divide
(MC6888X, MC68040)

FSGLDIV

Operation: FPn ÷ Source ♦ FPn

Assembler FSGLDIV.<fmt> <ea>,FPn
Syntax: FSGLDIV.X   FPm,FPn

Attributes: Format = (Byte, Word, Long, Single, Double, Extended, Packed)

Description: Converts the source operand to extended precision (if necessary) and divides that number into the number in the destination floating-point data register. Stores the result in the destination floating-point data register, rounded to single precision (despite the current rounding precision). This function is undefined for 0 ÷ 0 and infinity ÷ infinity.

Both the source and destination operands are assumed to be representable in the single-precision format. If either operand requires more than 24 bits of mantissa to be accurately represented, the extraneous mantissa bits are trancated prior to the division, hence the accuracy of the result is not guaranteed. Furthermore, the result exponent may exceed the range of single precision, regardless of the rounding precision selected in the floating-point control register mode control byte. Refer to **3.6.1 Underflow, Round, Overflow** for more information.

The accuracy of the result is not affected by the number of mantissa bits required to represent each input operand since the input operands just change to extended precision. The result mantissa is rounded to single precision, and the result exponent is rounded to extended precision, despite the rounding precision selected in the floating-point control register.

Operation Table:

DESTINATION		SOURCE[31]						
		+ In Range −		+ Zero −		+ Infinity −		
In Range	+	Divide		$+inf^2$	$-inf^2$	+0.0	−0.0	
	−	(Single Precision)		$-inf^2$	$+inf^2$	−0.0	+0.0	
Zero	+	+0.0	−0.0	NAN[3]		+0.0	−0.0	
	−	−0.0	+0.0			−0.0	+0.0	
Infinity	+	+inf	−inf	+inf	−inf	NAN[3]		
	−	−inf	+inf	−inf	+inf			

NOTES:
1. If the source operand is a NAN, refer to **1.6.5 NANs** for more information.
2. Sets the DZ bit in the floating-point status register exception byte.
3. Sets the OPERR bit in the floating-point status register exception byte.

Single-Precision Divide
(MC6888X, MC68040)

Floating-Point Status Register:

Condition Codes:	Affected as described in **3.6.2 Conditional Testing**.
Quotient Byte:	Not affected.
Exception Byte:	BSUN Cleared
	SNAN Refer to **1.6.5 NANs**.
	OPERR Set for 0 ÷ 0 or infinity ÷ infinity.
	OVFL Refer to overflow in the appropriate user's manual.
	UNFL Refer to underflow in the appropriate user's manual.
	DZ Set if the source is zero and the destination is in range; cleared otherwise.
	INEX2 Refer to inexact result in the appropriate user's manual.
	INEX1 If <fmt> is packed, refer to the appropriate user's manual for inexact result on decimal input; cleared otherwise.
Accrued Exception Byte:	Affected as described in IEEE exception and trap compatibility in the appropriate user's manual.

Instruction Format:

15	14	13	12	11	10	9	8	7	6	5	4	3	2	1	0
1	1	1	1	COPROCESSOR ID			0	0	0	EFFECTIVE ADDRESS MODE			REGISTER		
0	R/M	0	SOURCE SPECIFIER			DESTINATION REGISTER			0	1	0	0	1	0	0

Instruction Fields:

Coprocessor ID field—Specifies which coprocessor in the system is to execute this instruction. Motorola assemblers default to ID = 1 for the floating-point coprocessor.

FSGLDIV

Single-Precision Divide
(MC6888X, MC68040)

FSGLDIV

Effective Address field—Determines the addressing mode for external operands.
If R/M = 0, this field is unused and should be all zeros.
If R/M = 1, this field is encoded with an M68000 family addressing mode as listed in the following table:

Addressing Mode	Mode	Register	Addressing Mode	Mode	Register
Dn*	000	reg. number:Dn	(xxx).W	111	000
An	—	—	(xxx).L	111	001
(An)	010	reg. number:An	#<data>	111	100
(An) +	011	reg. number:An			
– (An)	100	reg. number:An			
(d$_{16}$,An)	101	reg. number:An	(d$_{16}$,PC)	111	010
(d$_8$,An,Xn)	110	reg. number:An	(d$_8$,PC,Xn)	111	011
(bd,An,Xn)	110	reg. number:An	(bd,PC,Xn)	111	011
([bd,An,Xn],od)	110	reg. number:An	([bd,PC,Xn],od)	111	011
([bd,An],Xn,od)	110	reg. number:An	([bd,PC],Xn,od)	111	011

*Only if <fmt> is byte, word, long, or single.

R/M field—Specifies the source operand address mode.
  0—The operation is register to register.
  1—The operation is <ea> to register.

Source Specifier field—Specifies the source register or data format.
  If R/M = 0, specifies the source floating-point data register.
  If R/M = 1, specifies the source data format:
    000—Long-Word Integer (L)
    001—Single-Precision Real (S)
    010—Extended-Precision Real (X)
    011—Packed-Decimal Real (P)
    100—Word Integer (W)
    101—Double-Precision Real (D)
    110—Byte Integer (B)

Destination Register field—Specifies the destination floating-point data register.

FSGLMUL   Single-Precision Multiply   FSGLMUL
(MC6888X, MC68040)

Operation: Source x FPn ♦ FPn

Assembler   FSGLMUL.<fmt> <ea>,FPn
Syntax: FSGLMUL.X FPm,FPn

Attributes: Format = (Byte, Word, Long, Single, Double, Extended, Packed)

Description: Converts the source operand to extended precision (if necessary) and multiplies that number by the number in the destination floating-point data register. Stores the result in the destination floating-point data register, rounded to single precision (regardless of the current rounding precision).

Both the source and destination operands are assumed to be representable in the single-precision format. If either operand requires more than 24 bits of mantissa to be accurately represented, the extraneous mantissa bits are truncated prior to the multipliction; hence, the accuracy of the result is not guaranteed. Furthermore, the result exponent may exceed the range of single precision, regardless of the rounding precision selected in the floating-point control register mode control byte. Refer to **3.6.1 Underflow, Round, Overflow** for more information.

Operation Table:

DESTINATION		SOURCE[1]						
		+ In Range **−**		**+** Zero **−**		**+** Infinity **−**		
In Range	**+**	Multiply		+0.0	−0.0	+inf		−inf
	−	(Single Precision)		−0.0	+0.0	−inf		+inf
Zero	**+**	+0.0	−0.0	+0.0	−0.0	NAN[2]		
	−	−0.0	+0.0	−0.0	+0.0			
Infinity	**+**	+inf	−inf	NAN[2]		+inf		−inf
	−	−inf	+inf			−inf		+inf

NOTES:
1. If the source operand is a NAN, refer to **1.6.5 NANs** for more information.
2. Sets the OPERR bit in the floating-point status register exception byte.

NOTE

The input operand mantissas truncate to single precision before the multiply operation. The result mantissa rounds to single precision despite the rounding precision selected in the floating-point control register.

FSGLMUL

Single-Precision Multiply
(MC6888X, MC68040)

FSGLMUL

Floating-Point Status Register:

Condition Codes: Affected as described in **3.6.2 Conditional Testing**.

Quotient Byte: Not affected.

Exception Byte:

BSUN	Cleared
SNAN	Refer to **1.6.5 NANs**.
OPERR	Set if one operand is zero and the other is infinity; cleared otherwise.
OVFL	Refer to overflow in the appropriate user's manual.
UNFL	Refer to underflow in the appropriate user's manual.
DZ	Cleared
INEX2	Refer to inexact result in the appropriate user's manual.
INEX1	If <fmt> is packed, refer to inexact result on decimal input in the appropriate user's manual; cleared otherwise.

Accrued Exception Byte: Affected as described in IEEE exception and trap compatibility in the appropriate user's manual.

Instruction Format:

15	14	13	12	11	10	9	8	7	6	5	4	3	2	1	0
1	1	1	1	COPROCESSOR ID			0	0	0	EFFECTIVE ADDRESS MODE			REGISTER		
0	R/M	0	SOURCE SPECIFIER			DESTINATION REGISTER		0	1	0	0	1	1	1

Instruction Fields:

Coprocessor ID field—Specifies which coprocessor in the system is to execute this instruction. Motorola assemblers default to ID = 1 for the floating-point coprocessor.

Effective Address field—Determines the addressing mode for external operands.

If R/M = 0, this field is unused and should be all zeros.

If R/M = 1, this field is encoded with an M68000 family addressing mode as listed in the following table:

Addressing Mode	Mode	Register	Addressing Mode	Mode	Register
Dn*	000	reg. number:Dn	(xxx).W	111	000
An	—	—	(xxx).L	111	001
(An)	010	reg. number:An	#<data>	111	100
(An) +	011	reg. number:An			
– (An)	100	reg. number:An			
(d_{16},An)	101	reg. number:An	(d_{16},PC)	111	010
(d_8,An,Xn)	110	reg. number:An	(d_8,PC,Xn)	111	011
(bd,An,Xn)	110	reg. number:An	(bd,PC,Xn)	111	011
([bd,An,Xn],od)	110	reg. number:An	([bd,PC,Xn],od)	111	011
([bd,An],Xn,od)	110	reg. number:An	([bd,PC],Xn,od)	111	011

*Only if <fmt> is byte, word, long, or single.

R/M field—Specifies the source operand address mode.

  0—The operation is register to register.

  1—The operation is <ea> to register.

Source Specifier field—Specifies the source register or data format.

  If R/M = 0, specifies the source floating-point data register.

  If R/M = 1, specifies the source data format:

    000—Long-Word Integer (L)

    001—Single-Precision Real (S)

    010—Extended-Precision Real (X)

    011—Packed-Decimal Real (P)

    100—Word Integer (W)

    101—Double-Precision Real (D)

    110—Byte Integer (B)

Destination Register field—Specifies the destination floating-point data register.

Operation: Sine of Source → FPn

Assembler
Syntax:
FSIN.<fmt> <ea>,FPn
FSIN.X FPm,FPn
FSIN.X FPn

Attributes: Format = (Byte, Word, Long, Single, Double, Extended, Packed)

Description: Converts the source operand to extended precision (if necessary) and calculates the sine of that number. Stores the result in the destination floating-point data register. This function is not defined for source operands of ±infinity. If the source operand is not in the range of $[-2\pi...+2\pi]$, the argument is reduced to within that range before the sine is calculated. However, large arguments may lose accuracy during reduction, and very large arguments (greater than approximately 10^{20}) lose all accuracy. The result is in the range of $[-1...+1]$.

Operation Table:

DESTINATION	SOURCE[1]					
	+	In Range	–	+	Zero	–	+	Infinity	–
Result		Sine		+0.0		–0.0		NAN[2]	

NOTES:
1. If the source operand is a NAN, refer to **1.6.5 NANs** for more information.
2. Sets the OPERR bit in the floating-point status register exception byte.

Floating-Point Status Register:

Condition Codes: Affected as described in **3.6.2 Conditional Testing**.

Quotient Byte: Not affected.

Exception Byte:

BSUN	Cleared
SNAN	Refer to **1.6.5 NANs.**
OPERR	Set if the source is ±infinity; cleared otherwise.
OVFL	Cleared
UNFL	Refer to underflow in the appropriate user's manual.
DZ	Cleared
INEX2	Refer to inexact result in the appropriate user's manual.
INEX1	If <fmt> is packed, refer to inexact result on decimal input in the appropriate user's manual; cleared otherwise.

Accrued Exception Byte: Affected as described in IEEE exception and trap compatibility in the appropriate user's manual.

Instruction Format:

15	14	13	12	11	10	9	8	7	6	5	4	3	2	1	0
1	1	1	1	COPROCESSOR ID			0	0	0	EFFECTIVE ADDRESS					
										MODE			REGISTER		
0	R/M	0	SOURCE SPECIFIER			DESTINATION REGISTER			0	0	0	1	1	1	0

Instruction Fields:

Coprocessor ID field—Specifies which coprocessor in the system is to execute this instruction. Motorola assemblers default to ID = 1 for the floating-point coprocessor.

Effective Address field—Determines the addressing mode for external operands.
If R/M = 0, this field is unused and should be all zeros.
If R/M = 1, this field is encoded with an M68000 family addressing mode as listed
in the following table:

Addressing Mode	Mode	Register	Addressing Mode	Mode	Register
Dn*	000	reg. number:Dn	(xxx).W	111	000
An	—	—	(xxx).L	111	001
(An)	010	reg. number:An	#<data>	111	100
(An) +	011	reg. number:An			
– (An)	100	reg. number:An			
(d$_{16}$,An)	101	reg. number:An	(d$_{16}$,PC)	111	010
(d$_8$,An,Xn)	110	reg. number:An	(d$_8$,PC,Xn)	111	011
(bd,An,Xn)	110	reg. number:An	(bd,PC,Xn)	111	011
([bd,An,Xn],od)	110	reg. number:An	([bd,PC,Xn],od)	111	011
([bd,An],Xn,od)	110	reg. number:An	([bd,PC],Xn,od)	111	011

*Only if <fmt> is byte, word, long, or single.

R/M field—Specifies the source operand address mode.
　0—The operation is register to register.
　1—The operation is <ea> to register.

Source Specifier field—Specifies the source register or data format.
　If R/M = 0, specifies the source floating-point data register.
　If R/M = 1, specifies the source data format:
　　000—Long-Word Integer (L)
　　001—Single-Precision Real (S)
　　010—Extended-Precision Real (X)
　　011—Packed-Decimal Real (P)
　　100—Word Integer (W)
　　101—Double-Precision Real (D)
　　110—Byte Integer (B)

Destination Register field—Specifies the destination floating-point data register. If
R/M = 0 and the source and destination fields are equal, then the input operand is
taken from the specified floating-point data register, and the result is written into
the same register. If the single register syntax is used, Motorola assemblers set
the source and destination fields to the same value.

FSINCOS Simultaneous Sine and Cosine FSINCOS
(MC6888X, M68040FPSP)

Operation: Sine of Source ♦ FPs
Cosine of Source ♦ FPc

Assembler FSINCOS.<fmt> <ea>,FPc,FPs
Syntax: FSINCOS.X FPm,FPc,FPs

Attributes: Format = (Byte, Word, Long, Single, Double, Extended, Packed)

Description: Converts the source operand to extended precision (if necessary) and calculates both the sine and the cosine of that number. Calculates both functions simultaneously; thus, this instruction is significantly faster than performing separate FSIN and FCOS instructions. Loads the sine and cosine results into the destination floating-point data register. Sets the condition code bits according to the sine result. If FPs and FPc are specified to be the same register, the cosine result is first loaded into the register and then is overwritten with the sine result. This function is not defined for source operands of ±infinity.

If the source operand is not in the range of $[-2\pi...+2\pi]$, the argument is reduced to within that range before the sine and cosine are calculated. However, large arguments may lose accuracy during reduction, and very large arguments (greater than approximately 10^{20}) lose all accuracy. The results are in the range of $[-1...+1]$.

Operation Table:

DESTINATION	SOURCE[1]							
	+	In Range	−	+	Zero	−	+	Infinity −
FPs		Sine		+0.0		−0.0		NAN[2]
FPc		Cosine			+1.0			NAN[2]

NOTES:
1. If the source operand is a NAN, refer to **1.6.5 NANs** for more information.
2. Sets the OPERR bit in the floating-point status register exception byte.

FSINCOS Simultaneous Sine and Cosine FSINCOS
(MC6888X, M68040FPSP)

Floating-Point Status Register:

Condition Codes:	Affected as described in **3.6.2 Conditional Testing** (for the sine result).
Quotient Byte:	Not affected.
Exception Byte:	

	BSUN	Cleared
	SNAN	Refer to **1.6.5 NANs**.
	OPERR	Set if the source is ±infinity; cleared otherwise.
	OVFL	Cleared
	UNFL	Set if a sine underflow occurs, in which case the cosine result is 1. Cosine cannot underflow. Refer to underflow in the appropriate user's manual.
	DZ	Cleared
	INEX2	Refer to inexact result in the appropriate user's manual.
	INEX1	If <fmt> is packed, refer to inexact result on decimal input in the appropriate user's manual; cleared otherwise.

Accrued Exception Byte: Affected as described in IEEE exception and trap compatibility in the appropriate user's manual.

Instruction Format:

15	14	13	12	11	10	9	8	7	6	5	4	3	2	1	0
1	1	1	1	COPROCESSOR ID			0	0	0	EFFECTIVE ADDRESS					
										MODE			REGISTER		
0	R/M	0	SOURCE SPECIFIER			DESTINATION REGISTER, FPs			0	1	1	0	DESTINATION REGISTER, FPc		

Instruction Fields:

Coprocessor ID field—Specifies which coprocessor in the system is to execute this instruction. Motorola assemblers default to ID = 1 for the floating-point coprocessor.

FSINCOS Simultaneous Sine and Cosine FSINCOS
(MC6888X, M68040FPSP)

Effective Address field—Determines the addressing mode for external operands.

If R/M = 0, this field is unused and should be all zeros.

If R/M = 1, this field is encoded with an M68000 family addressing mode as listed in the following table:

Addressing Mode	Mode	Register	Addressing Mode	Mode	Register
Dn*	000	reg. number:Dn	(xxx).W	111	000
An	—	—	(xxx).L	111	001
(An)	010	reg. number:An	#<data>	111	100
(An)+	011	reg. number:An			
−(An)	100	reg. number:An			
(d$_{16}$,An)	101	reg. number:An	(d$_{16}$,PC)	111	010
(d$_8$,An,Xn)	110	reg. number:An	(d$_8$,PC,Xn)	111	011
(bd,An,Xn)	110	reg. number:An	(bd,PC,Xn)	111	011
([bd,An,Xn],od)	110	reg. number:An	([bd,PC,Xn],od)	111	011
([bd,An],Xn,od)	110	reg. number:An	([bd,PC],Xn,od)	111	011

*Only if <fmt> is byte, word, long, or single.

R/M field—Specifies the source operand address mode.

    0—The operation is register to register.

    1—The operation is <ea> to register.

Source Specifier field—Specifies the source register or data format.

    If R/M = 0, specifies the source floating-point data register.

    If R/M = 1, specifies the source data format:

        000—Long-Word Integer (L)

        001—Single-Precision Real (S)

        010—Extended-Precision Real (X)

        011—Packed-Decimal Real (P)

        100—Word Integer (W)

        101—Double-Precision Real (D)

        110—Byte Integer (B)

Destination Register, FPc field—Specifies the destination floating-point data register, FPc. The cosine result is stored in this register.

FSINCOS Simultaneous Sine and Cosine FSINCOS
(MC6888X, M68040FPSP)

Destination Register, FPs field—Specifies the destination floating-point data register, FPs. The sine result is stored in this register. If FPc and FPs specify the same floating-point data register, the sine result is stored in the register, and the cosine result is discarded.

If R/M = 0 and the source register field is equal to either of the destination register fields, the input operand is taken from the specified floating-point data register, and the appropriate result is written into the same register.

5

Operation: Hyperbolic Sine of Source ♦ FPn

Assembler   FSINH.<fmt> <ea>,FPn
Syntax: FSINH.X FPm,FPn
              FSINH.X FPn

Attributes: Format = (Byte, Word, Long, Single, Double, Extended, Packed)

Description: Converts the source operand to extended precision (if necessary) and calculates the hyperbolic sine of that number. Stores the result in the destination floating-point data register.

Operation Table:

	SOURCE					
DESTINATION	+ In Range –	+	Zero –	+	Infinity –
Result	Hyperbolic Sine	+0.0	–0.0	+inf	–inf

NOTE: If the source operand is a NAN, refer to **1.6.5 NANs** for more information.

Floating-Point Status Register:

Condition Codes: Affected as described in **3.6.2 Conditional Testing**.

Quotient Byte: Not affected.

Exception Byte: BSUN   Cleared
              SNAN   Refer to **1.6.5 NANs**.
              OPERR   Cleared
              OVFL   Refer to overflow in the appropriate user's manual.
              UNFL   Refer to underflow in the appropriate user's manual.
              DZ   Cleared
              INEX2   Refer to inexact result in the appropriate user's manual.
              INEX1   If <fmt> is packed, refer to inexact result on decimal input in the appropriate user's manual; cleared otherwise.

Accrued Exception Byte: Affected as described in IEEE exception and trap compatibility in the appropriate user's manual.

Instruction Format:

15	14	13	12	11	10	9	8	7	6	5	4	3	2	1	0
1	1	1	1	COPROCESSOR ID			0	0	0	EFFECTIVE ADDRESS MODE			REGISTER		
0	R/M	0	SOURCE SPECIFIER			DESTINATION REGISTER			0	0	0	0	0	1	0

Instruction Fields:

Coprocessor ID field—Specifies which coprocessor in the system is to execute this instruction. Motorola assemblers default to ID = 1 for the floating-point coprocessor.

Effective Address field—Determines the addressing mode for external operands.

If R/M = 0, this field is unused and should be all zeros.

If R/M = 1, this field is encoded with an M68000 family addressing mode as listed in the following table:

Addressing Mode	Mode	Register	Addressing Mode	Mode	Register
Dn*	000	reg. number:Dn	(xxx).W	111	000
An	—	—	(xxx).L	111	001
(An)	010	reg. number:An	#<data>	111	100
(An) +	011	reg. number:An			
– (An)	100	reg. number:An			
(d$_{16}$,An)	101	reg. number:An	(d$_{16}$,PC)	111	010
(d$_8$,An,Xn)	110	reg. number:An	(d$_8$,PC,Xn)	111	011
(bd,An,Xn)	110	reg. number:An	(bd,PC,Xn)	111	011
([bd,An,Xn],od)	110	reg. number:An	([bd,PC,Xn],od)	111	011
([bd,An],Xn,od)	110	reg. number:An	([bd,PC],Xn,od)	111	011

*Only if <fmt> is byte, word, long, or single.

R/M field—Specifies the source operand address mode.
  0—The operation is register to register.
  1—The operation is <ea> to register.

Source Specifier field—Specifies the source register or data format.
  If R/M = 0, specifies the source floating-point data register.
  If R/M = 1, specifies the source data format:
    000—Long-Word Integer (L)
    001—Single-Precision Real (S)
    010—Extended-Precision Real (X)
    011—Packed-Decimal Real (P)
    100—Word Integer (W)
    101—Double-Precision Real (D)
    110—Byte Integer (B)

Destination Register field—Specifies the destination floating-point data register. If R/M = 0 and the source and destination fields are equal, the input operand is taken from the specified floating-point data register, and the result is written into the same register. If the single register syntax is used, Motorola assemblers set the source and destination fields to the same value.

5

Operation: Square Root of Source $\rightarrow$ FPn

Assembler Syntax:
FSQRT.<fmt> <ea>,FPn
FSQRT.X FPm,FPn
FSQRT.X FPn
*FrSQRT.<fmt> <ea>,FPn
*FrSQRT FPm,FPn
*FrSQRT FPn
where r is rounding precision, S or D

*Supported by MC68040 only

Attributes: Format = (Byte, Word, Long, Single, Double, Extended, Packed)

Description: Converts the source operand to extended precision (if necessary) and calculates the square root of that number. Stores the result in the destination floating-point data register. This function is not defined for negative operands.

FSQRT will round the result to the precision selected in the floating-point control register. FSFSQRT and FDFSQRT will round the result to single or double precision, respectively, regardless of the rounding precision selected in the floating-point control register.

Operation Table:

DESTINATION	SOURCE[1]					
	+ In Range **−**		**+** Zero **−**		**+** Infinity **−**	
Result	$\sqrt{x}$	NAN[2]	+0.0	−0.0	+inf	NAN[2]

NOTES:
1. If the source operand is a NAN, refer to **1.6.5 NANs** for more information.
2. Sets the OPERR bit in the floating-point status register exception byte.

FSQRT

Floating-Point Square Root
(MC6888X, MC68040)
FSQRT

Floating-Point Status Register:

Condition Codes: Affected as described in **3.6.2 Conditional Testing**.

Quotient Byte: Not affected.

Exception Byte:
BSUN	Cleared
SNAN	Refer to **1.6.5 NANs**.
OPERR	Set if the source operand is not zero and is negative; cleared otherwise.
OVFL	Cleared
UNFL	Cleared
DZ	Cleared
INEX2	Refer to exception processing in the appropriate user's manual.
INEX1	If <fmt> is packed, refer to exception processing in the appropriate user's manual; cleared otherwise.

Accrued Exception Byte: Affected as described in exception processing in the appropriate user's manual.

Instruction Format:

15	14	13	12	11	10	9	8	7	6	5	4	3	2	1	0
1	1	1	1	COPROCESSOR ID			0	0	0	EFFECTIVE ADDRESS					
										MODE			REGISTER		
0	R/M	0	SOURCE SPECIFIER			DESTINATION REGISTER			OPMODE						

Instruction Fields:

Effective Address field—Determines the addressing mode for external operands.

If R/M = 0, this field is unused and should be all zeros.

If R/M = 1, specifies the location of the source operand. Only data addressing modes can be used as listed in the following table:

Addressing Mode	Mode	Register	Addressing Mode	Mode	Register
Dn*	000	reg. number:Dn	(xxx).W	111	000
An	—	—	(xxx).L	111	001
(An)	010	reg. number:An	#<data>	111	100
(An) +	011	reg. number:An			
– (An)	100	reg. number:An			
(d$_{16}$,An)	101	reg. number:An	(d$_{16}$,PC)	111	010
(d$_8$,An,Xn)	110	reg. number:An	(d$_8$,PC,Xn)	111	011
(bd,An,Xn)	110	reg. number:An	(bd,PC,Xn)	111	011
([bd,An,Xn],od)	110	reg. number:An	([bd,PC,Xn],od)	111	011
([bd,An],Xn,od)	110	reg. number:An	([bd,PC],Xn,od)	111	011

*Only if <fmt> is byte, word, long, or single.

R/M field—Specifies the source operand address mode.

0—The operation is register to register.

1—The operation is <ea> to register.

Source Specifier field—Specifies the source register or data format.

If R/M = 0, specifies the source floating-point data register.

If R/M = 1, specifies the source data format:

000—Long-Word Integer (L)

001—Single-Precision Real (S)

010—Extended-Precision Real (X)

011—Packed-Decimal Real (P)*

100—Word Integer (W)

101—Double-Precision Real (D)

110—Byte Integer (B)

*This encoding will cause an unimplemented data type exception in the MC68040 to allow emulation in software.

Destination Register field—Specifies the destination floating-point data register. If R/M = 0 and the source and destination fields are equal, the input operand is taken from the specified floating-point data register, and the result is written into the same register. If the single register syntax is used, Motorola assemblers set the source and destination fields to the same value.

Opmode field—Specifies the instruction and rounding precision.

0000100	FSQRT	Rounding precision specified by the floating-point control register.
1000001	FSSQRT	Single-precision rounding specified.
1000101	FDSQRT	Double-precision rounding specified.

5

Operation: FPn – Source ◆ FPn

**Assembler
Syntax:**

FSUB.<fmt> <ea>,FPn
FSUB.X FPm,FPn
*FrSUB.<fmt> <ea>,FPn
*FrSUB.X FPm,FPn
where r is rounding precision, S or D

*Supported by MC68040 only

Attributes: Format = (Byte, Word, Long, Single, Double, Extended, Packed)

Description: Converts the source operand to extended precision (if necessary) and subtracts that number from the number in the destination floating-point data register. Stores the result in the destination floating-point data register.

Operation Table:

DESTINATION		SOURCE[1]						
		+	In Range	–	+	Zero	–	+	Infinity	–
In Range	+ –		Subtract			Subtract		–inf	+inf
Zero	+ –		Subtract		+0.0[2] +0.0		+0.0 +0.0[2]	–inf	+inf
Infinity	+ –		+inf –inf			+inf –inf		NAN[3] –inf	–inf NAN[3]

NOTES:
1. If the source operand is a NAN, refer to **1.6.5 NANs** for more information.
2. Returns +0.0 in rounding modes RN, RZ, and RP; returns –0.0 in RM.
3. Sets the OPERR bit in the floating-point status register exception byte.

Floating-Point Status Register:

Condition Codes:	Affected as described in **3.6.2 Conditional Testing**.
Quotient Byte:	Not affected.

Exception Byte:

BSUN	Cleared
SNAN	Refer to **1.6.5 NANs**.
OPERR	Set if both the source and destination are like-signed infinities; cleared otherwise.
OVFL	Refer to exception processing in the appropriate user's manual.
UNFL	Refer to exception processing in the appropriate user's manual.
DZ	Cleared
INEX2	Refer to exception processing in the appropriate user's manual.
INEX1	If <fmt> is packed, refer to exception processing in the appropriate user's manual; cleared otherwise.

Accrued Exception Byte: Affected as described in IEEE exception and trap compatibility in the appropriate user's manual.

Instruction Format:

15	14	13	12	11	10	9	8	7	6	5	4	3	2	1	0
1	1	1	1	COPROCESSOR ID			0	0	0	EFFECTIVE ADDRESS					
										MODE			REGISTER		
0	R/M	0	SOURCE SPECIFIER			DESTINATION REGISTER			OPMODE						

Instruction Fields:

Effective Address field—Determines the addressing mode for external operands.

If R/M = 0, this field is unused and should be all zeros.

If R/M = 1, specifies the location of the source operand. Only data addressing modes can be used as listed in the following table:

Addressing Mode	Mode	Register	Addressing Mode	Mode	Register
Dn*	000	reg. number:Dn	(xxx).W	111	000
An	—	—	(xxx).L	111	001
(An)	010	reg. number:An	#<data>	111	100
(An) +	011	reg. number:An			
– (An)	100	reg. number:An			
(d₁₆,An)	101	reg. number:An	(d₁₆,PC)	111	010
(d₈,An,Xn)	110	reg. number:An	(d₈,PC,Xn)	111	011
(bd,An,Xn)	110	reg. number:An	(bd,PC,Xn)	111	011
([bd,An,Xn],od)	110	reg. number:An	([bd,PC,Xn],od)	111	011
([bd,An],Xn,od)	110	reg. number:An	([bd,PC],Xn,od)	111	011

*Only if <fmt> is Byte, Word, Long or Single.

R/M field—Specifies the source operand address mode.

0—The operation is register to register.

1—The operation is <ea> to register.

Source Specifier field—Specifies the source register or data format.

If R/M = 0, specifies the source floating-point data register.

If R/M = 1, specifies the source data format:

000—Long-Word Integer (L)

001—Single-Precision Real (S)

010—Extended-Precision Real (X)

011—Packed-Decimal Real (P)*

100—Word Integer (W)

101—Double-Precision Real (D)

110—Byte Integer (B)

*This encoding will cause an unimplemented data type exception in the MC68040 to allow emulation in software.

Destination Register field—Specifies the destination floating-point data register.

Opmode field—Specifies the instruction and rounding precision.

0101000	FSUB	Rounding precision specified by the floating-point control register.
1101000	FSSUB	Single-precision rounding specified.
1101100	FDSUB	Double-precision rounding specified.

5

Operation: Tangent of Source ♦ FPn

Assembler FTAN.<fmt> <ea>,FPn
Syntax: FTAN.X FPm,FPn
 FTAN.X FPn

Attributes: Format = (Byte, Word, Long, Single, Double, Extended, Packed)

Description: Converts the source operand to extended precision (if necessary) and calculates the tangent of that number. Stores the result in the destination floating-point data register. This function is not defined for source operands of ±infinity. If the source operand is not in the range of $[-\pi/2...+\pi/2]$, the argument is reduced to within that range before the tangent is calculated. However, large arguments may lose accuracy during reduction, and very large arguments (greater than approximately 10^{20}) lose all accuracy.

Operation Table:

DESTINATION	SOURCE[1]					
	+	In Range	−	+	Zero	−	+	Infinity	−
Result		Tangent		+0.0		−0.0		NAN[2]	

NOTES:
1. If the source operand is a NAN, refer to **1.6.5 NANs** for more information.
2. Sets the OPERR bit in the floating-point status register exception byte.

Floating-Point Status Register:

Condition Codes:	Affected as described in **3.6.2 Conditional Testing**.
Quotient Byte:	Not affected.

Exception Byte:

BSUN	Cleared
SNAN	Refer to **1.6.5 NANs**.
OPERR	Set if the source is ±infinity; cleared otherwise.
OVFL	Refer to overflow in the appropriate user's manual.
UNFL	Refer to underflow in the appropriate user's manual.
DZ	Cleared
INEX2	Refer to inexact result in the appropriate user's manual.
INEX1	If <fmt> is packed, refer to inexact result on decimal input in the appropriate user's manual; cleared otherwise.

Accrued Exception Byte: Affected as described in IEEE exception and trap compatibility in the appropriate user's manual.

Instruction Format:

15	14	13	12	11	10	9	8	7	6	5	4	3	2	1	0
											EFFECTIVE ADDRESS				
1	1	1	1	COPROCESSOR ID			0	0	0	MODE			REGISTER		
0	R/M	0	SOURCE SPECIFIER			DESTINATION REGISTER			0	0	0	1	1	1	1

Instruction Fields:

Coprocessor ID field—Specifies which coprocessor in the system is to execute this instruction. Motorola assemblers default to ID = 1 for the floating-point coprocessor.

Effective Address field—Determines the addressing mode for external operands.
If R/M = 0, this field is unused and should be all zeros.
If R/M = 1, this field is encoded with an M68000 family addressing mode as listed in the following table:

Addressing Mode	Mode	Register	Addressing Mode	Mode	Register
Dn*	000	reg. number:Dn	(xxx).W	111	000
An	—	—	(xxx).L	111	001
(An)	010	reg. number:An	#<data>	111	100
(An) +	011	reg. number:An			
– (An)	100	reg. number:An			
(d16,An)	101	reg. number:An	(d16,PC)	111	010
(d8,An,Xn)	110	reg. number:An	(d8,PC,Xn)	111	011
(bd,An,Xn)	110	reg. number:An	(bd,PC,Xn)	111	011
([bd,An,Xn],od)	110	reg. number:An	([bd,PC,Xn],od)	111	011
([bd,An],Xn,od)	110	reg. number:An	([bd,PC],Xn,od)	111	011

*Only if <fmt> is byte, word, long, or single.

R/M field—Specifies the source operand address mode.
　0—The operation is register to register.
　1—The operation is <ea> to register.

Source Specifier field—Specifies the source register or data format.
　If R/M = 0, specifies the source floating-point data register.
　If R/M = 1, specifies the source data format:
　　000—Long-Word Integer (L)
　　001—Single-Precision Real (S)
　　010—Extended-Precision Real (X)
　　011—Packed-Decimal Real (P)
　　100—Word Integer (W)
　　101—Double-Precision Real (D)
　　110—Byte Integer (B)

Destination Register field—Specifies the destination floating-point data register. If R/M = 0 and the source and destination fields are equal, the input operand is taken from the specified floating-point data register, and the result is written into the same register. If the single register syntax is used, Motorola assemblers set the source and destination fields to the same value.

Operation: Hyperbolic Tangent of Source ♦ FPn

Assembler
Syntax:
FTANH.<fmt> <ea>,FPn
FTANH.X FPm,FPn
FTANH.X FPn

Attributes: Format = (Byte, Word, Long, Single, Double, Extended, Packed)

Description: Converts the source operand to extended precision (if necessary) and calculates the hyperbolic tangent of that number. Stores the result in the destination floating-point data register.

Operation Table:

DESTINATION	SOURCE					
	+ In Range −		+ Zero −		+ Infinity −	
Result	Hyperbolic Tangent		+0.0	−0.0	+1.0	−1.0

NOTE: If the source operand is a NAN, refer to **1.6.5 NANs** for more information.

Floating-Point Status Register:

Condition Codes: Affected as described in **3.6.2 Conditional Testing**.

Quotient Byte: Not affected.

Exception Byte:
BSUN   Cleared
SNAN   Refer to **1.6.5 NANs**.
OPERR   Cleared
OVFL   Cleared
UNFL   Refer to underflow in the appropriate user's manual.
DZ   Cleared
INEX2   Refer to inexact result in the appropriate user's manual.
INEX1   If <fmt> is packed, refer to inexact result on decimal input in the appropriate user's manual; cleared otherwise.

Accrued Exception Byte: Affected as described in IEEE exception and trap compatibility in the appropriate user's manual.

Instruction Format:

15	14	13	12	11	10	9	8	7	6	5	4	3	2	1	0
1	1	1	1	COPROCESSOR ID			0	0	0	EFFECTIVE ADDRESS MODE			REGISTER		
0	R/M	0	SOURCE SPECIFIER			DESTINATION REGISTER			0	0	0	1	0	0	1

Instruction Fields:

Coprocessor ID field—Specifies which coprocessor in the system is to execute this instruction. Motorola assemblers default to ID = 1 for the floating-point coprocessor.

Effective Address field—Determines the addressing mode for external operands.
If R/M = 0, this field is unused and should be all zeros.
If R/M = 1, this field is encoded with an M68000 family addressing mode as listed in the following table:

Addressing Mode	Mode	Register
Dn*	000	reg. number:Dn
An	—	—
(An)	010	reg. number:An
(An) +	011	reg. number:An
– (An)	100	reg. number:An
(d$_{16}$,An)	101	reg. number:An
(d$_8$,An,Xn)	110	reg. number:An
(bd,An,Xn)	110	reg. number:An
([bd,An,Xn],od)	110	reg. number:An
([bd,An],Xn,od)	110	reg. number:An

Addressing Mode	Mode	Register
(xxx).W	111	000
(xxx).L	111	001
#<data>	111	100
(d$_{16}$,PC)	111	010
(d$_8$,PC,Xn)	111	011
(bd,PC,Xn)	111	011
([bd,PC,Xn],od)	111	011
([bd,PC],Xn,od)	111	011

*Only if <fmt> is byte, word, long, or single.

R/M field—Specifies the source operand address mode.
0—The operation is register to register.
1—The operation is <ea> to register.

Source Specifier field—Specifies the source register or data format.
If R/M = 0, specifies the source floating-point data register.
If R/M = 1, specifies the source data format:
   000—Long-Word Integer (L)
   001—Single-Precision Real (S)
   010—Extended-Precision Real (X)
   011—Packed-Decimal Real (P)
   100—Word Integer (W)
   101—Double-Precision Real (D)
   110—Byte Integer (B)

Destination Register field—Specifies the destination floating-point data register. If R/M = 0 and the source and destination fields are equal, the input operand is taken from the specified floating-point data register, and the result is written into the same register. If the single register syntax is used, Motorola assemblers set the source and destination fields to the same value.

5

Operation: $10^{\text{Source}} \to FPn$

Assembler   FTENTOX.<fmt> <ea>,FPn
Syntax: FTENTOX.X FPm,FPn
                   FTENTOX.X FPn

Attributes: Format = (Byte, Word, Long, Single, Double, Extended, Packed)

Description: Converts the source operand to extended precision (if necessary) and calculates 10 to the power of that number. Stores the result in the destination floating-point data register.

Operation Table:

DESTINATION	SOURCE					
	+	In Range	−	+	Zero	−
Result		10^x			+1.0	

+	Infinity	−
+inf		+0.0

NOTE: If the source operand is a NAN, refer to **1.6.5 NANs** for more information.

Floating-Point Status Register:

Condition Codes: Affected as described in **3.6.2 Conditional Testing.**

Quotient Byte: Not affected.

Exception Byte: BSUN   Cleared
                     SNAN   Refer to **1.6.5 NANs**.
                     OPERR   Cleared
                     OVFL   Refer to overflow in the appropriate user's manual.
                     UNFL   Refer to underflow in the appropriate user's manual.
                     DZ   Cleared
                     INEX2   Refer to inexact result in the appropriate user's manual.
                     INEX1   If <fmt> is packed, refer to the appropriate user's manual inexact result on decimal input; cleared otherwise.

Accrued Exception Byte: Affected as described in IEEE exception and trap compatibility in the appropriate user's manual.

Instruction Format:

15	14	13	12	11	10	9	8	7	6	5	4	3	2	1	0
1	1	1	1	COPROCESSOR ID			0	0	0	EFFECTIVE ADDRESS MODE			REGISTER		
0	R/M	0	SOURCE SPECIFIER			DESTINATION REGISTER			0	0	1	0	0	1	0

Instruction Fields:

Coprocessor ID field—Specifies which coprocessor in the system is to execute this instruction. Motorola assemblers default to ID = 1 for the floating-point coprocessor.

Effective Address field—Determines the addressing mode for external operands.

If R/M = 0, this field is unused and should be all zeros.

If R/M = 1, this field is encoded with an M68000 family addressing mode as listed in the following table:

Addressing Mode	Mode	Register	Addressing Mode	Mode	Register
Dn*	000	reg. number:Dn	(xxx).W	111	000
An	—	—	(xxx).L	111	001
(An)	010	reg. number:An	#<data>	111	100
(An)+	011	reg. number:An			
–(An)	100	reg. number:An			
(d16,An)	101	reg. number:An	(d16,PC)	111	010
(d8,An,Xn)	110	reg. number:An	(d8,PC,Xn)	111	011
(bd,An,Xn)	110	reg. number:An	(bd,PC,Xn)	111	011
([bd,An,Xn],od)	110	reg. number:An	([bd,PC,Xn],od)	111	011
([bd,An],Xn,od)	110	reg. number:An	([bd,PC],Xn,od)	111	011

*Only if <fmt> is byte, word, long, or single.

R/M field—Specifies the source operand address mode.
0—The operation is register to register.
1—The operation is <ea> to register.

Source Specifier field—Specifies the source register or data format.
If R/M = 0, specifies the source floating-point data register.
If R/M = 1, specifies the source data format:
000—Long-Word Integer (L)
001—Single-Precision Real (S)
010—Extended-Precision Real (X)
011—Packed-Decimal Real (P)
100—Word Integer (W)
101—Double-Precision Real (D)
110—Byte Integer (B)

Destination Register field—Specifies the destination floating-point data register. If R/M = 0 and the source and destination fields are equal, the input operand is taken from the specified floating-point data register, and the result is written into the same register. If the single register syntax is used, Motorola assemblers set the source and destination fields to the same value.

5

FTRAPcc   Trap on Floating-Point Condition   FTRAPcc
(MC6888X, MC68040)

Operation: If Condition True
              Then TRAP

Assembler   FTRAPcc
Syntax: FTRAPcc.W #<data>
          FTRAPcc.L #<data>

Attributes: Size = (Word, Long)

Description: If the selected condition is true, the processor initiates exception processing. A vector number is generated to reference the TRAPcc exception vector. The stacked program counter points to the next instruction. If the selected condition is not true, there is no operation performed and execution continues with the next instruction in sequence. The immediate data operand is placed in the word(s) following the conditional predicate word and is available for user definition for use within the trap handler.

The conditional specifier cc selects one of the 32 conditional tests defined in **3.6.2 Conditional Testing**.

Floating-Point Status Register:

Condition Codes:	Not affected.
Quotient Byte:	Not affected.

Exception Byte: BSUN   Set if the NAN condition code is set and the condition selected is an IEEE nonaware test.

SNAN	Not Affected.
OPERR	Not Affected.
OVFL	Not Affected.
UNFL	Not Affected.
DZ	Not Affected.
INEX2	Not Affected.
INEX1	Not Affected.

Accrued Exception Byte: The IOP bit is set if the BSUN bit is set in the exception byte; no other bit is affected.

FTRAPcc   Trap on Floating-Point Condition   FTRAPcc
(MC6888X, MC68040)

Instruction Format:

15	14	13	12	11	10	9	8	7	6	5	4	3	2	1	0
1	1	1	1	COPROCESSOR ID			0	0	1	1	1	1	MODE		
0	0	0	0	0	0	0	0	0	0	CONDITIONAL PREDICATE					
16-BIT OPERAND OR MOST SIGNIFICANT WORD OF 32-BIT OPERAND (IF NEEDED)															
LEAST SIGNIFICANT WORD OR 32-BIT OPERAND (IF NEEDED)															

Instruction Fields:

Mode field—Specifies the form of the instruction.

    010—The instruction is followed by a word operand.

    011—The instruction is followed by a long-word operand.

    100—The instruction has no operand.

Conditional Predicate field—Specifies one of 32 conditional tests as described in **3.6.2 Conditional Testing.**

Operand field—Contains an optional word or long-word operand that is user defined.

NOTE

When a BSUN exception occurs, a preinstruction exception is taken by the main processor. If the exception handler returns without modifying the image of the program counter on the stack frame (to point to the instruction following the FTRAPcc), it must clear the cause of the exception (by clearing the NAN bit or disabling the BSUN trap), or the exception occurs again immediately upon return to the routine that caused the exception.

Test Floating-Point Operand
(MC6888X, MC68040)

Operation: Condition Codes for Operand ♦ FPCC

Assembler FTST.<fmt> <ea>
Syntax: FTST.X FPm

Attributes: Format = (Byte, Word, Long, Single, Double, Extended, Packed)

Description: Converts the source operand to extended precision (if necessary) and sets the condition code bits according to the data type of the result.

Operation Table: The contents of this table differ from the other operation tables. A letter in an entry of this table indicates that the designated condition code bit is always set by the FTST operation. All unspecified condition code bits are cleared during the operation.

	SOURCE							
DESTINATION	+	In Range	–	+	Zero	–	+	Infinity	–
Result	none		N	Z		NZ	I		NI

NOTE: If the source operand is a NAN, set the NAN condition code bit. If the source operand is an SNAN, set the SNAN bit in the floating-point status register exception byte.

Floating-Point Status Register:

Condition Codes: Affected as described in **3.6.2 Conditional Testing**.

Quotient Byte: Not affected.

Exception Byte: BSUN   Cleared
                SNAN   Refer to **1.6.5 NANs**.
                OPERR   Cleared
                OVFL   Cleared
                UNFL   Cleared
                DZ   Cleared
                INEX2   Cleared
                INEX1   If <fmt> is packed, refer to exception processing in the appropriate user's manual; cleared otherwise.

Accrued Exception Byte: Affected as described in exception processing in the appropriate user's manual.

5

FTST

Test Floating-Point Operand
(MC6888X, MC68040)

FTST

Instruction Format:

15	14	13	12	11	10	9	8	7	6	5	4	3	2	1	0
1	1	1	1	COPROCESSOR ID			0	0	0	EFFECTIVE ADDRESS					
										MODE			REGISTER		
0	R/M	0	SOURCE SPECIFIER			DESTINATION REGISTER			0	1	1	1	0	1	0

Instruction Fields:

Effective Address field—Determines the addressing mode for external operands.

If R/M = 0, this field is unused and should be all zeros.

If R/M = 1, specifies the location of the source operand. Only data addressing modes can be used as listed in the following table:

Addressing Mode	Mode	Register	Addressing Mode	Mode	Register
Dn*	000	reg. number:Dn	(xxx).W	111	000
An	—	—	(xxx).L	111	001
(An)	010	reg. number:An	#<data>	111	100
(An) +	011	reg. number:An			
– (An)	100	reg. number:An			
(d$_{16}$,An)	101	reg. number:An	(d$_{16}$,PC)	111	010
(d$_8$,An,Xn)	110	reg. number:An	(d$_8$,PC,Xn)	111	011
(bd,An,Xn)	110	reg. number:An	(bd,PC,Xn)	111	011
([bd,An,Xn],od)	110	reg. number:An	([bd,PC,Xn],od)	111	011
([bd,An],Xn,od)	110	reg. number:An	([bd,PC],Xn,od)	111	011

*Only if <fmt> is byte, word, long, or single.

R/M field—Specifies the source operand address mode.
  0—The operation is register to register.
  1—The operation is <ea> to register.

Source Specifier field—Specifies the source register or data format.
  If R/M = 0, specifies the source floating-point data register.
  If R/M = 1, specifies the source data format:
    000—Long-Word Integer (L)
    001—Single-Precision Real (S)
    010—Extended-Precision Real (X)
    011—Packed-Decimal Real (P)*
    100—Word Integer (W)
    101—Double-Precision Real (D)
    110—Byte Integer (B)
  *This encoding will cause an unimplemented data type
  exception in the MC68040 to allow emulation in software.

5

Destination Register field—Since the floating-point unit uses a common command
  word format for all of the arithmetic instructions (including FTST), this field is
  treated in the same manner for FTST as for the other arithmetic instructions, even
  though the destination register is not modified. This field should be set to zero to
  maintain compatibility with future devices; however, the floating-point unit does
  not signal an illegal instruction trap if it is not zero.

Operation: $2^{Source} \rightarrow FPn$

Assembler FTWOTOX.<fmt> <ea>,FPn
Syntax: FTWOTOX.X FPm,FPn
FTWOTOX.X FPn

Attributes: Format = (Byte, Word, Long, Single, Double, Extended, Packed)

Description: Converts the source operand to extended precision (if necessary) and calculates two to the power of that number. Stores the result in the destination floating-point data register.

Operation Table:

DESTINATION	SOURCE					
	+ In Range –		+ Zero –		+ Infinity –	
Result	2^x		+1.0		+inf	+0.0

NOTE: If the source operand is a NAN, refer to **1.6.5 NANs** for more information.

Floating-Point Status Register:

Condition Codes: Affected as described in **3.6.2 Conditional Testing**.

Quotient Byte: Not affected.

Exception Byte:
BSUN   Cleared
SNAN   Refer to **1.6.5 NANs**.
OPERR   Cleared
OVFL   Refer to overflow in the appropriate user's manual.
UNFL   Refer to underflow in the appropriate user's manual.
DZ   Cleared
INEX2   Refer to inexact result in the appropriate user's manual.
INEX1   If <fmt> is packed, refer to inexact result on decimal input in the appropriate user's manual; cleared otherwise.

Accrued Exception Byte: Affected as described in IEEE exception and trap compatibility in the appropriate user's manual.

FTWOTOX 2^x FTWOTOX

(MC6888X, M68040FPSP)

Instruction Format:

15	14	13	12	11	10	9	8	7	6	5	4	3	2	1	0
1	1	1	1	COPROCESSOR ID			0	0	0	EFFECTIVE ADDRESS MODE			REGISTER		
0	R/M	0	SOURCE SPECIFIER			DESTINATION REGISTER			0	0	1	0	0	0	1

Instruction Fields:

Coprocessor ID field—Specifies which coprocessor in the system is to execute this instruction. Motorola assemblers default to ID = 1 for the floating-point coprocessor.

Effective Address field—Determines the addressing mode for external operands.

If R/M = 0, this field is unused and should be all zeros.

If R/M = 1, this field is encoded with an M68000 family addressing mode as listed in the following table:

Addressing Mode	Mode	Register		Addressing Mode	Mode	Register
Dn*	000	reg. number:Dn		(xxx).W	111	000
An	—	—		(xxx).L	111	001
(An)	010	reg. number:An		#<data>	111	100
(An) +	011	reg. number:An				
– (An)	100	reg. number:An				
(d$_{16}$,An)	101	reg. number:An		(d$_{16}$,PC)	111	010
(d$_8$,An,Xn)	110	reg. number:An		(d$_8$,PC,Xn)	111	011
(bd,An,Xn)	110	reg. number:An		(bd,PC,Xn)	111	011
([bd,An,Xn],od)	110	reg. number:An		([bd,PC,Xn],od)	111	011
([bd,An],Xn,od)	110	reg. number:An		([bd,PC],Xn,od)	111	011

*Only if <fmt> is byte, word, long, or single.

R/M field—Specifies the source operand address mode.
  0—The operation is register to register.
  1—The operation is <ea> to register.

Source Specifier field—Specifies the source register or data format.
  If R/M = 0, specifies the source floating-point data register.
  If R/M = 1, specifies the source data format:
    000—Long-Word Integer (L)
    001—Single-Precision Real (S)
    010—Extended-Precision Real (X)
    011—Packed-Decimal Real (P)
    100—Word Integer (W)
    101—Double-Precision Real (D)
    110—Byte Integer (B)

Destination Register field—Specifies the destination floating-point data register. If R/M = 0 and the source and destination fields are equal, the input operand is taken from the specified floating-point data register, and the result is written into the same register. If the single register syntax is used, Motorola assemblers set the source and destination fields to the same value.

SECTION 6
SUPERVISOR (PRIVILEGED) INSTRUCTIONS

This section contains information about the supervisor privileged instructions for the M68000 family. Each instruction is described in detail, and the instruction descriptions are arranged in alphabetical order by instruction mnemonic.

Any differences within the M68000 family of instructions are identified in the instruction. If an instruction only applies to a certain processor or processors, the processor(s) that the instruction pertains to is identified under the title of the instruction. For example:

Invalidate Cache Lines
(MC68040)

All references to the MC68000, MC68020, and MC68030 include references to the corresponding embedded controllers, MC68EC000, MC68EC020, and MC68EC030. All references to the MC68040 include the MC68LC040 and MC68EC040. This applies throughout this section unless otherwise specified.

If the instruction applies to all the M68000 family but a processor or processors may use a different instruction field, instruction format, etc., the differences will be identified within the paragraph. For example:

MC68020, MC68030, and MC68040 only

(bd,An,Xn)*	110	reg. number:An	(bd,PC,Xn)*	—	—

*Can be used with CPU32 processor.

The following instructions are listed separately for each processor due to the many differences involved within the instruction:

PFLUSH	Flush ATC Entries
PMOVE	Move PMMU Register
PTEST	Test Logical Address

Appendix A Processor Instruction Summary provides a listing of all processors and the instructions that apply to them for quick reference.

AND Immediate to the Status Register
(M68000 Family)

Operation: If Supervisor State
　Then Source ∧ SR ♦ SR
Else TRAP

**Assembler
Syntax:**　ANDI #<data>,SR

Attributes:　Size = (Word)

Description: Performs an AND operation of the immediate operand with the contents of the status register and stores the result in the status register. All implemented bits of the status register are affected.

Condition Codes:

X	N	Z	V	C
*	*	*	*	*

X—Cleared if bit 4 of immediate operand is zero; unchanged otherwise.
N—Cleared if bit 3 of immediate operand is zero; unchanged otherwise.
Z—Cleared if bit 2 of immediate operand is zero; unchanged otherwise.
V—Cleared if bit 1 of immediate operand is zero; unchanged otherwise.
C—Cleared if bit 0 of immediate operand is zero; unchanged otherwise.

Instruction Format:

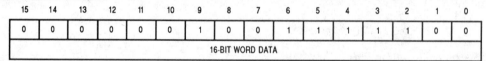

15	14	13	12	11	10	9	8	7	6	5	4	3	2	1	0
0	0	0	0	0	0	1	0	0	1	1	1	1	1	0	0
16-BIT WORD DATA															

6

Operation: If Supervisor State
                          Then Invalidate Selected Cache Lines
                    Else TRAP

Assembler
Syntax: CINVL <caches>,(An)
                   CINVP <caches>,(An)
                   CINVA <caches>

Where <caches> specifies the instruction cache,
data cache, both caches, or neither cache.

Attributes: Unsized

Description: Invalidates selected cache lines. The data cache, instruction cache, both
caches, or neither cache can be specified. Any dirty data in data cache lines that
invalidate are lost; the CPUSH instruction must be used when dirty data may be
contained in the data cache.

Specific cache lines can be selected in three ways:

1. CINVL invalidates the cache line (if any) matching the physical address in the
   specified address register.

2. CINVP invalidates the cache lines (if any) matching the physical memory page
   in the specified address register. For example, if 4K-byte page sizes are
   selected and An contains $12345000, all cache lines matching page
   $12345000 invalidate.

3. CINVA invalidates all cache entries.

Condition Codes:
  Not affected.

6

Invalidate Cache Lines
(MC68040, MC68LC040)

Instruction Format:

15	14	13	12	11	10	9	8	7	6	5	4	3	2	1	0
1	1	1	1	0	1	0	0	CACHE		0	SCOPE		REGISTER		

Instruction Fields:

Cache field—Specifies the Cache.
  00—No Operation
  01—Data Cache
  10—Instruction Cache
  11—Data and Instruction Caches

Scope field—Specifies the Scope of the Operation.
  00—Illegal (causes illegal instruction trap)
  01—Line
  10—Page
  11—All

Register field—Specifies the address register for line and page operations. For line operations, the low-order bits 3–0 of the address are don't cares. Bits 11–0 or 12–0 of the address are don't care for 4K-byte or 8K-byte page operations, respectively.

6

cpRESTORE

Coprocessor
Restore Functions
(MC68020, MC68030)

cpRESTORE

Operation: If Supervisor State
           Then Restore Internal State of Coprocessor
       Else TRAP

**Assembler
Syntax:**   cpRESTORE <ea>

Attributes: Unsized

Description: Restores the internal state of a coprocessor usually after it has been saved by a preceding cpSAVE instruction.

Condition Codes:
    Not affected.

Instruction Format:

15	14	13	12	11	10	9	8	7	6	5	4	3	2	1	0
1	1	1	1	COPROCESSOR ID			1	0	1	EFFECTIVE ADDRESS					
										MODE			REGISTER		

**Coprocessor
Restore Functions
(MC68020, MC68030)**

Instruction Fields:

Coprocessor ID field—Identifies the coprocessor that is to be restored. Coprocessor ID of 000 results in an F-line exception for the MC68030.

Effective Address field—Specifies the location where the internal state of the coprocessor is located. Only postincrement or control addressing modes can be used as listed in the following table:

Addressing Mode	Mode	Register	Addressing Mode	Mode	Register
Dn	—	—	(xxx).W	111	000
An	—	—	(xxx).L	111	001
(An)	010	reg. number:An	#<data>	111	100
(An) +	011	reg. number:An			
– (An)	—	—			
(d_{16},An)	101	reg. number:An	(d_{16},PC)	111	010
(d_8,An,Xn)	110	reg. number:An	(d_8,PC,Xn)	111	011
(bd,An,Xn)	110	reg. number:An	(bd,PC,Xn)	111	011
([bd,An,Xn],od)	110	reg. number:An	([bd,PC,Xn],od)	111	011
([bd,An],Xn,od)	110	reg. number:An	([bd,PC],Xn,od)	111	011

NOTE

If the format word returned by the coprocessor indicates "come again", pending interrupts are not serviced.

cpSAVE

Coprocessor Save Function
(MC68020, MC68030)

cpSAVE

Operation: If Supervisor State
   Then Save Internal State of Coprocessor
   Else TRAP

Assembler
Syntax: cpSAVE <ea>

Attributes: Unsized

Description: Saves the internal state of a coprocessor in a format that can be restored by a cpRESTORE instruction.

Condition Codes:
   Not affected.

Instruction Format:

15	14	13	12	11	10	9	8	7	6	5	4	3	2	1	0
1	1	1	1	COPROCESSOR ID			1	0	0	EFFECTIVE ADDRESS					
										MODE			REGISTER		

Instruction Fields:

   Coprocessor ID field—Identifies the coprocessor for this operation. Coprocessor ID of 000 results in an F-line exception for the MC68030.

   Effective Address field—Specifies the location where the internal state of the coprocessor is to be saved. Only predecrement or control alterable addressing modes can be used as listed in the following table:

Addressing Mode	Mode	Register	Addressing Mode	Mode	Register
Dn	—	—	(xxx).W	111	000
An	—	—	(xxx).L	111	001
(An)	010	reg. number:An	#<data>	—	—
(An) +	—	—			
− (An)	100	reg. number:An			
(d$_{16}$,An)	101	reg. number:An	(d$_{16}$,PC)	—	—
(d$_8$,An,Xn)	110	reg. number:An	(d$_8$,PC,Xn)	—	—
(bd,An,Xn)	110	reg. number:An	(bd,PC,Xn)	—	—
([bd,An,Xn],od)	110	reg. number:An	([bd,PC,Xn],od)	—	—
([bd,An],Xn,od)	110	reg. number:An	([bd,PC],Xn,od)	—	—

CPUSH
Push and Invalidate Cache Lines
(MC68040, MC68LC040)
CPUSH

Operation: If Supervisor State
    Then If Data Cache
        Then Push Selected Dirty Data Cache Lines
      Invalidate Selected Cache Lines
    Else TRAP

Assembler   CPUSHL <caches>,(An)
Syntax: CPUSHP <caches>,(An)
           CPUSHA <caches>

           Where <caches> specifies the instruction cache, data cache,
           both caches, or neither cache.

Attributes: Unsized

Description: Pushes and then invalidates selected cache lines. The data cache, instruction cache, both caches, or neither cache can be specified. When the data cache is specified, the selected data cache lines are first pushed to memory (if they contain dirty data) and then invalidated. Selected instruction cache lines are invalidated.

Specific cache lines can be selected in three ways:

1. CPUSHL pushes and invalidates the cache line (if any) matching the physical address in the specified address register.

2. CPUSHP pushes and invalidates the cache lines (if any) matching the physical memory page in the specified address register. For example, if 4K-byte page sizes are selected and An contains $12345000, all cache lines matching page $12345000 are selected.

3. CPUSHA pushes and invalidates all cache entries.

Condition Codes:
Not affected.

Instruction Format:

15	14	13	12	11	10	9	8	7	6	5	4	3	2	1	0
1	1	1	1	0	1	0	0	CACHE		1	SCOPE		REGISTER		

Instruction Fields:

Cache field—Specifies the Cache.
00—No Operation
01—Data Cache
10—Instruction Cache
11—Data and Instruction Caches

Scope field—Specifies the Scope of the Operation.
00—Illegal (causes illegal instruction trap)
01—Line
10—Page
11—All

Register field—Specifies the address register for line and page operations. For line operations, the low-order bits 3–0 of the address are don't care. Bits 11–0 or 12–0 of the address are don't care for 4K-byte or 8K-byte page operations, respectively.

6

EORI
to SR

Exclusive-OR Immediate to the Status Register
(M68000 Family)

EORI
to SR

Operation: If Supervisor State
Then Source $\oplus$ SR $\rightarrow$ SR
Else TRAP

Assembler
Syntax: EORI #<data>,SR

Attributes: Size = (Word)

Description: Performs an exclusive-OR operation on the contents of the status register using the immediate operand and stores the result in the status register. All implemented bits of the status register are affected.

Condition Codes:

X	N	Z	V	C
*	*	*	*	*

X—Changed if bit 4 of immediate operand is one; unchanged otherwise.
N—Changed if bit 3 of immediate operand is one; unchanged otherwise.
Z—Changed if bit 2 of immediate operand is one; unchanged otherwise.
V—Changed if bit 1 of immediate operand is one; unchanged otherwise.
C—Changed if bit 0 of immediate operand is one; unchanged otherwise.

Instruction Format:

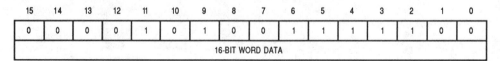

15	14	13	12	11	10	9	8	7	6	5	4	3	2	1	0
0	0	0	0	1	0	1	0	0	1	1	1	1	1	0	0
16-BIT WORD DATA															

FRESTORE

FRESTORE Restore Internal **FRESTORE**
Floating-Point State
(MC68881, MC68882, MC68040 only)

Operation: If in Supervisor State
Then FPU State Frame ♦ Internal State
Else TRAP

**Assembler
Syntax:** FRESTORE <ea>

Attributes: Unsized

Description: Aborts the execution of any floating-point operation in progress and loads a new floating-point unit internal state from the state frame located at the effective address. The first word at the specified address is the format word of the state frame. It specifies the size of the frame and the revision number of the floating-point unit that created it. A format word is invalid if it does not recognize the size of the frame or the revision number does not match the revision of the floating-point unit. If the format word is invalid, FRESTORE aborts, and a format exception is generated. If the format word is valid, the appropriate state frame is loaded, starting at the specified location and proceeding through higher addresses.

The FRESTORE instruction does not normally affect the programmer's model registers of the floating-point coprocessor, except for the NULL state size, as described below. It is only for restoring the user invisible portion of the machine. The FRESTORE instruction is used with the FMOVEM instruction to perform a full context restoration of the floating-point unit, including the floating-point data registers and system control registers. To accomplish a complete restoration, the FMOVEM instructions are first executed to load the programmer's model, followed by the FRESTORE instruction to load the internal state and continue any previously suspended operation.

6

The current implementation supports the following four state frames:

NULL: This state frame is 4 bytes long, with a format word of $0000. An FRESTORE operation with this size state frame is equivalent to a hardware reset of the floating-point unit. The programmer's model is set to the reset state, with nonsignaling NANs in the floating-point data registers and zeros in the floating-point control register, floating-point status register, and floating-point instruction address register. (Thus, it is unnecessary to load the programmer's model before this operation.)

IDLE: This state frame is 4 bytes long in the MC68040, 28 ($1C) bytes long in the MC68881, and 60 ($3C) bytes long in the MC68882. An FRESTORE operation with this state frame causes the floating-point unit to be restored to the idle state, waiting for the initiation of the next instruction, with no exceptions pending. The programmer's model is not affected by loading this type of state frame.

UNIMP: This state frame is generated only by the MC68040. It is 48 ($30) bytes long. An FSAVE that generates this size frame indicates either an unimplemented floating-point instruction or only an E1 exception is pending. This frame is never generated when an unsupported data type exception is pending or an E3 exception is pending. If both E1 and E3 exceptions are pending, a BUSY frame is generated.

BUSY: This state frame is 96 ($60) bytes long in the MC68040, 184 ($B8) bytes long in the MC68881, and 216 ($D8) bytes long in the MC68882. An FRESTORE operation with this size state frame causes the floating-point unit to be restored to the busy state, executing the instructions that were suspended by a previous FSAVE operation. The programmer's model is not affected by loading this type of state frame; however, the completion of the suspended instructions after the restore is executed may modify the programmer's model.

Floating-Point Status Register: Cleared if the state size is NULL; otherwise, not affected.

FRESTORE

**Restore Internal
Floating-Point State
(MC68881, MC68882, MC68040 only)**

FRESTORE

Instruction Format:

15	14	13	12	11	10	9	8	7	6	5	4	3	2	1	0
1	1	1	1	COPROCESSOR ID			1	0	1	EFFECTIVE ADDRESS					
										MODE			REGISTER		

Instruction Field:

Effective Address field—Determines the addressing mode for the state frame. Only postincrement or control addressing modes can be used as listed in the following table:

Addressing Mode	Mode	Register
Dn	—	—
An	—	—
(An)	010	reg. number:An
(An)+	011	reg. number:An
−(An)	—	—
(d_{16},An)	101	reg. number:An
(d_8,An,Xn)	110	reg. number:An
(bd,An,Xn)	110	reg. number:An
([bd,An,Xn],od)	110	reg. number:An
([bd,An],Xn,od)	110	reg. number:An

Addressing Mode	Mode	Register
(xxx).W	111	000
(xxx).L	111	001
#<data>	—	—
(d_{16},PC)	111	010
(d_8,PC,Xn)	111	011
(bd,PC,Xn)	111	011
([bd,PC,Xn],od)	111	011
([bd,PC],Xn,od)	111	011

6

FSAVE   Save Internal Floating-Point State   FSAVE
(MC68881, MC68882, MC68040 only)

Operation: If in Supervisor State
                    Then FPU Internal State ✦ State Frame
                    Else TRAP

**Assembler
Syntax:**   FSAVE <ea>

Attributes: Unsized

Description: FSAVE allows the completion of any floating-point operation in progress for the MC68040. It saves the internal state of the floating-point unit in a state frame located at the effective address. After the save operation, the floating-point unit is in the idle state, waiting for the execution of the next instruction. The first word written to the state frame is the format word specifying the size of the frame and the revision number of the floating-point unit.

Any floating-point operations in progress when an FSAVE instruction is encountered can be completed before the FSAVE executes, saving an IDLE state frame. Execution of instructions already in the floating-point unit pipeline continues until completion of all instructions in the pipeline or generation of an exception by one of the instructions. An IDLE state frame is created by the FSAVE if no exceptions occurred; otherwise, a BUSY or an UNIMP stack frame is created.

FSAVE suspends the execution of any operation in progress and saves the internal state in a state frame located at the effective address for the MC68881/MC68882. After the save operation, the floating-point coprocessor is in the idle state, waiting for the execution of the next instruction. The first word written to the state frame is the format word, specifying the size of the frame and the revision number of the floating-point coprocessor. The microprocessor unit initiates the FSAVE instruction by reading the floating-point coprocessor save CIR. The floating-point coprocessor save CIR is encoded with a format word that indicates the appropriate action to be taken by the main processor. The current implementation of the floating-point coprocessor always returns one of five responses in the save CIR:

Value	Definition
$0018	Save NULL state frame
$0118	Not ready, come again
$0218	Illegal, take format exception
$XX18	Save IDLE state frame
$XXB4	Save BUSY state frame

NOTE: XX is the floating-point coprocessor version number.

The not ready format word indicates that the floating-point coprocessor is not prepared to perform a state save and that the microprocessor unit should process interrupts, if necessary, and re-read the save CIR. The floating-point coprocessor uses this format word to cause the main processor to wait while an internal operation completes, if possible, to allow an IDLE frame rather than a BUSY frame to be saved. The illegal format word aborts an FSAVE instruction that is attempted while the floating-point coprocessor executes a previous FSAVE instruction. All other format words cause the microprocessor unit to save the indicated state frame at the specified address. For state frame details see state frames in the appropriate user's manual.

The following state frames apply to both the MC68040 and the MC68881/MC68882.

NULL: This state frame is 4 bytes long. An FSAVE instruction that generates this state frame indicates that the floating-point unit state has not been modified since the last hardware reset or FRESTORE instruction with a NULL state frame. This indicates that the programmer's model is in the reset state, with nonsignaling NANs in the floating-point data registers and zeros in the floating-point control register, floating-point status register, and floating-point instruction address register. (Thus, it is not necessary to save the programmer's model.)

IDLE: This state frame is 4 bytes long in the MC68040, 28 ($1C) bytes long in the MC68881, and 60 ($3C) bytes long in the MC68882. An FSAVE instruction that generates this state frame indicates that the floating-point unit finished in an idle condition and is without any pending exceptions waiting for the initiation of the next instruction.

UNIMP: This state frame is generated only by the MC68040. It is 48 ($30) bytes long. An FSAVE that generates this size frame indicates either an unimplemented floating-point instruction or that only an E1 exception is pending. This frame is never generated when an unsupported data type exception or an E3 exception is pending. If both E1 and E3 exceptions are pending, a BUSY frame is generated.

BUSY: This state frame is 96 ($60) bytes long in the MC68040, 184 ($B8) bytes long in the MC68881, and 216 ($D8) bytes long in the MC68882. An FSAVE instruction that generates this size state frame indicates that the floating-point unit encountered an exception while attempting to complete the execution of the previous floating-point instructions.

6

FSAVE

Save Internal Floating-Point State
(MC68881, MC68882, MC68040 only)

FSAVE

The FSAVE does not save the programmer's model registers of the floating-point unit; it saves only the user invisible portion of the machine. The FSAVE instruction may be used with the FMOVEM instruction to perform a full context save of the floating-point unit that includes the floating-point data registers and system control registers. To accomplish a complete context save, first execute an FSAVE instruction to suspend the current operation and save the internal state, then execute the appropriate FMOVEM instructions to store the programmer's model.

Floating-Point Status Register: Not affected.

Instruction Format:

15	14	13	12	11	10	9	8	7	6	5	4	3	2	1	0
1	1	1	1	COPROCESSOR ID			1	0	0	EFFECTIVE ADDRESS					
										MODE			REGISTER		

Instruction Field:

Effective Address field—Determines the addressing mode for the state frame. Only predecrement or control alterable addressing modes can be used as listed in the following table:

Addressing Mode	Mode	Register		Addressing Mode	Mode	Register
Dn	—	—		(xxx).W	111	000
An	—	—		(xxx).L	111	001
(An)	010	reg. number:An		#<data>	—	—
(An) +	—	—				
−(An)	100	reg. number:An				
(d16,An)	101	reg. number:An		(d16,PC)	—	—
(d8,An,Xn)	110	reg. number:An		(d8,PC,Xn)	—	—
(bd,An,Xn)	110	reg. number:An		(bd,PC,Xn)	—	—
([bd,An,Xn],od)	110	reg. number:An		([bd,PC,Xn],od)	—	—
([bd,An],Xn,od)	110	reg. number:An		([bd,PC],Xn,od)	—	—

6

MOVE
from SR

Move from the Status Register
(MC68EC000, MC68010, MC68020,
MC68030, MC68040, CPU32)

MOVE
from SR

Operation: If Supervisor State
                     Then SR ◆ Destination
                 Else TRAP

Assembler
Syntax: MOVE SR,<ea>

Attributes: Size = (Word)

Description: Moves the data in the status register to the destination location. The destination is word length. Unimplemented bits are read as zeros.

Condition Codes:
   Not affected.

Instruction Format:

15	14	13	12	11	10	9	8	7	6	5	4	3	2	1	0
0	1	0	0	0	0	0	0	1	1	EFFECTIVE ADDRESS					

| | | | | | | | | | | MODE | | | REGISTER | | |

Move from the Status Register
(MC68EC000, MC68010, MC68020,
MC68030, MC68040, CPU32)

Instruction Field:

Effective Address field—Specifies the destination location. Only data alterable addressing modes can be used as listed in the following tables:

Addressing Mode	Mode	Register
Dn	000	reg. number:Dn
An	—	—
(An)	010	reg. number:An
(An) +	011	reg. number:An
−(An)	100	reg. number:An
(d_{16},An)	101	reg. number:An
(d_8,An,Xn)	110	reg. number:An

Addressing Mode	Mode	Register
(xxx).W	111	000
(xxx).L	111	001
#<data>	—	—
(d_{16},PC)	—	—
(d_8,PC,Xn)	—	—

MC68020, MC68030, and MC68040 only

Addressing Mode	Mode	Register
(bd,An,Xn)*	110	reg. number:An
([bd,An,Xn],od)	110	reg. number:An
([bd,An],Xn,od)	110	reg. number:An

Addressing Mode	Mode	Register
(bd,PC,Xn)*	—	—
([bd,PC,Xn],od)	—	—
([bd,PC],Xn,od)	—	—

*Available for the CPU32.

NOTE

Use the MOVE from CCR instruction to access only the condition codes.

6

Move to the Status Register
(M68000 Family)

Operation: If Supervisor State
                   Then Source ♦ SR
                   Else TRAP

**Assembler
Syntax:**   MOVE <ea>,SR

Attributes: Size = (Word)

Description: Moves the data in the source operand to the status register. The source operand is a word, and all implemented bits of the status register are affected.

Condition Codes:
   Set according to the source operand.

Instruction Format:

15	14	13	12	11	10	9	8	7	6	5	4	3	2	1	0
0	1	0	0	0	1	1	0	1	1	EFFECTIVE ADDRESS					

| | | | | | | | | | | MODE | | | REGISTER | | |

MOVE to SR

MOVE to SR

Move to the Status Register
(M68000 Family)

Instruction Field:

Effective Address field—Specifies the location of the source operand. Only data addressing modes can be used as listed in the following tables:

Addressing Mode	Mode	Register		Addressing Mode	Mode	Register
Dn	000	reg. number:Dn		(xxx).W	111	000
An	—	—		(xxx).L	111	001
(An)	010	reg. number:An		#<data>	111	100
(An)+	011	reg. number:An				
-(An)	100	reg. number:An				
(d$_{16}$,An)	101	reg. number:An		(d$_{16}$,PC)	111	010
(d$_8$,An,Xn)	110	reg. number:An		(d$_8$,PC,Xn)	111	011

MC68020, MC68030, and MC68040 only

Addressing Mode	Mode	Register		Addressing Mode	Mode	Register
(bd,An,Xn)*	110	reg. number:An		(bd,PC,Xn)*	111	011
([bd,An,Xn],od)	110	reg. number:An		([bd,PC,Xn],od)	111	011
([bd,An],Xn,od)	110	reg. number:An		([bd,PC],Xn,od)	111	011

*Available for the CPU32.

6

Move User Stack Pointer
(M68000 Family)

Operation: If Supervisor State
        Then USP ♦ An or An ♦ USP
        Else TRAP

Assembler   MOVE USP,An
Syntax: MOVE An,USP

Attributes: Size = (Long)

Description: Moves the contents of the user stack pointer to or from the specified address register.

Condition Codes:
    Not affected.

Instruction Format:

15	14	13	12	11	10	9	8	7	6	5	4	3	2	1	0
0	1	0	0	1	1	1	0	0	1	1	0	dr	REGISTER		

6

Instruction Fields:

dr field—Specifies the direction of transfer.
    0—Transfer the address register to the user stack pointer.
    1—Transfer the user stack pointer to the address register.

Register field—Specifies the address register for the operation.

Operation: If Supervisor State
    Then Rc ♦ Rn or Rn ♦ Rc
Else TRAP

Assembler MOVEC Rc,Rn
Syntax: MOVEC Rn,Rc

Attributes: Size = (Long)

Description: Moves the contents of the specified control register (Rc) to the specified general register (Rn) or copies the contents of the specified general register to the specified control register. This is always a 32-bit transfer, even though the control register may be implemented with fewer bits. Unimplemented bits are read as zeros.

Condition Codes:
Not affected.

Instruction Format:

15	14	13	12	11	10	9	8	7	6	5	4	3	2	1	0
0	1	0	0	1	1	1	0	0	1	1	1	1	0	1	dr
A/D	REGISTER			CONTROL REGISTER											

Instruction Fields:

dr field—Specifies the direction of the transfer.
    0—Control register to general register.
    1—General register to control register.

A/D field—Specifies the type of general register.
    0—Data Register
    1—Address Rregister

Register field—Specifies the register number.

Control Register field—Specifies the control register.

Hex[1]	Control Register
MC68010/MC68020/MC68030/MC68040/CPU32	
000	Source Function Code (SFC)
001	Destination Function Code (DFC)
800	User Stack Pointer (USP)
801	Vector Base Register (VBR)
MC68020/MC68030/MC68040	
002	Cache Control Register (CACR)
802	Cache Address Register (CAAR)[2]
803	Master Stack Pointer (MSP)
804	Interrupt Stack Pointer (ISP)
MC68040/MC68LC040	
003	MMU Translation Control Register (TC)
004	Instruction Transparent Translation Register 0 (ITT0)
005	Instruction Transparent Translation Register 1 (ITT1)
006	Data Transparent Translation Register 0 (DTT0)
007	Data Transparent Translation Register 1 (DTT1)
805	MMU Status Register (MMUSR)
806	User Root Pointer (URP)
807	Supervisor Root Pointer (SRP)
MC68EC040 only	
004	Instruction Access Control Register 0 (IACR0)
005	Instruction Access Control Register 1 (IACR1)
006	Data Access Control Register 0 (DACR1)
007	Data Access Control Register 1 (DACR1)

NOTES:
1. Any other code causes an illegal instruction exception.
2. For the MC68020 and MC68030 only.

MOVES

Move Address Space

(MC68010, MC68020, MC68030, MC68040, CPU32)

Operation: If Supervisor State
Then Rn ♦ Destination [DFC] or Source [SFC] ♦ Rn
Else TRAP

Assembler MOVES Rn,<ea>
Syntax: MOVES <ea>,Rn

Attributes: Size = (Byte, Word, Long)

Description: This instruction moves the byte, word, or long operand from the specified general register to a location within the address space specified by the destination function code (DFC) register, or it moves the byte, word, or long operand from a location within the address space specified by the source function code (SFC) register to the specified general register.

If the destination is a data register, the source operand replaces the corresponding low-order bits of that data register, depending on the size of the operation. If the destination is an address register, the source operand is sign-extended to 32 bits and then loaded into that address register.

Condition Codes:
Not affected.

Instruction Format:

15	14	13	12	11	10	9	8	7	6	5	4	3	2	1	0
0	0	0	0	1	1	1	0	SIZE		EFFECTIVE ADDRESS MODE			REGISTER		
A/D	REGISTER			dr	0	0	0	0	0	0	0	0	0	0	0

Instruction Fields:

Size field—Specifies the size of the operation.
00—Byte Operation
01—Word Operation
10—Long Operation

Effective Address field—Specifies the source or destination location within the alternate address space. Only memory alterable addressing modes can be used as listed in the following tables:

Addressing Mode	Mode	Register	Addressing Mode	Mode	Register
Dn	—	—	(xxx).W	111	000
An	—	—	(xxx).L	111	001
(An)	010	reg. number:An	#<data>	—	—
(An) +	011	reg. number:An			
–(An)	100	reg. number:An			
(d_{16},An)	101	reg. number:An	(d_{16},PC)	—	—
(d_8,An,Xn)	110	reg. number:An	(d_8,PC,Xn)	—	—

MC68020, MC68030, and MC68040 only

(bd,An,Xn)*	110	reg. number:An	(bd,PC,Xn)*	—	—
([bd,An,Xn],od)	110	reg. number:An	([bd,PC,Xn],od)	—	—
([bd,An],Xn,od)	110	reg. number:An	([bd,PC],Xn,od)	—	—

*Available for the CPU32.

A/D field—Specifies the type of general register.
0—Data Register
1—Address Register

Register field—Specifies the register number.

dr field—Specifies the direction of the transfer.
0—From <ea> to general register.
1—From general register to <ea>.

NOTE

The value stored is undefined for either of the two following examples with the same address register as both source and destination.

    MOVES.x An,(An)+

    MOVES.x An,–(An)

The current implementations of the MC68010, MC68020, MC68030, and MC68040 store the incremented or decremented value of An. Check the following code sequence to determine what value is stored for each case.

    MOVEA.L #$1000,A0

    MOVES.L A0,(A0)+

    MOVES.L A0,–(A0)

Because the MC68040 implements a merged instruction and data space, the MC68040's integer unit into data references (SFC/DFC = 5 or 1) translates MOVES accesses to the "instruction" address spaces (SFC/DFC = 6 or 2). The data memory unit handles these translated accesses as normal data accesses. If the access fails due to an ATC fault or a physical bus error, the resulting access error stack frame contains the converted function code in the TM field for the faulted access. To maintain cache coherency, MOVES accesses to write the "instruction" address space must be preceded by invalidation of the instruction cache line containing the referenced location.

Inclusive-OR Immediate to the Status Register
(M68000 Family)

Operation: If Supervisor State
                      Then Source V SR ◆ SR
                   Else TRAP

Assembler
Syntax: ORI #<data>,SR

Attributes: Size = (Word)

Description: Performs an inclusive-OR operation of the immediate operand and the status register's contents and stores the result in the status register. All implemented bits of the status register are affected.

Condition Codes:

X	N	Z	V	C
*	*	*	*	*

X—Set if bit 4 of immediate operand is one; unchanged otherwise.
N—Set if bit 3 of immediate operand is one; unchanged otherwise.
Z—Set if bit 2 of immediate operand is one; unchanged otherwise.
V—Set if bit 1 of immediate operand is one; unchanged otherwise.
C—Set if bit 0 of immediate operand is one; unchanged otherwise.

Instruction Format:

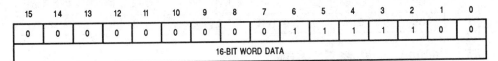

15	14	13	12	11	10	9	8	7	6	5	4	3	2	1	0
0	0	0	0	0	0	0	0	0	1	1	1	1	1	0	0
16-BIT WORD DATA																

PBcc

Branch on PMMU Condition
(MC68851)

PBcc

Operation: If Supervisor State
                         Then If cc True
                             Then (PC) + d$_n$ ♦ PC
                         Else TRAP

Assembler
Syntax: PBcc.<size><label>

Attributes: Size = (Word, Long)

Description: If the specified paged memory management unit condition is met, execution continues at location (PC) + displacement. The displacement is a twos complement integer that counts the relative distance in bytes. The value in the program counter is the address of the displacement word(s). The displacement may be either 16 or 32 bits.

The condition specifier cc indicates the following conditions:

Specifier	Description	Condition Field		Specifier	Description	Condition Field
BS	B set	000000		BC	B clear	000001
LS	L set	000010		LC	L clear	000011
SS	S set	000100		SC	S clear	000101
AS	A set	000110		AC	A clear	000111
WS	W set	001000		WC	W clear	001001
IS	I set	001010		IC	I clear	001011
GS	G set	001100		GC	G clear	001101
CS	C set	001110		CC	C clear	001111

PMMU Status Register: Not affected.

Instruction Format:

15	14	13	12	11	10	9	8	7	6	5	4	3	2	1	0
1	1	1	1	0	0	0	0	1	SIZE	MC68851 CONDITION					
16-BIT DISPLACEMENT OR MOST SIGNIFICANT WORD OF 32-BIT DISPLACEMENT															
LEAST SIGNIFICANT WORD OF 32-BIT DISPLACEMENT (IF NEEDED)															

Instruction Fields:

Size field—Specifies the size of the displacement.
0—Displacement is 16 bits.
1—Displacement is 32 bits.

MC68851 Condition field—Specifies the coprocessor condition to be tested. This field is passed to the MC68851, which provides directives to the main processor for processing this instruction.

Word Displacement field—The shortest displacement form for MC68851 branches is 16 bits.

Long-Word Displacement field—Allows a displacement larger than 16 bits.

6

Operation: If Supervisor State
    Then If cc False
      Then (Dn–1 ⬧ Dn; If Dn < > –1 then (PC) + d ≥ PC)
    Else No Operation
    Else TRAP

Assembler
Syntax: PDBcc Dn, <label>

Attributes: Size = (Word)

Description: This instruction is a looping primitive of three parameters: an MC68851 condition, a counter (an MC68020 data register), and a 16-bit displacement. The instruction first tests the condition to determine if the termination condition for the loop has been met. If so, the main processor executes the next instruction in the instruction stream. If the termination condition is not true, the low-order 16 bits of the counter register are decremented by one. If the result is not –1, execution continues at the location specified by the current value of the program counter plus the sign-extended 16-bit displacement. The value of the program counter used in the branch address calculation is the address of the PDBcc instruction plus two.

The condition specifier cc indicates the following conditions:

Specifier	Description	Condition Field	Specifier	Description	Condition Field
BS	B set	000000	BC	B clear	000001
LS	L set	000010	LC	L clear	000011
SS	S set	000100	SC	S clear	000101
AS	A set	000110	AC	A clear	000111
WS	W set	001000	WC	W clear	001001
IS	I set	001010	IC	I clear	001011
GS	G set	001100	GC	G clear	001101
CS	C set	001110	CC	C clear	001111

PMMU Status Register: Not affected.

Instruction Format:

15	14	13	12	11	10	9	8	7	6	5	4	3	2	1	0
1	1	1	1	0	0	0	0	0	1	0	0	1	COUNT REGISTER		
0	0	0	0	0	0	0	0	0	0	MC68851 CONDITION					
16-BIT DISPLACEMENT															

Instruction Fields:

Register field—Specifies the data register in the main processor to be used as the counter.

MC68851 Condition field—Specifies the MC68851 condition to be tested. This field is passed to the MC68851, which provides directives to the main processor for processing this instruction.

Displacement field—Specifies the distance of the branch in bytes.

6

Operation: If Supervisor State
    Then Invalidate ATC Entries for Destination Addresses
Else TRAP

Assembler   PFLUSHA
Syntax: PFLUSH FC,MASK
              PFLUSH FC,MASK,<ea>

Attributes: Unsized

Description: PFLUSH invalidates address translation cache entries. The instruction has three forms. The PFLUSHA instruction invalidates all entries. When the instruction specifies a function code and mask, the instruction invalidates all entries for a selected function code(s). When the instruction also specifies an <ea>, the instruction invalidates the page descriptor for that effective address entry in each selected function code.

The mask operand contains three bits that correspond to the three function code bits. Each bit in the mask that is set to one indicates that the corresponding bit of the FC operand applies to the operation. Each bit in the mask that is zero indicates a bit of FC and of the ignored function code. For example, a mask operand of 100 causes the instruction to consider only the most significant bit of the FC operand. If the FC operand is 001, function codes 000, 001, 010, and 011 are selected.

The FC operand is specified in one of the following ways:
1. Immediate—Three bits in the command word.
2. Data Register—The three least significant bits of the data register specified in the instruction.
3. Source Function Code (SFC) Register
4. Destination Function Code (DFC) Register

Condition Codes:
Not affected.

MMU Status Register:
Not affected.

Instruction Format:

15	14	13	12	11	10	9	8	7	6	5	4	3	2	1	0
1	1	1	1	0	0	0	0	0	0		EFFECTIVE ADDRESS MODE			REGISTER	
0	0	1	MODE			0	0	MASK			FC				

Instruction Fields:

Effective Address field—Specifies a control alterable address. The address translation cache entry for this address is invalidated. Valid addressing modes are in the following table:

Addressing Mode	Mode	Register	Addressing Mode	Mode	Register
Dn	—	—	(xxx).W	111	000
An	—	—	(xxx).L	111	001
(An)	010	reg. number:An	#<data>	—	—
(An) +	—	—			
−(An)	—	—			
(d_{16},An)	101	reg. number:An	(d_{16},PC)	—	—
(d_8,An,Xn)	110	reg. number:An	(d_8,PC,Xn)	—	—
(bd,An,Xn)	110	reg. number:An	(bd,PC,Xn)	—	—
([bd,An,Xn],od)	110	reg. number:An	([bd,PC,Xn],od)	—	—
([bd,An],Xn,od)	110	reg. number:An	([bd,PC],Xn,od)	—	—

6

NOTE

The address field must provide the memory management unit with the effective address to be flushed from the address translation cache, not the effective address describing where the PFLUSH operand is located. For example, to flush the address translation cache entry corresponding to a logical address that is temporarily stored on top of the system stack, the instruction PFLUSH [(SP)] must be used since PFLUSH (SP) would invalidate the address translation cache entry mapping the system stack (i.e., the effective address passed to the memory management unit is the effective address of the system stack, not the effective address formed by the operand located on the top of the stack).

Mode field—Specifies the type of flush operation.
001—Flush all entries.
100—Flush by function code only.
110—Flush by function code and effective address.

Mask field—Mask for selecting function codes. Ones in the mask correspond to applicable bits; zeros are bits to be ignored. When mode is 001, mask must be 000.

FC field—Function code of entries to be flushed. If the mode field is 001, FC field must be 00000; otherwise:

10XXX — Function code is specified as bits XXX.
01DDD — Function code is specified as bits 2–0 of data register DDD.
00000 — Function code is specified as SFC register.
00001 — Function code is specified as DFC register.

6

PFLUSH

Operation: If Supervisor State
   Then Invalidate Instruction and Data ATC Entries for Destination
   Address
   Else TRAP

Assembler   PFLUSH (An)
Syntax: PFLUSHN (An)
   PFLUSHA
   PFLUSHAN

Attributes: Unsized

Description: Invalidates address translation cache entries in both the instruction and
data address translation caches. The instruction has two forms. The PFLUSHA
instruction invalidates all entries. The PFLUSH (An) instruction invalidates the entry
in each address translation cache which matches the logical address in An and the
specified function code.

The function code for PFLUSH is specified in the destination function code register.
Destination function code values of 1 or 2 will result in flushing of user address
translation cache entries in both address translation caches; whereas, values of 5
or 6 will result in flushing of supervisor address translation cache entries. PFLUSH
is undefined for destination function code values of 0, 3, 4, and 7 and may cause
flushing of an unexpected entry.

6

The PFLUSHN and PFLUSHAN instructions have a global option specified and
invalidate only nonglobal entries. For example, if only page descriptors for
operating system code have the global bit set, these two PFLUSH variants can be
used to flush only user address translation cache entries during task swaps.

Condition Codes:
   Not affected.

PFLUSH

Flush ATC Entries
(MC68040, MC68LC040)

Instruction Format:

Postincrement Source and Destination

15	14	13	12	11	10	9	8	7	6	5	4	3	2	1	0
1	1	1	1	0	1	0	1	0	0	0	OPMODE		REGISTER		

Instruction Fields:

Opmode field—Specifies the flush operation.

Opcode	Operation	Assembler Syntax
00	Flush page entry if not global	PFLUSHN (An)
01	Flush page entry	PFLUSH (An)
10	Flush all except global entries	PFLUSHAN
11	Flush all entries	PFLUSHA

Register field—Specifies the address register containing the effective address to be flushed when flushing a page entry.

6

Operation: If Supervisor State
                 Then No Operation
                 Else TRAP

Assembler   PFLUSH (An)
Syntax: PFLUSHN (An)

Attributes: Unsized

Description: This instruction should not be executed when using an MC68EC040. The PFLUSH encoding suspends operation of the MC68EC040 for an indefinite period of time and subsequently continues with no adverse effects.

Condition Codes:
Not affected.

Instruction Format:

Postincrement Source and Destination

15	14	13	12	11	10	9	8	7	6	5	4	3	2	1	0
1	1	1	1	0	1	0	1	0	0	0	OPMODE		REGISTER		

Instruction Fields:

Opmode field—Specifies the flush operation.

Opcode	Operation	Assembler Syntax
00	Flush page entry if not global	PFLUSHN (An)
01	Flush page entry	PFLUSH (An)
10	Flush all except global entries	PFLUSHAN
11	Flush all entries	PFLUSHA

Register field—Specifies the address register containing the effective address to be flushed when flushing a page entry.

PFLUSH
PFLUSHA
PFLUSHS

Invalidate Entries in the ATC
(MC68851)

PFLUSH
PFLUSHA
PFLUSHS

Operation: If Supervisor State
               Then Address Translation Cache Entries For Destination Address
               Are Invalidated
               Else TRAP

Assembler   PFLUSHA
Syntax: PFLUSH FC,MASK
               PFLUSHS FC,MASK
               PFLUSH FC,MASK,<ea>
               PFLUSHS FC,MASK,<ea>

Attributes: Unsigned

Description: PFLUSHA invalidates all entries in the address translation cache.

PFLUSH invalidates a set of address translation cache entries whose function code
bits satisfy the relation: (address translation cache function code bits and mask) =
(FC and MASK) for all entries whose task alias matches the task alias currently
active when the instruction is executed. With an additional effective address
argument, PFLUSH invalidates a set of address translation cache entries whose
function code satisfies the relation above and whose effective address field
matches the corresponding bits of the evaluated effective address argument. In both
of these cases, address translation cache entries whose SG bit is set will not be
invalidated unless the PFLUSHS is specified.

The function code for this operation may be specified as follows:
   1. Immediate—The function code is four bits in the command word.
   2. Data Register—The function code is in the lower four bits of the MC68020
      data register specified in the instruction.
   3. Source Function Code (SFC) Register—The function code is in the CPU SFC
      register. Since the SFC of the MC68020 has only three implemented bits, only
      function codes $0–$7 can be specified in this manner.
   4. Destination Function Code (DFC) Register—The function code is in the CPU
      DFC register. Since the DFC of the MC68020 has only three implemented
      bits, only function codes $0–$7 can be specified in this manner.

6

PFLUSH
PFLUSHA
PFLUSHS

Invalidate Entries in the ATC
(MC68851)

PMMU Status Register: Not affected.

Instruction Format:

15	14	13	12	11	10	9	8	7	6	5	4	3	2	1	0
											EFFECTIVE ADDRESS				
1	1	1	1	0	0	0	0	0	0		MODE			REGISTER	
0	0	1	MODE			0	MASK				FC				

Instruction Fields:

Effective Address field—Specifies an address whose page descriptor is to be flushed from (invalidated) the address translation cache. Only control alterable addressing modes can be used as listed in the following table:

Addressing Mode	Mode	Register	Addressing Mode	Mode	Register
Dn	—	—	(xxx).W	111	000
An	—	—	(xxx).L	111	001
(An)	010	reg. number:An	#<data>	—	—
(An) +	—	—			
–(An)	—	—			
(d$_{16}$,An)	101	reg. number:An	(d$_{16}$,PC)	—	—
(d$_8$,An,Xn)	110	reg. number:An	(d$_8$,PC,Xn)	—	—
(bd,An,Xn)	110	reg. number:An	(bd,PC,Xn)	—	—
([bd,An,Xn],od)	110	reg. number:An	([bd,PC,Xn],od)	—	—
([bd,An],Xn,od)	110	reg. number:An	([bd,PC],Xn,od)	—	—

6

PFLUSH
PFLUSHA
PFLUSHS

Invalidate Entries in the ATC (MC68851)

PFLUSH
PFLUSHA
PFLUSHS

NOTE

The effective address field must provide the MC68851 with the effective address of the entry to be flushed from the address translation cache, not the effective address describing where the PFLUSH operand is located. For example, in order to flush the address translation cache entry corresponding to a logical address that is temporarily stored on the top of the system stack, the instruction PFLUSH [(SP)] must be used since PFLUSH (SP) would invalidate the address translation cache entry mapping the system stack (i.e., the effective address passed to the MC68851 is the effective address of the system stack, not the effective address formed by the operand located on the top of the stack).

Mode field—Specifies how the address translation cache is to be flushed.
    001—Flush all entries.
    100—Flush by function code only.
    101—Flush by function code including shared entries.
    110—Flush by function code and effective address.
    111—Flush by function code and effective address including shared entries.

Mask field—Indicates which bits are significant in the function code compare. A zero indicates that the bit position is not significant; a one indicates that the bit position is significant. If mode = 001 (flush all entries), mask must be 0000.

FC field—Function code of address to be flushed. If the mode field is 001 (flush all entries), function code must be 00000; otherwise:
    1DDDD — Function code is specified as four bits DDDD.
    01RRR — Function code is contained in CPU data register RRR.
    00000 — Function code is contained in CPU SFC register.
    00001 — Function code is contained in CPU DFC register.

PFLUSHR   Invalidate ATC and RPT Entries   PFLUSHR
(MC68851)

Operation: If Supervisor State
Then RPT Entry (If Any) Matching Root Pointer Specified by
<ea> Corresponding Address Translation Cache Entries Are
Invalidated
Else TRAP

Assembler
Syntax: PFLUSHR<ea>

Attributes: Unsized

Description: The quad word pointed to by <ea> is regarded as a previously used value of the CPU root pointer register. The root pointer table entry matching this CPU root pointer register (if any) is flushed, and all address translation cache entries loaded with this value of CPU root pointer register (except for those that are globally shared) are invalidated. If no entry in the root pointer table matches the operand of this instruction, no action is taken.

If the supervisor root pointer is not in use, the operating system should not issue the PFLUSHR command to destroy a task identified by the current CPU root pointer register. It should wait until the CPU root pointer register has been loaded with the root pointer identifying the next task until using the PFLUSHR instruction. At any time, execution of the PFLUSHR instruction for the current CPU root pointer register causes the current task alias to be corrupted.

Instruction Format:

15	14	13	12	11	10	9	8	7	6	5	4	3	2	1	0
1	1	1	1	0	0	0	0	0	0	EFFECTIVE ADDRESS				
										MODE			REGISTER		
1	0	1	0	0	0	0	0	0	0	0	0	0	0	0	0

Invalidate ATC and RPT Entries
(MC68851)

Instruction Field:

Effective Address field—Specifies the address of a previous value of the CPU root pointer register register. Only memory addressing modes can be used as listed in the following table:

Addressing Mode	Mode	Register
Dn	—	—
An	—	—
(An)	010	reg. number:An
(An) +	011	reg. number:An
−(An)	100	reg. number:An
(d_{16},An)	101	reg. number:An
(d_8,An,Xn)	110	reg. number:An
(bd,An,Xn)	110	reg. number:An
([bd,An,Xn],od)	110	reg. number:An
([bd,An],Xn,od)	110	reg. number:An

Addressing Mode	Mode	Register
(xxx).W	111	000
(xxx).L	111	001
#<data>	111	100
(d_{16},PC)	111	010
(d_8,PC,Xn)	111	011
(bd,PC,Xn)	111	011
([bd,PC,Xn],od)	111	011
([bd,PC],Xn,od)	111	011

NOTE

The effective address usage of this instruction is different than that of other PFLUSH variants.

6

Operation: If Supervisor State
                        Then Search Translation Table and Make Address Translation
                        Cache Entry for Effective Address
                   Else TRAP

Assembler   PLOADR FC,<ea>
Syntax: PLOADW FC,<ea>

Attributes: Unsized

Description: For the MC68851, PLOAD searches the translation table for a translation of the specified effective address. If one is found, it is flushed from the address translation cache, and an entry is made as if a bus master had run a bus cycle. Used and modified bits in the table are updated as part of the table search. The MC68851 ignores the logical bus arbitration signals during the flush and load phases at the end of this instruction. This prevents the possibility of an entry temporarily disappearing from the address translation cache and causing a false table search.

This instruction will cause a paged memory management unit illegal operation exception (vector $39) if the E-bit of the translation control register is clear.

The function code for this operation may be specified to be:

1. Immediate—The function code is specified as four bits in the command word.
2. Data Register—The function code is contained in the lower four bits in the MC68020 data register specified in the instruction.
3. Source Function Code (SFC) Register—The function code is in the CPU SFC register. Since the SFC of the MC68020 has only three implemented bits, only function codes $0–$7 can be specified in this manner.
4. Destination Function Code (DFC) Register—The function code is in the CPU DFC register. Since the DFC of the MC68020 has only three implemented bits, only function codes $0–$7 can be specified in this manner.

6

For the MC68030, PLOAD searches the address translation cache for the specified effective address. It also searches the translation table for the descriptor corresponding to the specified effective address. It creates a new entry as if the MC68030 had attempted to access that address. Sets the used and modified bits appropriately as part of the search. The instruction executes despite the value of the E-bit in the translation control register or the state of the MMUDIS signal.

The <function code> operand is specified in one of the following ways:
1. Immediate—Three bits in the command word.
2. Data Register—The three least significant bits of the data register specified in the instruction.
3. Source Function Code (SFC) Register
4. Destination Function Code (DFC) Register

The effective address field specifies the logical address whose translation is to be loaded.

PLOADR causes U bits in the translation tables to be updated as if a read access had occurred. PLOADW causes U and M bits in the translation tables to be updated as if a write access had occurred.

PMMU Status Register: Not affected.

Instruction Format:

15	14	13	12	11	10	9	8	7	6	5	4	3	2	1	0
1	1	1	1	0	0	0	0	0	0	EFFECTIVE ADDRESS MODE		REGISTER			
0	0	1	0	0	0	R/W	0	0	0	0	FC				

Instruction Fields:

Effective Address field—Specifies the logical address whose translation is to be loaded into the address translation cache. Only control alterable addressing modes are allowed as listed in the following table:

Addressing Mode	Mode	Register	Addressing Mode	Mode	Register
Dn	—	—	(xxx).W	111	000
An	—	—	(xxx).L	111	001
(An)	010	reg. number:An	#<data>	—	—
(An) +	—	—			
–(An)	—	—			
(d$_{16}$,An)	101	reg. number:An	(d$_{16}$,PC)	—	—
(d$_8$,An,Xn)	110	reg. number:An	(d$_8$,PC,Xn)	—	—
(bd,An,Xn)	110	reg. number:An	(bd,PC,Xn)	—	—
([bd,An,Xn],od)	110	reg. number:An	([bd,PC,Xn],od)	—	—
([bd,An],Xn,od)	110	reg. number:An	([bd,PC],Xn,od)	—	—

NOTE

The effective address field must provide the MC68851 with the effective address of the entry to be loaded into the address translation cache, not the effective address describing where the PLOAD operand is located. For example, to load an address translation cache entry to map a logical address that is temporarily stored on the system stack, the instruction PLOAD [(SP)] must be used since PLOAD (SP) would load an address translation cache entry mapping the system stack (i.e., the effective address passed to the MC68851 is the effective address of the system stack, not the effective address formed by the operand located on the top of the stack).

R/W field—Specifies whether the tables should be updated for a read or a write.
1—Read
0—Write

FC field (MC68851)—Function code of address to load.

    1DDDD — Function code is specified as four bits DDDD.

    01RRR — Function code is contained in CPU data register RRR.

    00000 — Function code is contained in CPU SFC register.

    00001 — Function code is contained in CPU DFC register.

FC field (MC68030)—Function code of address corresponding to entry to be loaded.

    10XXX — Function code is specified as bits XXX.

    01DDD — Function code is specified as bits 2–0 of data register DDD.

    00000 — Function code is specified as SFC register.

    00001 — Function code is specified as DFC register.

6

PMOVE
Move to/from MMU Registers
(MC68030 only)
PMOVE

Operation: If Supervisor State
        Then (Source) ♦ MRn or MRn ♦ (Destination)

Assembler   PMOVE MRn,<ea>
Syntax: PMOVE <ea>,MRn
         PMOVEFD <ea>,MRn

Attributes: Size = (Word, Long, Quad)

Description: Moves the contents of the source effective address to the specified memory management unit register or moves the contents of the memory management unit register to the destination effective address.

The instruction is a quad-word (8 byte) operation for the CPU root pointer and the supervisor root pointer. It is a long-word operation for the translation control register and the transparent translation registers (TT0 and TT1). It is a word operation for the MMU status register.

The PMOVEFD form of this instruction sets the FD-bit to disable flushing the address translation cache when a new value loads into the supervisor root pointer, CPU root pointer, TT0, TT1 or translation control register (but not the MMU status register).

Writing to the following registers has the indicated side effects:

CPU Root Pointer—When the FD-bit is zero, it flushes the address translation cache. If the operand value is invalid for a root pointer descriptor, the instruction takes an memory management unit configuration error exception after moving the operand to the CPU root pointer.

Supervisor Root Pointer—When the FD-bit is zero, it flushes the address translation cache. If the operand value is invalid as a root pointer descriptor, the instruction takes an memory management unit configuration error exception after moving the operand to the supervisor root pointer.

Translation Control Register—When the FD-bit is zero, it flushes the address translation cache. If the E-bit = 1, consistency checks are performed on the PS and TIx fields. If the checks fail, the instruction takes an memory management unit configuration exception after moving the operand to the translation control register. If the checks pass, the translation control register is loaded with the operand and the E-bit is cleared.

TT0, TT1—When the FD-bit is zero, it flushes the address translation cache. It enables or disables the transparent translation register according to the E-bit written. If the E-bit = 1, the transparent translation register is enabled. If the E-bit = 0, the register is disabled.

Condition Codes:
Not affected.

MMU Status Register:
Not affected (unless the MMU status register is specified as the destination operand).

Instruction Format:

SRP, CRP, and TC Registers

15	14	13	12	11	10	9	8	7	6	5	4	3	2	1	0
1	1	1	1	0	0	0	0	0	0			EFFECTIVE ADDRESS MODE		REGISTER	
0	1	0	P-REGISTER			R/W	FD	0	0	0	0	0	0	0	0

Instruction Fields:

Effective Address field—Specifies the memory location for the transfer. Only control alterable addressing modes can be used as in the following table:

Addressing Mode	Mode	Register	Addressing Mode	Mode	Register
Dn	—	—	(xxx).W	111	000
An	—	—	(xxx).L	111	001
(An)	010	reg. number:An	#<data>	—	—
(An) +	—	—			
–(An)	—	—			
(d_{16},An)	101	reg. number:An	(d_{16},PC)	—	—
(d_8,An,Xn)	110	reg. number:An	(d_8,PC,Xn)	—	—
(bd,An,Xn)	110	reg. number:An	(bd,PC,Xn)	—	—
([bd,An,Xn],od)	110	reg. number:An	([bd,PC,Xn],od)	—	—
([bd,An],Xn,od)	110	reg. number:An	([bd,PC],Xn,od)	—	—

6

P-Register field—Specifies the memory management unit register.
000—Translation Control Register
010—Supervisor Root Pointer
011—CPU Root Pointer

R/W field—Specifies the direction of transfer.
0—Memory to memeory management unit register.
1—Memeory management unit register to memory.

FD field—Disables flushing of the address translation cache on writes to memeory management unit registers.
0—Address translation cache is flushed.
1—Address translation cache is not flushed.

Instruction Format:

MMU Status Register

15	14	13	12	11	10	9	8	7	6	5	4	3	2	1	0
1	1	1	1	0	0	0	0	0	0			EFFECTIVE ADDRESS			
												MODE		REGISTER	
0	1	1	0	0	0	R/W	0	0	0	0	0	0	0	0	0

Instruction Fields:

Effective Address field—Specifies the memory location for the transfer. Control alterable addressing modes shown for supervisor root pointer register apply.

R/W field—Specifies the direction of transfer.
0—Memory to MMU status register.
1—MMU status register to memory.

NOTE

The syntax of assemblers for the MC68851 use the symbol PMMU status register for the MMU status register.

6

PMOVE PMOVE

Move to/from MMU Registers
(MC68030 only)

Instruction Format:

TT Registers

15	14	13	12	11	10	9	8	7	6	5	4	3	2	1	0
1	1	1	1	0	0	0	0	0	0	EFFECTIVE ADDRESS					
1	1	1	1	0	0	0	0	0	0	MODE			REGISTER		
0	0	0	P-REGISTER			R/W	FD	0	0	0	0	0	0	0	0

Instruction Fields:

Effective Address field—Specifies the memory location for the transfer. Control alterable addressing modes shown for supervisor root pointer register apply.

P-Register field—Specifies the transparent translation register.
010—Transparent Translation Register 0
011—Transparent Translation Register 1

R/W field—Specifies the direction of transfer.
0—Memory to MMU status register.
1—MMU status register to memory.

FD field—Disables flushing of the address translation cache.
0—Address translation cache is flushed.
1—Address translation cache does not flush.

PMOVE Move to/from MMU Registers PMOVE
(MC68EC030)

Operation: If Supervisor State
Then (Source) ♦ MRn or MRn ♦ (Destination)

Assembler PMOVE MRn,<ea>
Syntax: PMOVE <ea>,MRn

Attributes: Size = (Word, Long, Quad)

Description: Moves the contents of the source effective address to an access control register or moves the contents of an access control register to the destination effective address.

The instruction is a long-word operation for the access control registers (AC0 and AC1). It is a word operation for the access control unit status register (ACUSR).

Writing to the ACx registers enables or disables the access control register according to the E-bit written. If the E-bit = 1, the access control register is enabled. If the E-bit = 0, the register is disabled

Condition Codes:
Not affected.

ACUSR:
Not affected unless the ACUSR is specified as the destination operand.

Instruction Format:

ACUSR

15	14	13	12	11	10	9	8	7	6	5	4	3	2	1	0
1	1	1	1	0	0	0	0	0	0	EFFECTIVE ADDRESS MODE			REGISTER		
0	1	1	0	0	0	R/W	0	0	0	0	0	0	0	0	0

Instruction Fields:

Effective Address field—Specifies the memory location for the transfer.

R/W field—Specifies the direction of transfer.
    0—Memory to ACUSR
    1—ACUSR to memory

6

NOTE

Assembler syntax for the MC68851 uses the symbol PMMU status register for the ACUSR; and for the MC68030, the symbols TT0 and TT1 for AC0 and AC1.

Instruction Format:

ACx Registers

15	14	13	12	11	10	9	8	7	6	5	4	3	2	1	0
											EFFECTIVE ADDRESS				
1	1	1	1	0	0	0	0	0	0		MODE			REGISTER	
0	0	0	P-REGISTER			R/W	0	0	0	0	0	0	0	0	0

Instruction Fields:

Effective Address field—Specifies the memory location for the transfer.

P-Register field—Specifies the ACx register.
001—Access Control Register 0
011—Access Control Register 1

R/W field—Specifies the direction of transfer.
0—Memory to ACUSR
1—ACUSR to memory

6

PMOVE

Move PMMU Register
(MC68851)

PMOVE

Operation: If Supervisor State
  Then MC68851 Register ♦ Destination
  Or Source ♦ MC68851 Register
  Else TRAP

Assembler   PMOVE <PMMU Register>,<ea>
Syntax: PMOVE <ea>,<PMMU Register>

Attributes: Size = (Byte, Word, Long, Double Long)

Description: The contents of the MC68851 register copies to the address specified by <ea>, or the data at <ea> copies into the MC68851 register.

The instruction is a quad-word operation for CPU root pointer, supervisor root pointer, and DMA root pointer registers. It is a long-word operation for the translation control register and a word operation for the breakpoint acknowledge control, breakpoint acknowledge data, access control, PMMU status, and PMMU cache status registers. PMOVE is a byte operation for the current access level, valid access level, and stack change control registers.

The following side effects occur when data is read into certain registers:

CPU Root Pointer—Causes the internal root pointer table to be searched for the new value. If there is no matching value, an entry in the root pointer table is selected for replacement, and all address translation cache entries associated with the replaced entry are invalidated.

Supervisor Root Pointer—Causes all entries in the address translation cache that were formed with the supervisor root pointer (even globally shared entries) to be invalidated.

DMA Root Pointer—Causes all entries in the address translation cache that were formed with the DMA root pointer (even globally shared entries) to be invalidated.

Translation Control Register—If data written to the translation control register attempts to set the E-bit and the E-bit is currently clear, a consistency check is performed on the IS, TIA, TIB, TIC, TID, and PS fields.

6

PMMU Status Register: Not affected unless the PMMU status register is written to by the instruction.

Instruction Format 1:

PMOVE to/from TC, CRP, DRP, SRP, CAL, VAL, SCC, AC

15	14	13	12	11	10	9	8	7	6	5	4	3	2	1	0
1	1	1	1	0	0	0	0	0	0	EFFECTIVE ADDRESS					

| | | | | | | | | | | MODE | | | REGISTER | | |

| 0 | 1 | 0 | P-REGISTER ||| R/W | 0 | 0 | 0 | 0 | 0 | 0 | 0 | 0 | 0 |

Instruction Fields:

Effective Address field—for memory-to-register transfers, any addressing mode is allowed as listed in the following table:

Addressing Mode	Mode	Register		Addressing Mode	Mode	Register
Dn*	000	reg. number:Dn		(xxx).W	111	000
An*	001	reg. number:An		(xxx).L	111	001
(An)	010	reg. number:An		#<data>	111	100
(An) +	011	reg. number:An				
–(An)	100	reg. number:An				
(d$_{16}$,An)	101	reg. number:An		(d$_{16}$,PC)	111	010
(d$_8$,An,Xn)	110	reg. number:An		(d$_8$,PC,Xn)	111	011
(bd,An,Xn)	110	reg. number:An		(bd,PC,Xn)	111	011
([bd,An,Xn],od)	110	reg. number:An		([bd,PC,Xn],od)	111	011
([bd,An],Xn,od)	110	reg. number:An		([bd,PC],Xn,od)	111	011

*PMOVE to CRP, SRP, and DMA root pointer not allowed with these modes.

For register-to-memory transfers, only alterable addressing modes can be used as listed in the following table:

Addressing Mode	Mode	Register	Addressing Mode	Mode	Register
Dn*	000	reg. number:Dn	(xxx).W	111	000
An*	001	reg. number:An	(xxx).L	111	001
(An)	010	reg. number:An	#<data>	—	—
(An)+	011	reg. number:An			
–(An)	100	reg. number:An			
(d_{16},An)	101	reg. number:An	(d_{16},PC)	—	—
(d_8,An,Xn)	110	reg. number:An	(d_8,PC,Xn)	—	—
(bd,An,Xn)	110	reg. number:An	(bd,PC,Xn)	—	—
([bd,An,Xn],od)	110	reg. number:An	([bd,PC,Xn],od)	—	—
([bd,An],Xn,od)	110	reg. number:An	([bd,PC],Xn,od)	—	—

*PMOVE from CRP, SRP, and DMA root pointer not allowed with these modes.

Register field—Specifies the MC68851 register.
000—Translation Control Register
001—DMA Root Pointer
010—Supervisor Root Pointer
011—CPU Root Pointer
100—Current Access Level
101—Valid Access Level
110—Stack Change Control Register
111—Access Control Register

R/W field—Specifies the direction of transfer.
0—Transfer <ea> to MC68851 register.
1—Transfer MC68851 register to <ea>.

Instruction Format 2:

PMOVE to/from BADx, BACx

15	14	13	12	11	10	9	8	7	6	5	4	3	2	1	0
1	1	1	1	0	0	0	0	0	0	— EFFECTIVE ADDRESS MODE			REGISTER		
0	1	1	P-REGISTER		R/W	0	0	0	0	NUM				0	0

Instruction Fields:

Effective Address field—Same as format 1.

P-Register field—Specifies the type of MC68851 register.
100—Breakpoint Acknowledge Data
101—Breakpoint Acknowledge Control

R/W field—Specifies the direction of transfer.
0—Transfer <ea> to MC68851 register
1—Transfer MC68851 register to <ea>

Num field—Specifies the number of the BACx or BADx register to be used.

Instruction Format 3:

PMOVE to/from PSR, from PCSR

15	14	13	12	11	10	9	8	7	6	5	4	3	2	1	0
											EFFECTIVE ADDRESS				
1	1	1	1	0	0	0	0	0	0		MODE			REGISTER	
0	1	1	P-REGISTER			R/W	0	0	0	0	0	0	0	0	0

Instruction Fields:

Effective Address field—Same as format 1.

P Register field—Specifies the MC68851 register.
000 — PMMU Status Register
001 — PMMU Cache Status Register

R/W field—Specifies direction of transfer.
0—Transfer <ea> to MC68851 register.
1—Transfer MC68851 register to <ea> (must be one to access PMMU cache status register using this format).

Operation: If Supervisor State
Then MC68851 State Frame ✦ Internal State, Programmer
Registers
Else TRAP

**Assembler
Syntax:**   PRESTORE <ea>

Attributes: Unsized, Privileged

Description: The MC68851 aborts execution of any operation in progress. New programmer registers and internal states are loaded from the state frame located at the effective address. The first word at the specified address is the format word of the state frame, specifying the size of the frame and the revision number of the MC68851 that created it. The MC68020 writes the first word to the MC68851 restore coprocessor interface register, initiating the restore operation. Then it reads the response coprocessor interface register to verify that the MC68851 recognizes the format as valid. The format is invalid if the MC68851 does not recognize the frame size or the revision number does not match. If the format is invalid, the MC68020 takes a format exception, and the MC68851 returns to the idle state with its user visible registers unchanged. However, if the format is valid, then the appropriate state frame loads, starting at the specified location and proceeding up through the higher addresses.

The PRESTORE instruction restores the nonuser visible state of the MC68851 as well as the PMMU status register, CPU root pointer, supervisor root pointer, current access level, valid access level, and stack change control registers of the user programming model. In addition, if any breakpoints are enabled, all breakpoint acknowledge control and breakpoint acknowledge data registers are restored. This instruction is the inverse of the PSAVE instruction.

The current implementation of the MC68851 supports four state frame sizes:

NULL: This state frame is 4 bytes long, with a format word of $0. A PRESTORE with this size state frame places the MC68851 in the idle state with no coprocessor or module operations in progress.

IDLE: This state frame is 36 ($24) bytes long. A PRESTORE with this size state frame causes the MC68851 to place itself in an idle state with no coprocessor operations in progress and no breakpoints enabled. A module operation may or may not be in progress. This state frame restores the minimal set of MC68851 registers.

6

PRESTORE   PMMU Restore Function   PRESTORE
(MC68851)

MID-COPROCESSOR: This state frame is 44 ($2C) bytes long. A PRESTORE with this size frame restores the MC68851 to a state with a coprocessor operation in progress and no breakpoints enabled.

BREAKPOINTS ENABLED: This state frame is 76 ($4C) bytes long. A PRESTORE with this size state frame restores all breakpoint registers, along with other states. A coprocessor operation may or may not be in progress.

PMMU Status Register: Set according to restored data.

Instruction Format:

15	14	13	12	11	10	9	8	7	6	5	4	3	2	1	0
1	1	1	1	0	0	0	1	0	1	EFFECTIVE ADDRESS MODE / REGISTER				

Instruction Fields:

Effective Address field—Specifies the source location. Only control or post-increment addressing modes can be used as listed in the following table:

Addressing Mode	Mode	Register		Addressing Mode	Mode	Register
Dn	—	—		(xxx).W	111	000
An	—	—		(xxx).L	111	001
(An)	010	reg. number:An		#<data>	—	—
(An)+	011	reg. number:An				
–(An)	—	—				
(d16,An)	101	reg. number:An		(d16,PC)	111	010
(d8,An,Xn)	110	reg. number:An		(d8,PC,Xn)	111	011
(bd,An,Xn)	110	reg. number:An		(bd,PC,Xn)	111	011
([bd,An,Xn],od)	110	reg. number:An		([bd,PC,Xn],od)	111	011
([bd,An],Xn,od)	110	reg. number:An		([bd,PC],Xn,od)	111	011

PSAVE

(MC68851)

PSAVE

Operation: If Supervisor State
   Then MC68851 Internal State, Programmer Registers ♦ State Frame
   Else TRAP

**Assembler
Syntax:**   PSAVE <ea>

Attributes: Unsized, Privileged

Description: The MC68851 suspends execution of any operation that it is performing
and saves its internal state and some programmer registers in a state frame located
at the effective address. The following registers are copied: PMMU status, control
root pointer, supervisor root pointer, current access level, valid access level, and
stack change control. If any breakpoint is enabled, all breakpoint acknowledge
control and breakpoint acknowledge data registers are copied. After the save
operation, the MC68851 is in an idle state waiting for another operation to be
requested. Programmer registers are not changed.

The state frame format saved by the MC68851 depends on its state at the time of
the PSAVE operation. In the current implementation, three state frames are
possible:

IDLE: This state frame is 36 ($24) bytes long. A PSAVE of this size state frame
   indicates that the MC68851 was in an idle state with no coprocessor
   operations in progress and no breakpoints enabled. A module call
   operation may or may not have been in progress when this state frame
   was saved.

MID-COPROCESSOR: This state frame is 44 ($2C) bytes long. A PSAVE of this
   size frame indicates that the MC68851 was in a state with a coprocessor
   or module call operation in progress and no breakpoints enabled.

BREAKPOINTS ENABLED: This state frame is 76 ($4C) bytes long. A PSAVE of
   this size state frame indicates that one or more breakpoints were
   enabled. A coprocessor or module call operation may or may not have
   been in progress.

PMMU Status Register: Not affected

Instruction Format:

15	14	13	12	11	10	9	8	7	6	5	4	3	2	1	0
											EFFECTIVE ADDRESS				
1	1	1	1	0	0	0	1	0	0		MODE			REGISTER	

Instruction Fields:

Effective Address field—Specifies the destination location. Only control or predecrement addressing modes can be used as listed in the following table:

Addressing Mode	Mode	Register	Addressing Mode	Mode	Register
Dn	—	—	(xxx).W	111	000
An	—	—	(xxx).L	111	001
(An)	010	reg. number:An	#<data>	—	—
(An) +	—	—			
−(An)	100	reg. number:An			
(d$_{16}$,An)	101	reg. number:An	(d$_{16}$,PC)	—	—
(d$_8$,An,Xn)	110	reg. number:An	(d$_8$,PC,Xn)	—	—
(bd,An,Xn)	110	reg. number:An	(bd,PC,Xn)	—	—
([bd,An,Xn],od)	110	reg. number:An	([bd,PC,Xn],od)	—	—
([bd,An],Xn,od)	110	reg. number:An	([bd,PC],Xn,od)	—	—

6

PScc

Set on PMMU unit Condition
(MC68851)

Operation: If Supervisor State
            Then If cc True
               Then 1s ♦ Destination
               Else 0s ♦ Destination
            Else TRAP

Assembler
Syntax: PScc <ea>

Attributes: Size = (Byte)

Description: The specified MC68851 condition code is tested. If the condition is true, the byte specified by the effective address is set to TRUE (all ones); otherwise, that byte is set to FALSE (all zeros).

The condition code specifier cc may specify the following conditions:

Specifier	Description	Condition Field	Specifier	Description	Condition Field
BS	B set	000000	BC	B clear	000001
LS	L set	000010	LC	L clear	000011
SS	S set	000100	SC	S clear	000101
AS	A set	000110	AC	A clear	000111
WS	W set	001000	WC	W clear	001001
IS	I set	001010	IC	I clear	001011
GS	G set	001100	GC	G clear	001101
CS	C set	001110	CC	C clear	001111

PMMU Status Register: Not affected

6

Instruction Format:

15	14	13	12	11	10	9	8	7	6	5	4	3	2	1	0
1	1	1	1	0	0	0	0	0	1			EFFECTIVE ADDRESS			
										MODE			REGISTER		
0	0	0	0	0	0	0	0	0	0			MC68851 CONDITION			

Instruction Fields:

Effective Address field—Specifies the destination location. Only data alterable addressing modes can be used as listed in the following table:

Addressing Mode	Mode	Register	Addressing Mode	Mode	Register
Dn	000	reg. number:Dn	(xxx).W	111	000
An	—	—	(xxx).L	111	001
(An)	010	reg. number:An	#<data>	—	—
(An) +	011	reg. number:An			
−(An)	100	reg. number:An			
(d_{16},An)	101	reg. number:An	(d_{16},PC)	—	—
(d_8,An,Xn)	110	reg. number:An	(d_8,PC,Xn)	—	—
(bd,An,Xn)	110	reg. number:An	(bd,PC,Xn)	—	—
([bd,An,Xn],od)	110	reg. number:An	([bd,PC,Xn],od)	—	—
([bd,An],Xn,od)	110	reg. number:An	([bd,PC],Xn,od)	—	—

MC68851 Condition field—Specifies the coprocessor condition to be tested. This field is passed to the MC68851, which provides directives to the main processor for processing this instruction.

Operation: If Supervisor State
        Then Logical Address Status ♦ MMUSR
    Else TRAP

Assembler   PTESTR FC,<ea>,#<level>
Syntax: PTESTR FC,<ea>,#<level>,An
    PTESTW FC,<ea>,#<level>
    PTESTW FC,<ea>,#<level>,An

Attributes: Unsized

Description: This instruction searches the address translation cache or the translation tables to a specified level. Searching for the translation descriptor corresponding to the <ea> field, it sets the bits of the MMU status register according to the status of the descriptor. Optionally, PTEST stores the physical address of the last table entry accessed during the search in the specified address register. The PTEST instruction searches the address translation cache or the translation tables to obtain status information, but alters neither the used or modified bits of the translation tables nor the address translation cache. When the level operand is zero, only the transparent translation of either read or write accesses causes the operations of the PTESTR and PTESTW to return different results.

The <function code> operand is specified as one of the following:
1. Immediate—Three bits in the command word.
2. Data Register—The three least significant bits of the data register specified in the instruction.
3. Source Function Code (SFC) Register
4. Destination Function Code (DFC) Register

The effective address is the address to test. The <level> operand specifies the level of the search. Level 0 specifies searching the addrass translation cache only. Levels 1–7 specify searching the translation tables only. The search ends at the specified level. A level 0 test does not return the same MMU status register values as a test at a nonzero level number.

Execution of the instruction continues to the requested level or until detecting one of the following conditions:

• Invalid Descriptor

• Limit Violation

• Bus Error Assertion (Physical Bus Error)

6

The instruction accumulates status as it accesses successive table entries. When the instruction specifies an address translation cache search with an address register operand, the MC68030 takes an F-line unimplemented instruction exception.

If there is a parameter specification for a translation table search, the physical address of the last descriptor successfully fetched loads into the address register. A successfully fetched descriptor occurs only if all portions of the descriptor can be read by the MC68030 without abnormal termination of the bus cycle. If the root pointer's DT field indicates page descriptor, the returned address is $0. For a long descriptor, the address of the first long word is returned. The size of the descriptor (short or long) is not returned and must be determined from a knowledge of the translation table.

Condition Codes:
Not affected.

MMUSR:

B	L	S	W	I	M	T							N
*	*	*	0	*	*	*	0	0	0	0	0	0	*

The MMU status register contains the results of the search. The values in the fields of the MMU status register for an address translation cache search are given in the following table:

MMUSR Bit	PTEST, Level 0	PTEST, Levels 1–7
Bus Error (B)	This bit is set if the bus error bit is set in the ATC entry for the specified logical address.	This bit is set if a bus error is encountered during the table search for the PTEST instruction.
Limit (L)	This bit is cleared.	This bit is set if an index exceeds a limit during the table search.
Supervisor Violation (S)	This bit is cleared.	This bit is set if the S-bit of a long (S) format table descriptor or long format page descriptor encountered during the search is set and if the FC2-bit of the function code specified by the PTEST instruction is not equal to one. The S-bit is undefined if the I-bit is set.
Write Protected (W)	The bit is set if the WP-bit of the ATC entry is set. It is undefined if the I-bit is set.	This bit is set if a descriptor or page descriptor is encountered with the WP-bit set during the table search. The W-bit is undefined if the I-bit is set.
Invalid (I)	This bit indicates an invalid translation. The I-bit is set if the translation for the specified logical address is not resident in the ATC or if the B-bit of the corresponding ATC entry is set.	This bit indicates an invalid translation. The I-bit is set if the DT field of a table or a page descriptor encountered during the search is set to invalid or if either the B or L bits of the MMUSR are set during the table search.
Modified (M)	This bit is set if the ATC entry corresponding to the specified address has the modified bit set. It is undefined if the I-bit is set.	This bit is set if the page descriptor for the specified address has the modified bit set. It is undefined if I-bit is set.
Transparent (T)	This bit is set if a match occurred in either (or both) of the transparent translation registers (TT0 or TT1).	This bit is set to zero.
Number of Levels (N)	This 3-bit field is set to zero.	This 3-bit field contains the actual number of tables accessed during the search.

6

Test a Logical Address
(MC68030 only)

Instruction Format:

15	14	13	12	11	10	9	8	7	6	5	4	3	2	1	0
1	1	1	1	0	0	0	0	0	0		EFFECTIVE ADDRESS				
											MODE			REGISTER	
1	0	0		LEVEL		R/W	A		REGISTER			FC			

Instruction Fields:

Effective Address field—Specifies the logical address to be tested. Only control alterable addressing modes can be used as listed in the following table:

Addressing Mode	Mode	Register	Addressing Mode	Mode	Register
Dn	—	—	(xxx).W	111	000
An	—	—	(xxx).L	111	001
(An)	010	reg. number:An	#<data>	—	—
(An) +	—	—			
-(An)	—	—			
(d_{16},An)	101	reg. number:An	(d_{16},PC)	—	—
(d_8,An,Xn)	110	reg. number:An	(d_8,PC,Xn)	—	—
(bd,An,Xn)	110	reg. number:An	(bd,PC,Xn)	—	—
([bd,An,Xn],od)	110	reg. number:An	([bd,PC,Xn],od)	—	—
([bd,An],Xn,od)	110	reg. number:An	([bd,PC],Xn,od)	—	—

Level field—Specifies the highest numbered level to be searched in the table. When this field contains 0, the A field and the register field must also be 0. The instruction takes an F-line exception when the level field is 0 and the A field is not 0.

R/W field—Specifies simulating a read or write bus cycle (no difference for MC68030 MMU).
0—Write
1—Read

A field—Specifies the address register option.
0—No address register.
1—Return the address of the last descriptor searched in the address register specified in the register field.

Register field—Specifies an address register for the instruction. When the A field contains 0, this field must contain 0.

FC field—Function code of address to be tested.

10XXX — Function code is specified as bits XXX.

01DDD — Function code is specified as bits 2–0 of data register DDD

00000 — Function code is specified as source function code register.

00001 — Function code is specified as destination function code register.

6

Test a Logical Address
(MC68EC030)

Operation: If Supervisor State
    Then Logical Address Status ♦ ACUSR
    Else TRAP

Assembler   PTESTR FC,<ea>
Syntax: PTESTW FC,<ea>

Attributes: Unsized

Description: This instruction searches the access control registers for the address descriptor corresponding to the <ea> field and sets the bit of the access control unit status register (ACUSR) according to the status of the descriptor.

The <function code> operand is specified in one of the following ways:

1. Immediate—Three bits in the command word.
2. Data Register—The three least significant bits of the data register specified in the instruction.
3. Source Function Code (SFC) Register
4. Destination Function Code (DFC) Register

The effective address is the address to test.

Condition Codes:
    Not affected.

ACUSR:

x	x	x	0	x	x	x	0	0	AC	0	0	0	x	x	x

x = May be 0 or 1.

The AC-bit is set if a match occurs in either (or both) of the access control registers.

Instruction Format:

15	14	13	12	11	10	9	8	7	6	5	4	3	2	1	0
1	1	1	1	0	0	0	0	0	0		EFFECTIVE ADDRESS				
											MODE		REGISTER		
1	0	0	0	0	0	R/W	0	REGISTER			FC				

Instruction Fields:

Effective Address field—Specifies the logical address to be tested. Only control alterable addressing modes can be used as listed in the following table:

Addressing Mode	Mode	Register	Addressing Mode	Mode	Register
Dn	—	—	(xxx).W	111	000
An	—	—	(xxx).L	111	001
(An)	010	reg. number:An	#<data>	—	—
(An) +	—	—			
−(An)	—	—			
(d$_{16}$,An)	101	reg. number:An	(d$_{16}$,PC)	—	—
(d$_8$,An,Xn)	110	reg. number:An	(d$_8$,PC,Xn)	—	—
(bd,An,Xn)	110	reg. number:An	(bd,PC,Xn)	—	—
([bd,An,Xn],od)	110	reg. number:An	([bd,PC,Xn],od)	—	—
([bd,An],Xn,od)	110	reg. number:An	([bd,PC],Xn,od)	—	—

R/W field—Specifies simulating a read or write bus cycle.
0—Write
1—Read

Register field—Specifies an address register for the instruction. When the A field contains 0, this field must contain 0.

FC field—Function code of address to be tested.
10XXX — Function code is specified as bits XXX.
01DDD — Function code is specified as bits 2–0 of data register DDD.
00000 — Function code is specified as source function code register.
00001 — Function code is specified as destination function code register.

NOTE

Assembler syntax for the MC68030 is PTESTR FC,<ea>,#0
and PTESTW FC,<ea>,#0.

Operation: If Supervisor State
               Then Logical Address Status ♦ MMUSR; Entry ♦ ATC
               Else TRAP

Assembler   PTESTR (An)
Syntax: PTESTW (An)

Attributes: Unsized

Description: This instruction searches the translation tables for the page descriptor corresponding to the test address in An and sets the bits of the MMU status register according to the status of the descriptors. The upper address bits of the translated physical address are also stored in the MMU status register. The PTESTR instruction simulates a read access and sets the U-bit in each descriptor during table searches; PTESTW simulates a write access and also sets the M-bit in the descriptors, the address translation cache entry, and the MMU status register.

A matching entry in the address translation cache (data or instruction) specified by the function code will be flushed by PTEST. Completion of PTEST results in the creation of a new address translation cache entry.

The specification of the function code for the test address is in the destination function code (DFC) register. A PTEST instruction with a DFC value of 0, 3, 4, or 7 is undefined and will return an unknown value in the MMUSR.

Execution of the instruction continues until one of the following conditions occurs:

- Match with one of the two transparent translation registers.
- Transfer Error Assertion (physical transfer error)
- Invalid Descriptor
- Valid Page Descriptor

Condition Codes:
Not affected.

MMU Status Register:

PHYSICAL ADDRESS	B	G	U1	U0	S	CM	M		W	T	R
*	*	*	*	*	*	*	*	0	*	*	*

6

The MMUSR contains the results of the search. The values in the fields of the MMUSR for a search are:

Physical Address—This 20-bit field contains the upper bits of the translated physical address. Merging these bits with the lower bits of the logical address forms the actual physical address.

Bus Error (B)—Set if a transfer error is encountered during the table search for the PTEST instruction. If this bit is set, all other bits are zero.

Globally Shared (G)—Set if the G-bit is set in the page descriptor.

User Page Attributes (U1, U0)—Set if corresponding bits in the page descriptor are set.

Supervisor Protection (S)—Set if the S-bit in the page descriptor is set. This bit does not indicate that a violation has occurred.

Cache Mode (CM)—This 2-bit field is copied from the CM-bit in the page descriptor.

Modified (M)—Set if the M-bit is set in the page descriptor associated with the address.

Write Protect (W)—Set if the W-bit is set in any of the descriptors encountered during the table search. Setting of this bit does not indicate that a violation occurred.

Transparent Translation Register Hit (T)—Set if the PTEST address matches an instruction or data transparent translation register and the R-bit is set; all other bits are zero.

Resident (R)—Set if the PTEST address matches a transparent translation register or if the table search completes by obtaining a valid page descriptor.

Instruction Format:

15	14	13	12	11	10	9	8	7	6	5	4	3	2	1	0
1	1	1	1	0	1	0	1	0	1	R/W	0	1	REGISTER		

Instruction Fields:

R/W field—Specifies simulating a read or write bus transfer.
0—Write
1—Read

Register field—Specifies the address register containing the effective address for the instruction.

Operation: If Supervisor State
  Then No Operation, Possibly Run Extraneous Bus Cycles
  Else TRAP

Assembler   PTESTR (An)
Syntax: PTESTW (An)

Attributes: Unsized

Description: This instruction must not be executed on an MC68EC040. This instruction may cause extraneous bus cycles to occur and may result in unexpected exception types.

Instruction Format:

15	14	13	12	11	10	9	8	7	6	5	4	3	2	1	0
1	1	1	1	0	1	0	1	0	1	R/W	0	1	REGISTER		

Instruction Fields:

R/W field—Specifies simulating a read or write bus transfer.
  0—Write
  1—Read

Register field—Specifies the address register containing the effective address for the instruction.

6

Operation: If Supervisor State
      Then Information About Logical Address ♦ PSTATUS
     Else TRAP

Assembler   PTESTR FC,<ea>,#<level>,(An)
Syntax: PTESTW FC,<ea>,#<level>,(An)

Attributes: Unsized

Description: If the E-bit of the translation control register is set, information about the logical address specified by FC and <ea> is placed in the PMMU status register. If the E-bit of the translation control register is clear, this instruction will cause a paged memory management unit illegal operation exception (vector $39).

The function code for this operation may be specified as follows:

1. Immediate—The function code is four bits in the command word.

2. Data Register—The function code is in the lower four bits in the MC68020 data register specified in the instruction.

3. Source Function Code (SFC) Register—The function code is in the SFC register in the CPU. Since the SFC of the MC68020 has only three implemented bits, only function codes $0–$7 can be specified in this manner.

4. Destination Function Code (DFC) Register—The function code is in the DFC register in the CPU. Since the DFC of the MC68020 has only three implemented bits, only function codes $0–$7 can be specified in this manner.

The effective address field specifies the logical address to be tested.

The #<level> parameter specifies the depth to which the translation table is to be searched. A value of zero specifies a search of the address translation cache only. Values 1–7 cause the address translation cache to be ignored and specify the maximum number of descriptors to fetch.

NOTE

Finding an address translation cache entry with <level> set to zero may result in a different value in the PMMU status register than forcing a table search. Only the I, W, G, M, and C bits of the PMMU status register are always the same in both cases.

Either PTESTR or PTESTW must be specified. These two instructions differ in the setting of the A-bit of the PMMU status register. For systems where access levels are not in use, either PTESTR or PTESTW may be used. U and M bits in the translation table are not modified by this instruction.

If there is a specified address register parameter, the physical address of the last successfully fetched descriptor is loaded into the address register. A descriptor is successfully fetched if all portions of the descriptor can be read by the MC68851 without abnormal termination of the bus cycle. If the DT field of the root pointer used indicates page descriptor, the returned address is $0.

The PTEST instruction continues searching the translation tables until reaching the requested level or until a condition occurs that makes further searching impossible (i.e., a DT field set to invalid, a limit violation, or a bus error from memory). The information in the PMMU status register reflects the accumulated values.

PMMU Status Register:

Bus Error (B)—Set if a bus error was received during a descriptor fetch, or if <level> = 0 and an entry was found in the address translation cache with its BERR bit set; cleared otherwise.

Limit (L)—Set if the limit field of a long descriptor was exceeded; cleared otherwise.

Supervisor Violation (S)—Set if a long descriptor indicated supervisor-only access and the <fc> parameter did not have bit 2 set; cleared otherwise.

Access Level Violation (A)—If PTESTR was specified, set if the RAL field of a long descriptor would deny access. If PTESTW was specified, set if a WAL or RAL field of a long descriptor would deny access; cleared otherwise.

Write Protection (W)—Set if the WP-bit of a descriptor was set or if a WAL field of a long descriptor would deny access; cleared otherwise.

Invalid (I)—Set if a valid translation was not available; cleared otherwise.

Modified (M)—If the tested address is found in the address translation cache, set to the value of the M-bit in the address translation cache. If the tested address is found in the translation table, set if the M-bit of the page descriptor is set; cleared otherwise.

PTEST   Get Information About Logical Address   PTEST
(MC68851)

Gate (G)—If the tested address is found in the address translation cache, set to the value of the G-bit in the address translation cache. If the tested address is found in the translation table, set if the G-bit of the page descriptor is set; cleared otherwise.

Globally Shared (C)—Set if the address is globally shared; cleared otherwise.

Level Number (N)—Set to the number of levels searched. A value of zero indicates an early termination of the table search in the root pointer (DT = page descriptor) if the level specification was not zero. If the level specification was zero, N is always set to zero.

Instruction Format:

15	14	13	12	11	10	9	8	7	6	5	4	3	2	1	0
1	1	1	1	0	0	0	0	0	0	EFFECTIVE ADDRESS					
										MODE			REGISTER		
1	0	0	LEVEL			R/W	A-REGISTER			FC					

Instruction Fields:

Effective Address field—Specifies the logical address about which information is requested. Only control alterable addressing modes can be used as listed in the following table:

Addressing Mode	Mode	Register	Addressing Mode	Mode	Register
Dn	—	—	(xxx).W	111	000
An	—	—	(xxx).L	111	001
(An)	010	reg. number:An	#<data>	—	—
(An) +	—	—			
−(An)	—	—			
(d_{16},An)	101	reg. number:An	(d_{16},PC)	—	—
(d_8,An,Xn)	110	reg. number:An	(d_8,PC,Xn)	—	—
(bd,An,Xn)	110	reg. number:An	(bd,PC,Xn)	—	—
([bd,An,Xn],od)	110	reg. number:An	([bd,PC,Xn],od)	—	—
([bd,An],Xn,od)	110	reg. number:An	([bd,PC],Xn,od)	—	—

NOTE

The effective address field must provide the MC68851 with the effective address of the logical address to be tested, not the effective address describing where the PTEST operand is located. For example, to test a logical address that is temporarily stored on the system stack, the instruction PTEST [(SP)] must be used since PTEST (SP) would test the mapping of the system stack (i.e., the effective address passed to the MC68851 is the effective address of the system stack, not the effective address formed by the operand located on the top of the stack).

Level field—Specifies the depth to which the translation table should be searched.

R/W field—Specifies whether the A-bit should be updated for a read or a write.
  1—Read
  0—Write

A-Register field—Specifies the address register in which to load the last descriptor address.
  0xxx — Do not return the last descriptor address to an address register.
  1RRR — Return the last descriptor address to address register RRR.

NOTE

When the PTEST instruction specifies a level of zero, the A-register field must be 0000. Otherwise, an F-line exception is generated.

FC field—Function code of address to test.
  1DDDD — Function code is specified as four bits DDDD.
  01RRR — Function code is contained in CPU data register RRR.
  00000 — Function code is contained in CPU source function code register.
  00001 — Function code is contained in CPU destination function code register.

6

PTRAPcc   TRAP on PMMU Condition   PTRAPcc
(M68851)

Operation: If Supervisor State
                        Then If cc True
                            Then TRAP
                        Else TRAP

Assembler   PTRAPcc
Syntax: PTRAPcc.W #<data>
                 PTRAPcc.L #<data>

Attributes: Unsized or Size = (Word, Long)

Description: If the selected MC68851 condition is true, the processor initiates exception processing. The vector number is generated referencing the cpTRAPcc exception vector; the stacked program counter is the address of the next instruction. If the selected condition is not true, no operation is performed, and execution continues with the next instruction. The immediate data operand is placed in the next word(s) following the MC68851 condition and is available for user definition to be used within the trap handler. Following the condition word, there may be a user-defined data operand, specified as immediate data, to be used by the trap handler.

The condition specifier cc may specify the following conditions:

Specifier	Description	Condition Field	Specifier	Description	Condition Field
BS	B set	000000	BC	B clear	000001
LS	L set	000010	LC	L clear	000011
SS	S set	000100	SC	S clear	000101
AS	A set	000110	AC	A clear	000111
WS	W set	001000	WC	W clear	001001
IS	I set	001010	IC	I clear	001011
GS	G set	001100	GC	G clear	001101
CS	C set	001110	CC	C clear	001111

PMMU Status Register: Not affected

Instruction Format:

15	14	13	12	11	10	9	8	7	6	5	4	3	2	1	0
1	1	1	1	0	0	0	0	0	1	1	1	1	OPMODE		
0	0	0	0	0	0	0	0	0	0	MC68851 CONDITION					
16-BIT OPERAND OR MOST SIGNIFICANT WORD OF 32-BIT OPERAND (IF NEEDED)															
LEAST SIGNIFICANT WORD OF 32-BIT OPERAND (IF NEEDED)															

Instruction Fields:

Opmode field—Selects the instruction form.

010 — Instruction is followed by one operand word.

011 — Instruction is followed by two operand words.

100 — Instruction has no following operand words.

MC68851 Condition field—Specifies the coprocessor condition to be tested. This field is passed to the MC68851, which provides directives to the main processor for processing this instruction.

6

PVALID

Validate a Pointer
(MC68851)

PVALID

Operation: If (Source AL Bits) ♦ (Destination AL Bits)
Then TRAP

Assembler PVALID VAL,<ea>
Syntax: PVALID An,<ea>

Attributes: Size = (Long)

Description: The upper bits of the source, VAL or An, compare with the upper bits of the destination, <ea>. The ALC field of the access control register defines the number of bits compared. If the upper bits of the source are numerically greater than (less privileged than) the destination, they cause a memory management access level exception. Otherwise, execution continues with the next instruction. If the MC field of the access control register = 0, then this instruction always causes a paged memory management unit access level exception.

PMMU Status Register: Not affected.

Instruction Format 1:

VAL Contains Access Level to Test Against

15	14	13	12	11	10	9	8	7	6	5	4	3	2	1	0
1	1	1	1	0	0	0	0	0	0	|EFFECTIVE ADDRESS| MODE			REGISTER		
0	0	1	0	1	0	0	0	0	0	0	0	0	0	0	0

Instruction Field:

Effective Address field—Specifies the logical address to be evaluated and compared against the valid access level register. Only control alterable addressing modes can be used as listed in the following table:

Addressing Mode	Mode	Register	Addressing Mode	Mode	Register
Dn	—	—	(xxx).W	111	000
An	—	—	(xxx).L	111	001
(An)	010	reg. number:An	#<data>	—	—
(An) +	—	—			
− (An)	—	—			
(d_{16},An)	101	reg. number:An	(d_{16},PC)	—	—
(d_8,An,Xn)	110	reg. number:An	(d_8,PC,Xn)	—	—
(bd,An,Xn)	110	reg. number:An	(bd,PC,Xn)	—	—
([bd,An,Xn],od)	110	reg. number:An	([bd,PC,Xn],od)	—	—
([bd,An],Xn,od)	110	reg. number:An	([bd,PC],Xn,od)	—	—

6

Instruction Format 2:

Main Processor Register Contains Access Level to Test Against

15	14	13	12	11	10	9	8	7	6	5	4	3	2	1	0
											EFFECTIVE ADDRESS				
1	1	1	1	0	0	0	0	0	0		MODE			REGISTER	
0	0	1	0	1	0	0	0	0	0	0	0	0		REGISTER	

Instruction Fields:

Effective Address field—Specifies the logical address to be evaluated and compared against specified main processor address register. Only control alterable addressing modes can be used as listed in the following table:

Addressing Mode	Mode	Register	Addressing Mode	Mode	Register
Dn	—	—	(xxx).W	111	000
An	—	—	(xxx).L	111	001
(An)	010	reg. number:An	#<data>	—	—
(An) +	—	—			
– (An)	—	—			
(d_{16},An)	101	reg. number:An	(d_{16},PC)	—	—
(d_8,An,Xn)	110	reg. number:An	(d_8,PC,Xn)	—	—
(bd,An,Xn)	110	reg. number:An	(bd,PC,Xn)	—	—
([bd,An,Xn],od)	110	reg. number:An	([bd,PC,Xn],od)	—	—
([bd,An],Xn,od)	110	reg. number:An	([bd,PC],Xn,od)	—	—

NOTE

The effective address field must provide the MC68851 with the effective address of the logical address to be validated, not the effective address describing where the PVALID operand is located. For example, to validate a logical address that is temporarily stored on the system stack, the instruction PVALID VAL,[(SP)] must be used since PVALID VAL,(SP) would validate the mapping on the system stack (i.e., the effective address passed to the MC68851 is the effective address of the system stack, not the effective address formed by the operand located on the top of the stack).

Register field—Specifies the main processor address register to be used in the compare.

RESET

RESET

Operation: If Supervisor State
                      Then Assert $\overline{\text{RESET}}$ ($\overline{\text{RSTO}}$, MC68040 Only) Line
                      Else TRAP

**Assembler
Syntax:**   RESET

Attributes: Unsized

Description: Asserts the $\overline{\text{RSTO}}$ signal for 512 (124 for MC68000, MC68EC000, MC68HC000, MC68HC001, MC68008, MC68010, and MC68302) clock periods, resetting all external devices. The processor state, other than the program counter, is unaffected, and execution continues with the next instruction.

Condition Codes:
Not affected.

Instruction Format:

15	14	13	12	11	10	9	8	7	6	5	4	3	2	1	0
0	1	0	0	1	1	1	0	0	1	1	1	0	0	0	0

6

Operation: If Supervisor State
Then (SP) ♦ SR; SP + 2 ♦ SP; (SP) ♦ PC; SP + 4 ♦ SP;
Restore State and Deallocate Stack According to (SP)
Else TRAP

Assembler Syntax: RTE

Attributes: Unsized

Description: Loads the processor state information stored in the exception stack frame located at the top of the stack into the processor. The instruction examines the stack format field in the format/offset word to determine how much information must be restored.

Condition Codes:
Set according to the condition code bits in the status register value restored from the stack.

Instruction Format:

15	14	13	12	11	10	9	8	7	6	5	4	3	2	1	0
0	1	0	0	1	1	1	0	0	1	1	1	0	0	1	1

Format/Offset Word (in Stack Frame):

MC68010, MC68020, MC68030, MC68040, CPU32

15	14	13	12	11	10	9	8	7	6	5	4	3	2	1	0
FORMAT				0	0	VECTOR OFFSET									

Format Field of Format/Offset Word:

Contains the format code, which implies the stack frame size (including the format/offset word). For further information, refer to **Appendix B Exception Processing Reference**.

Load Status Register and Stop
(M68000 Family)

STOP

Operation: If Supervisor State
Then Immediate Data ♦ SR; STOP
Else TRAP

**Assembler
Syntax:** STOP #<data>

Attributes: Unsized

Description: Moves the immediate operand into the status register (both user and supervisor portions), advances the program counter to point to the next instruction, and stops the fetching and executing of instructions. A trace, interrupt, or reset exception causes the processor to resume instruction execution. A trace exception occurs if instruction tracing is enabled (T0 = 1, T1 = 0) when the STOP instruction begins execution. If an interrupt request is asserted with a priority higher than the priority level set by the new status register value, an interrupt exception occurs; otherwise, the interrupt request is ignored. External reset always initiates reset exception processing.

Condition Codes:
Set according to the immediate operand.

Instruction Format:

15	14	13	12	11	10	9	8	7	6	5	4	3	2	1	0
0	1	0	0	1	1	1	0	0	1	1	1	0	0	1	0
IMMEDIATE DATA															

Instruction Fields:

Immediate field—Specifies the data to be loaded into the status register.

6

SECTION 7
CPU32 INSTRUCTIONS

This section describes the instructions provided for the CPU32. The CPU32 can execute object code from an MC68000 and MC68010 and many of the instructions of the MC68020.

There are three new instructions provided for the CPU32: enter background mode (BGND), low-power stop (LPSTOP), and table lookup and interpolate (TBLS, TBLSN, TBLU, and TBLUN). Table 7-1 lists the MC68020 instructions not supported by the CPU32.

Table 7-1. MC68020 Instructions Not Supported

Mnemonic	Description
BFCHG	Test Bit Field and Change
BFCLR	Test Bit Field and Clear
BFEXTS	Signed Bit Field Extract
BFEXTU	Unsigned Bit Field Extract
BFFFO	Bit Field Find First One
BFINS	Bit Field Insert
BFSET	Test Bit Field and Set
BFTST	Test Bit Field
CALLM	CALL Module
CAS	Compare and Swap Operands
CAS2	Compare and Swap Dual Operands
cpBcc	Branch on Coprocessor Condition
cpDBcc	Test Coprocessor Condition Decrement and Branch
cpGEN	Coprocessor General Function
cpRESTORE	Coprocessor Restore Function
cpSAVE	Coprocessor Save Function
cpScc	Set on Coprocessor Condition
cpTRAPcc	Trap on Coprocessor Condition
RTM	Return from Module
PACK	Pack BCD
UNPK	Unpack BCD

Addressing in the CPU32 is register oriented. Most instructions allow the results of the specified operation to be placed either in a register or directly in memory. This flexibility eliminates the need for extra instructions to store register contents in memory. Table 7-2 lists the M68000 family addressing modes with cross-references to the MC68000, MC68010, CPU32, and MC68020. When referring to instructions in the previous sections, refer to Table 7-2 to identify the addressing modes available to the CPU32. Table 7-3 lists the instructions for the CPU32.

Table 7-2. M68000 Family Addressing Modes

Addressing Mode	Syntax	MC68000 MC68010	CPU32	MC68020
Register Indirect	Rn	X	X	X
Address Register Indirect	(An)	X	X	X
Address Register Indirect with Postincrement	(An)+	X	X	X
Address Register Indirect with Postdecrement	–(An)	X	X	X
Address Register Indirect with Displacement	(d_{16},An)	X	X	X
Address Register Indirect with Index (8-Bit Displacement)	(d_8,An,Xn)	X	X	X
Address Register Indirect with Index (Base Displacement)	$(d_8,An,Xn*SCALE)$		X	X
Memory Indirect with Postincrement	([bd,An],Xn,od)			X
Memory Indirect with Preincrement	([bd,An],Xn,od)			X
Absolute Short	(xxx).W	X	X	X
Absolute Long	(xxx).L	X	X	X
Program Counter Indirect with Displacement	(d_{16},PC)	X	X	X
Program Counter Indirect with Index (8-Bit Displacement)	(d_8,PC,Xn)	X	X	X
Program Counter Indirect with Index (Base Displacement)	$(d_8,PC,Xn*SCALE)$		X	X
Immediate	#<data>	X	X	X
PC Memory Indirect with Postincrement	([bd,PC],Xn,od)			X
PC Memory Indirect with Predecrement	([bd,PC],Xn,od)			X

NOTE: Xn,SIZE*SCALE—Denotes index register n (data or address), the index size (W for word, L for long word) and scale factor (1, 2, 4, or 8 for no-word, long-word, or 8 for quad-word scaling, respectively).
X—Supported

Table 7-3. CPU32 Instruction Set

Mnemonic	Description	Mnemonic	Description
ABCD	Add Decimal with Extend	MOVE	Move
ADD	Add	MOVEA	Move Address
ADDA	Add Address	MOVE from CCR	Move Condition Code Register
ADDI	Add Immediate	Move from SR	Move from Status Register
ADDQ	Add Quick	MOVE to SR	Move to Status Register
ADDX	Add with Extend	MOVE USP	Move User Stack Pointer
AND	Logical AND	MOVEC	Move Control Register
ANDI	Logical AND Immediate	MOVEM	Move Multiple Registers
ANDI to CCR	AND Immediate to Condition Code Register	MOVEP	Move Peripheral
		MOVEQ	Move Quick
ANDI to SR	AND Immediate to Status Register	MOVES	Move Alternate Address Space
ASL, ASR	Arithmetic Shift Left and Right	MULS	Signed Multiply
Bcc	Branch Conditionally	MULU	Unsigned Multiply
BCHG	Test Bit and Change	NBCD	Negate Decimal with Extend
BCLR	Test Bit and Clear	NEG	Negate
BGND	Enter Background Mode	NEGX	Negate with Extend
BKPT	Breakpoint	NOP	No Operation
BRA	Branch	NOT	Logical Complement
BSET	Test Bit and Set	PEA	Push Effective Address
BSR	Branch to Subroutine	RESET	Reset External Devices
BTST	Test Bit	ROL, ROR	Rotate Left and Right
CHK	Check Register Against Bound	ROXL, ROXR	Rotate with Extend Left and Right
CHK2	Check Register Against Upper and Lower Bound	RTD	Return and Deallocate
		RTE	Return from Exception
CLR	Clear	RTR	Return and Restore Codes
CMP	Compare	RTS	Return from Subroutine
CMPA	Compare Address	SBCD	Subtract Decimal with Extend
CMPI	Compare Immediate	Scc	Set Conditionally
CMPM	Compare Memory to Memory	STOP	Stop
CMP2	Compare Register Against Upper and Lower Bounds	SUB	Subtract
		SUBA	Subtract Address
DBcc	Test Condition, Decrement, and Branch	SUBI	Subtract Immediate
		SUBQ	Subtract Quick
DIVS, DIVSL	Signed Divide	SUBX	Subtract with Extend
DIVU, DIVUL	Unsigned Divide	SWAP	Swap Register Words
EOR	Logical Exclusive-OR	TAS	Test Operand and Set
EORI	Logical Exclusive-OR Immediate	TBLS, TBLSN	Signed/Unsigned Table Lookup and Interpolate
EORI to CCR	Exclusive-OR Immediate to Condition Code Register	TBLU, TBLUN	Signed/Unsigned Table Lookup and Interpolate
EORI to SR	Exclusive-OR Immediate to Status Register	TRAP	Trap
		TRAPcc	Trap Conditionally
EXG	Exchange Registers	TRAPV	Trap an Overflow
EXT, LSR	Sign-Extend	TST	Test Operand
ILLEGAL	Take Illegal Instruction Trap	UNLK	Unlink
JMP	Jump		
JSR	Jump to Subroutine		
LEA	Load Effective Address		
LINK	Link and Allocate		
LPSTOP	Low Power Stop		
LSL, LSR	Logical Shift Left and Right		

Operation: If Background Mode Enabled
Then Enter Background Mode
Else Format/Vector Offset ♦ –(SSP);
PC ♦ –(SSP)
SR ♦ –(SSP)
(Vector) ♦ PC

Assembler
Syntax: BGND

Attributes: Size = (Unsized)

Description: The processor suspends instruction execution and enters background mode if background mode is enabled. The freeze output is asserted to acknowledge entrance into background mode. Upon exiting background mode, instruction execution continues with the instruction pointed to by the current program counter.

If background mode is not enabled, the processor initiates illegal instruction exception processing. The vector number is generated to reference the illegal instruction exception vector. Refer to the appropriate user's manual for detailed information on background mode.

Condition Codes:

X	N	Z	V	C
—	—	—	—	—

X—Not affected.
N—Not affected.
Z—Not affected.
V—Not affected.
C—Not affected.

Instruction Format:

15	14	13	12	11	10	9	8	7	6	5	4	3	2	1	0
0	1	0	0	1	0	1	0	1	1	1	1	1	0	1	0

LPSTOP

Low-Power Stop
(CPU32)

LPSTOP

Operation: If Supervisor State
                     Immediate Data ◆ SR
                     Interrupt Mask ◆ External Bus Interface (EBI)
                     STOP
            Else TRAP

Assembler
Syntax: LPSTOP #<data>

Attributes: Size = (Word) Privileged

Description: The immediate operand moves into the entire status register, the program counter advances to point to the next instruction, and the processor stops fetching and executing instructions. A CPU LPSTOP broadcast cycle is executed to CPU space $3 to copy the updated interrupt mask to the external bus interface (EBI). The internal clocks are stopped.

Instruction execution resumes when a trace, interrupt, or reset exception occurs. A trace exception will occur if the trace state is on when the LPSTOP instruction is executed. If an interrupt request is asserted with a higher priority that the current priority level set by the new status register value, an interrupt exception occurs; otherwise, the interrupt request is ignored. If the bit of the immediate data corresponding to the S-bit is off, execution of the instruction will cause a privilege violation. An external reset always initiates reset exception processing.

Condition Codes:
Set according to the immediate operand.

Instruction Format:

15	14	13	12	11	10	9	8	7	6	5	4	3	2	1	0
1	1	1	1	1	0	0	0	0	0	0	0	0	0	0	0
0	0	0	0	0	0	0	1	1	1	0	0	0	0	0	0
IMMEDIATE DATA															

Instruction Fields:

Immediate field—Specifies the data to be loaded into the status register.

TBLS
TBLSN

TBLS
TBLSN

Table Lookup and Interpolate (Signed)
(CPU32)

Operation: Rounded:
ENTRY(n)+ {(ENTRY(n+1) − ENTRY(n)) x Dx 7–0} ÷ 256 ♦ Dx
Unrounded:
ENTRY(n) x 256 + {(ENTRY(n+1) − ENTRY(n)) x Dx 7–0} ♦ Dx

Where ENTRY(n) and ENTRY(n + 1) are either:
1. Consecutive entries in the table pointed to by the <ea> and indexed by Dx 15–8 × SIZE or;
2. The registers Dym, Dyn respectively.

Assembler	TBLS.<size> <ea>,Dx	Result rounded
Syntax:	TBLSN.<size> <ea>,Dx	Result not rounded
	TBLS.<size> Dym:Dyn, Dx	Result rounded
	TBLSN.<size> Dym:Dyn, Dx	Result not rounded

Attributes: Size = (Byte, Word, Long)

Description: The TBLS and TBLSN instructions allow the efficient use of piecewise linear compressed data tables to model complex functions. The TBLS instruction has two modes of operation: table lookup and interpolate mode and data register interpolate mode.

For table lookup and interpolate mode, data register Dx 15–0 contains the independent variable X. The effective address points to the start of a signed byte, word, or long-word table containing a linearized representation of the dependent variable, Y, as a function of X. In general, the independent variable, located in the low-order word of Dx, consists of an 8-bit integer part and an 8-bit fractional part. An assumed radix point is located between bits 7 and 8. The integer part, Dx 15–8, is scaled by the operand size and is used as an offset into the table. The selected entry in the table is subtracted from the next consecutive entry. A fractional portion of this difference is taken by multiplying by the interpolation fraction, Dx 7–0 .The adjusted difference is then added to the selected table entry. The result is returned in the destination data register, Dx.

TBLS
TBLSN

Table Lookup and Interpolate (Signed)
(CPU32)

TBLS
TBLSN

For register interpolate mode, the interpolation occurs using the Dym and Dyn registers in place of the two table entries. For this mode, only the fractional portion, Dx 7–0, is used in the interpolation, and the integer portion, Dx 15–8, is ignored. The register interpolation mode may be used with several table lookup and interpolations to model multidimensional functions.

Signed table entries range from -2^{n-1} to $2^{n-1} - 1$; whereas, unsigned table entries range from 0 to 2^{n-1} where n is 8, 16, or 32 for byte, word, and long-word tables, respectively.

Rounding of the result is optionally selected via the "R" instruction field. If R = 0 (TABLE), the fractional portion is rounded according to the round-to-nearest algorithm. The following table summerizes the rounding procedure:

Adjusted Difference Fraction	Rounding Adjustment
$\leq -1/2$	-1
$> -1/2$ and $< 1/2$	$+0$
$\geq 1/2$	$+1$

The adjusted difference is then added to the selected table entry. The rounded result is returned in the destination data register, Dx. Only the portion of the register corresponding to the selected size is affected.

	31 24	23 16	15 8	7 0
BYTE	UNAFFECTED	UNAFFECTED	UNAFFECTED	RESULT
WORD	UNAFFECTED	UNAFFECTED	RESULT	RESULT
LONG	RESULT	RESULT	RESULT	RESULT

7

TBLS
TBLSN

Table Lookup and Interpolate (Signed)
(CPU32)

TBLS
TBLSN

If R = 1 (TABLENR), the result is returned in register Dx without rounding. If the size is byte, the integer portion of the result is returned in Dx 15–8; the integer portion of a word result is stored in Dx 23–8; the least significant 24 bits of a long result are stored in Dx 31–8. Byte and word results are sign-extended to fill the entire 32-bit register.

	31　　　　24	23　　　　16	15　　　　8	7　　　　0
BYTE	SIGN-EXTENDED	SIGN-EXTENDED	RESULT	FRACTION
WORD	SIGN-EXTENDED	RESULT	RESULT	FRACTION
LONG	RESULT	RESULT	RESULT	FRACTION

NOTE

The long-word result contains only the least significant 24 bits of integer precision.

For all sizes, the 8-bit fractional portion of the result is returned to the low byte of the data register, Dx 7–0. User software can make use of the fractional data to reduce cumulative errors in lengthy calculations or implement rounding algorithms different from that provided by other forms of TBLS. The previously described assumed radix point places two restrictions on the programmer:

1. Tables are limited to 257 entries in length.
2. Interpolation resolution is limited to 1/256, the distance between consecutive table entries. The assumed radix point should not, however, be construed by the programmer as a requirement that the independent variable be calculated as a fractional number in the range $0 < x < 255$. On the contrary, X should be considered an integer in the range $0 < x < 65535$, realizing that the table is actually a compressed representation of a linearized function in which only every 256th value is actually stored in memory.

TBLS
TBLSN

Table Lookup and Interpolate (Signed)
(CPU32)

TBLS
TBLSN

Condition Codes:

X	N	Z	V	C
—	*	*	*	0

X—Not affected.
N—Set if the most significant bit of the result is set; cleared otherwise.
Z—Set if the result is zero; cleared otherwise.
V—Set if the integer portion of an unrounded long result is not in the range,
    $-(2^{23}) \leq \text{Result} \leq (2^{23}) - 1$; cleared otherwise.
C—Always cleared.

Instruction Format:

Table Lookup and Interpolate

15	14	13	12	11	10	9	8	7	6	5	4	3	2	1	0
												EFFECTIVE ADDRESS			
1	1	1	1	1	0	0	0	0	0		MODE			REGISTER	
0	REGISTER Dx			1	R	0	1	SIZE		0	0	0	0	0	0

Data Register Interpolate

15	14	13	12	11	10	9	8	7	6	5	4	3	2	1	0
1	1	1	1	1	0	0	0	0	0	0	0	0	REGISTER Dym		
0	REGISTER Dx			1	R	0	0	SIZE		0	0	0	REGISTER Dyn		

7

TBLS
TBLSN

Table Lookup and Interpolate (Signed)
(CPU32)

TBLS
TBLSN

Instruction Fields:

Effective address field (table lookup and interpolate mode only)—Specifies the destination location. Only control alterable addressing modes are allowed as listed in the following table:

Addressing Mode	Mode	Register	Addressing Mode	Mode	Register
Dn	—	—	(xxx).W	111	000
An	—	—	(xxx).L	111	001
(An)	—	—	#<data>	—	—
(An)+	—	—			
–(An)	100	reg. number:An			
(d$_{16}$,An)	101	reg. number:An	(d$_{16}$,PC)	111	010
(d$_8$,An,Xn)	110	reg. number:An	(d$_8$,PC,Xn)	111	011
(bd,An,Xn)	110	reg. number:An	(bd,PC,Xn)	111	011

Size Field—Specifies the size of operation.
  00—Byte Operation
  01—Word Operation
  10—Long Operation

Register field—Specifies the destination data register, Dx. On entry, the register contains the interpolation fraction and entry number.

Dym, Dyn field—If the effective address mode field is nonzero, this operand register is unused and should be zero. If the effective address mode field is zero, the surface interpolation variant of this instruction is implied, and Dyn specifies one of the two source operands.

Rounding mode field—The R-bit controls the rounding of the final result. When R = 0, the result is rounded according to the round-to-nearest algorithm. When R = 1, the result is returned unrounded.

TBLU
TBLUN
Table Lookup and Interpolation (Unsigned)
(CPU32)

TBLU
TBLUN

Operation: Rounded:

$ENTRY(n) + \{(ENTRY(n + 1) - ENTRY(n)) \times Dx\ 7-0\} \div 256 \blacklozenge Dx$

Unrounded:

$ENTRY(n) \times 256 + \{(ENTRY(n + 1) - ENTRY(n)) \times Dx\ 7-0\} \blacklozenge Dx$

Where ENTRY(n) and ENTRY(n + 1) are either:
1. Consecutive entries in the table pointed to by the <ea> and indexed by Dx 15–8 × SIZE or;
2. The registers Dym, Dyn respectively

Assembler   TBLU.<size> <ea>,Dx   Result rounded
Syntax: TBLUN.<size> <ea>,Dx   Result not rounded
                TBLU.<size> Dym:Dyn, Dx   Result rounded
                TBLUN.<size> Dym:Dyn, Dx   Result not rounded

Attributes: Size = (Byte, Word, Long)

Description: The TBLU and TBLUN instructions allow the efficient use of piecewise linear, compressed data tables to model complex functions. The TBLU instruction has two modes of operation: table lookup and interpolate mode and data register interpolate mode.

For table lookup and interpolate mode, data register Dx 15–0 contains the independent variable X. The effective address points to the start of a unsigned byte, word, or long-word table containing a linearized representation of the dependent variable, Y, as a function of X. In general, the independent variable, located in the low-order word of Dx, consists of an 8-bit integer part and an 8-bit fractional part. An assumed radix point is located between bits 7 and 8. The integer part, Dx 15–8, is scaled by the operand size and is used as an offset into the table. The selected entry in the table is subtracted from the next consecutive entry. A fractional portion of this difference is taken by multiplying by the interpolation fraction, Dx 7–0. The adjusted difference is then added to the selected table entry. The result is returned in the destination data register, Dx.

7

For register interpolate mode, the interpolation occurs using the Dym and Dyn registers in place of the two table entries. For this mode, only the fractional portion, Dx 7–0, is used in the interpolation and the integer portion, Dx 15–8, is ignored. The register interpolation mode may be used with several table lookup and interpolations to model multidimensional functions.

Signed table entries range from -2^{n-1} to $2^{n-1}-1$; whereas, unsigned table entries range from 0 to $2^{n}-1$ where n is 8, 16, or 32 for byte, word, and long-word tables, respectively. The unsigned and unrounded table results will be zero-extended instead of sign-extended.

Rounding of the result is optionally selected via the "R" instruction field. If R = 0 (TABLE), the fractional portion is rounded according to the round-to-nearest algorithm. The rounding procedure can be summarized by the following table:

Adjusted Difference Fraction	Rounding Adjustment
≥ 1/2	+1
< 1/2	+0

The adjusted difference is then added to the selected table entry. The rounded result is returned in the destination data register, Dx. Only the portion of the register corresponding to the selected size is affected.

	31 24	23 16	15 8	7 0
BYTE	UNAFFECTED	UNAFFECTED	UNAFFECTED	RESULT
WORD	UNAFFECTED	UNAFFECTED	RESULT	RESULT
LONG	RESULT	RESULT	RESULT	RESULT

If R = 1 (TBLUN), the result is returned in register Dx without rounding. If the size is byte, the integer portion of the result is returned in Dx 15–8; the integer portion of a word result is stored in Dx 23–8; the least significant 24 bits of a long result are stored in Dx 31–8. Byte and word results are sign-extended to fill the entire 32-bit register.

	31 24	23 16	15 8	7 0
BYTE	SIGN-EXTENDED	SIGN-EXTENDED	RESULT	FRACTION
WORD	SIGN-EXTENDED	RESULT	RESULT	FRACTION
LONG	RESULT	RESULT	RESULT	FRACTION

NOTE

The long-word result contains only the least significant 24 bits of integer precision.

For all sizes, the 8-bit fractional portion of the result is returned in the low byte of the data register, Dx 7–0. User software can make use of the fractional data to reduce cumulative errors in lengthy calculations or implement rounding algorithms different from that provided by other forms of TBLU. The previously described assumed radix point places two restrictions on the programmer:

1. Tables are limited to 257 entries in length.
2. Interpolation resolution is limited to 1/256, the distance between consecutive table entries. The assumed radix point should not, however, be construed by the programmer as a requirement that the independent variable be calculated as a fractional number in the range $0 \le X \le 255$. On the contrary, X should be considered to be an integer in the range $0 \le X \le 65535$, realizing that the table is actually a compressed representation of a linearized function in which only every 256th value is actually stored in memory.

Condition Codes:

X	N	Z	V	C
—	*	*	*	0

X—Not affected.
N—Set if the most significant bit of the result is set; cleared otherwise.
Z—Set if the result is zero; cleared otherwise.
V—Set if the integer portion of an unrounded long result is not in the range, $-(2^{23}) \le \text{Result} \le (2^{23}) - 1$; cleared otherwise.
C—Always cleared.

TBLU TBLUN Table Lookup and Interpolation (Unsigned) TBLU TBLUN

(CPU32)

Instruction Format:

Table Lookup and Interpolate

15	14	13	12	11	10	9	8	7	6	5	4	3	2	1	0
1	1	1	1	1	0	0	0	0	0	EFFECTIVE ADDRESS MODE			EFFECTIVE ADDRESS REGISTER		
0	REGISTER Dx			0	R	0	1	SIZE		0	0	0	0	0	0

Data Register Interpolate

15	14	13	12	11	10	9	8	7	6	5	4	3	2	1	0
1	1	1	1	1	0	0	0	0	0	0	0	0	REGISTER Dym		
0	REGISTER Dx			0	R	0	0	SIZE		0	0	0	REGISTER Dyn		

Instruction Fields:

Effective address field (table lookup and interpolate mode only)—Specifies the destination location. Only control alterable addressing modes are allowed as listed in the following table:

Addressing Mode	Mode	Register
Dn	—	—
An	—	—
(An)	010	reg. number:An
(An)+	—	—
–(An)	100	reg. number:An
(d_{16},An)	101	reg. number:An
(d_8,An,Xn)	110	reg. number:An
(bd,An,Xn)	110	reg. number:An

Addressing Mode	Mode	Register
(xxx).W	111	000
(xxx).L	111	001
#<data>	—	—
(d_{16},PC)	111	010
(d_8,PC,Xn)	111	011
(bd,PC,Xn)	111	011

Size field—Specifies the size of operation.

00—Byte Operation
01—Word Operation
10—Long Operation

TBLU
TBLUN
Table Lookup and Interpolation (Unsigned)
(CPU32)

Register field—Specifies the destination data register, Dx. On entry, the register contains the interpolation fraction and entry number.

Dym, Dyn field—If the effective address mode field is nonzero, this operand register is unused and should be zero. If the effective address mode field is zero, the surface interpolation variant of this instruction is implied, and Dyn specifies one of the two source operands.

Rounding mode field—The R-bit controls the rounding of the final result. When R = 0, the result is rounded according to the round-to-nearest algorithm. When R = 1, the result is returned unrounded.

7

SECTION 8
INSTRUCTION FORMAT SUMMARY

This section contains a listing of the M68000 family instructions in binary format. It is listed in opcode order for the M68000 family instruction set.

8.1 INSTRUCTION FORMAT

The following paragraphs present a summary of the binary encoding fields.

8.1.1 Coprocessor ID Field

This field specifies which coprocessor in a system is to perform the operation. When using directly supported floating-point instructions for the MC68040, this field must be set to one.

8.1.2 Effective Address Field

This field specifies which addressing mode is to be used. For some operations, there are hardware-enforced restrictions on the available addressing modes allowed.

8.1.3 Register/Memory Field

This field is common to all arithmetic instructions. A zero in this field indicates a register-to-register operation, and a one indicates an <ea>-to-register operation.

8.1.4 Source Specifier Field

This field is common to all arithmetic instructions. The value of the register/memory (R/M) field affects this field's definition. If R/M = 0, specifies the source floating-point data register (FPDR). If R/M = 1, specifies the source operand data format.

    000—Long-Word Integer (L)
    001—Single-Precision Real (S)
    010—Extended-Precision Real (X)
    011—Packed-Decimal Real (P)
    100—Word Integer (W)
    101—Double-Precision Real (D)
    110—Byte Integer (B)

8

8.1.5 Destination Register Field

This field is common to all arithmetic instructions. It specifies the FPDR that that will be the destination. The results are always stored in this register.

8.1.6 Conditional Predicate Field

This field is common to all conditional instructions and specifies the conditional test that is to be evaluated. Table 8-1 shows the binary encodings for the conditional tests.

8.1.7 Shift and Rotate Instructions

The following paragraphs define the fields used with the shift and rotate instructions.

8.1.7.1 COUNT REGISTER FIELD. If i/r = 0, this field contains the rotate (shift) count of 1–8 (a zero specifies 8). If i/r = 1, this field specifies a data register that contains the rotate (shift) count. The following shift and rotate fields are encoded as follows:

> dr field
> > 0—Rotate (shift) Right
> > 1—Rotate (shift) Left
>
> i/r field
> > 0—Immediate Rotate (shift) Count
> > 1—Register Rotate (shift) Count

8.1.7.2 REGISTER FIELD. This field specifies a data register to be rotated (shifted).

8

Table 8-1. Conditional Predicate Field Encoding

Conditional Predicate	Mnemonic	Definition
000000	F	False
000001	EQ	Equal
000010	OGT	Ordered Greater Than
000011	OGE	Ordered Greater Than or Equal
000100	OLT	Ordered Less Than
000101	OLE	Ordered Less Than or Equal
000110	OGL	Ordered Greater Than or Less Than
000111	OR	Ordered
001000	UN	Unordered
001001	UEQ	Unordered or Equal
001010	UGT	Unordered or Greater Than
001011	UGE	Unordered or Greater Than or Equal
001100	ULT	Unordered or Less Than
001101	ULE	Unordered or Less Than or Equal
001110	NE	Not Equal
001111	T	True
010000	SF	Signaling False
010001	SEQ	Signaling Equal
010010	GT	Greater Than
010011	GE	Greater Than or Equal
010100	LT	Less Than
010101	LE	Less Than or Equal
010110	GL	Greater Than or Less Than
010111	GLE	Greater Than or Less Than or Equal
011000	NGLE	Not (Greater Than or Less Than or Equal)
011001	NGL	Not (Greater Than or Less Than)
011010	NLE	Not (Less Than or Equal)
011011	NLT	Not (Less Than)
011100	NGE	Not (Greater Than or Equal)
011101	NGT	Not (Greater Than)
011110	SNE	Signaling Not Equal
011111	ST	Signaling True

8

8.1.8 Size Field

This field specifies the size of the operation. The encoding is as follows:

00—Byte Operation
01—Word Operation
10—Long Operation

8.1.9 Opmode Field

Refer to the applicable instruction descriptions for the encoding of this field in **Section 4 Integer Unit Instructions, Section 5 Floating-Point Instructions, Section 6 Supervisor (Priviledged) Instructions**, and **Section 7 CPU32 Instructions.**

8.1.10 Address/Data Field

This field specifies the type of general register. The encoding is:

0—Data Register
1—Address Register

8.2 OPERATION CODE MAP

Table 8-2 lists the encoding for bits 15–12 and the operation performed.

Table 8-2. Operation Code Map

Bits 15–12	Operation
0000	Bit Manipulation/MOVEP/Immediate
0001	Move Byte
0010	Move Long
0011	Move Word
0100	Miscellaneous
0101	ADDQ/SUBQ/Scc/DBcc/TRAPcc
0110	Bcc/BSR/BRA
0111	MOVEQ
1000	OR/DIV/SBCD
1001	SUB/SUBX
1010	(Unassigned, Reserved)
1011	CMP/EOR
1100	AND/MUL/ABCD/EXG
1101	ADD/ADDX
1110	Shift/Rotate/Bit Field
1111	Coprocessor Interface/MC68040 and CPU32 Extensions

8

M68000 FAMILY PROGRAMMER'S REFERENCE MANUAL   MOTOROLA

ORI to CCR

15	14	13	12	11	10	9	8	7	6	5	4	3	2	1	0
0	0	0	0	0	0	0	0	0	0	1	1	1	1	0	0
0	0	0	0	0	0	0	0	8-BIT BYTE DATA							

ORI to SR

15	14	13	12	11	10	9	8	7	6	5	4	3	2	1	0
0	0	0	0	0	0	0	0	0	1	1	1	1	1	0	0
16-BIT WORD DATA															

ORI

15	14	13	12	11	10	9	8	7	6	5	4	3	2	1	0
0	0	0	0	0	0	0	0	SIZE		EFFECTIVE ADDRESS					
										MODE			REGISTER		
16-BIT WORD DATA								8-BIT BYTE DATA							
32-BIT LONG DATA															

ANDI to CCR

15	14	13	12	11	10	9	8	7	6	5	4	3	2	1	0
0	0	0	0	0	0	1	0	0	0	1	1	1	1	0	0
0	0	0	0	0	0	0	0	8-BIT BYTE DATA							

ANDI to SR

15	14	13	12	11	10	9	8	7	6	5	4	3	2	1	0
0	0	0	0	0	0	1	0	0	1	1	1	1	1	0	0
16-BIT WORD DATA															

ANDI

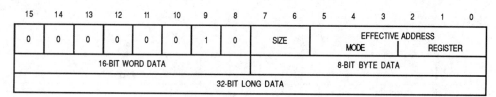

15	14	13	12	11	10	9	8	7	6	5	4	3	2	1	0
0	0	0	0	0	0	1	0	SIZE		EFFECTIVE ADDRESS					
										MODE			REGISTER		
16-BIT WORD DATA								8-BIT BYTE DATA							
32-BIT LONG DATA															

SUBI

15	14	13	12	11	10	9	8	7	6	5	4	3	2	1	0
0	0	0	0	0	1	0	0	SIZE		EFFECTIVE ADDRESS					
										MODE			REGISTER		
16-BIT WORD DATA								8-BIT BYTE DATA							
32-BIT LONG DATA															

RTM

15	14	13	12	11	10	9	8	7	6	5	4	3	2	1	0
0	0	0	0	0	1	1	0	1	1	0	0	D/A	REGISTER		

CALLM

15	14	13	12	11	10	9	8	7	6	5	4	3	2	1	0
0	0	0	0	0	1	1	0	1	1	EFFECTIVE ADDRESS					
										MODE			REGISTER		
0	0	0	0	0	0	0	0	ARGUMENT COUNT							

ADDI

15	14	13	12	11	10	9	8	7	6	5	4	3	2	1	0
0	0	0	0	0	1	1	0	SIZE		EFFECTIVE ADDRESS					
										MODE			REGISTER		
16-BIT WORD DATA								8-BIT BYTE DATA							
32-BIT LONG DATA															

CMP2

15	14	13	12	11	10	9	8	7	6	5	4	3	2	1	0
0	0	0	0	0	SIZE		0	1	1	EFFECTIVE ADDRESS					
										MODE			REGISTER		
D/A	REGISTER			0	0	0	0	0	0	0	0	0	0	0	0

CHK2

15	14	13	12	11	10	9	8	7	6	5	4	3	2	1	0
0	0	0	0	0	SIZE		0	1	1	EFFECTIVE ADDRESS					
										MODE			REGISTER		
D/A	REGISTER			1	0	0	0	0	0	0	0	0	0	0	0

8

EORI to CCR

15	14	13	12	11	10	9	8	7	6	5	4	3	2	1	0
0	0	0	0	1	0	1	0	0	0	1	1	1	1	0	0
0	0	0	0	0	0	0	0	BYTE DATA (8 BITS)							

EORI to SR

15	14	13	12	11	10	9	8	7	6	5	4	3	2	1	0
0	0	0	0	1	0	1	0	0	1	1	1	1	1	0	0
16-BIT WORD DATA															

EORI

15	14	13	12	11	10	9	8	7	6	5	4	3	2	1	0
0	0	0	0	1	0	1	0	SIZE		EFFECTIVE ADDRESS					
										MODE			REGISTER		
16-BIT WORD DATA								16-BIT BYTE DATA							
32-BIT LONG DATA															

CMPI

15	14	13	12	11	10	9	8	7	6	5	4	3	2	1	0
0	0	0	0	1	1	0	0	SIZE		EFFECTIVE ADDRESS					
										MODE			REGISTER		
16-BIT WORD DATA								8-BIT BYTE DATA							
32-BIT LONG DATA															

BTST

Bit Number Static, Specified as Immediate Data

15	14	13	12	11	10	9	8	7	6	5	4	3	2	1	0
0	0	0	0	1	0	0	0	0	0	EFFECTIVE ADDRESS					
										MODE			REGISTER		
0	0	0	0	0	0	0	0	BIT NUMBER							

BCHG

Bit Number Static, Specified as Immediate Data

15	14	13	12	11	10	9	8	7	6	5	4	3	2	1	0
0	0	0	0	1	0	0	0	0	1	EFFECTIVE ADDRESS					
										MODE			REGISTER		
0	0	0	0	0	0	0	0	BIT NUMBER							

8

BCLR

Bit Number Static, Specified as Immediate Data

15	14	13	12	11	10	9	8	7	6	5	4	3	2	1	0
										EFFECTIVE ADDRESS					
0	0	0	0	1	0	0	0	1	0	MODE			REGISTER		
0	0	0	0	0	0	0	0	BIT NUMBER							

BSET

Bit Number Static, Specified as Immediate Data

15	14	13	12	11	10	9	8	7	6	5	4	3	2	1	0
										EFFECTIVE ADDRESS					
0	0	0	0	1	0	0	0	1	1	MODE			REGISTER		
0	0	0	0	0	0	0	BIT NUMBER								

MOVES

15	14	13	12	11	10	9	8	7	6	5	4	3	2	1	0
										EFFECTIVE ADDRESS					
0	0	0	0	1	1	1	0	SIZE		MODE			REGISTER		
A/D	REGISTER			dr	0	0	0	0	0	0	0	0	0	0	0

CAS2

15	14	13	12	11	10	9	8	7	6	5	4	3	2	1	0
0	0	0	0	1	SIZE		0	1	1	1	1	1	1	0	0
D/A1	Rn1			0	0	0	Du1			0	0	0	Dc1		
D/A2	Rn2			0	0	0	Du2			0	0	0	Dc2		

CAS

15	14	13	12	11	10	9	8	7	6	5	4	3	2	1	0
										EFFECTIVE ADDRESS					
0	0	0	0	1	SIZE		0	1	1	MODE			REGISTER		
0	0	0	0	0	0	0	Du			0	0	0	Dc		

BTST

Bit Number Dynamic, Specified in a Register

15	14	13	12	11	10	9	8	7	6	5	4	3	2	1	0
										EFFECTIVE ADDRESS					
0	0	0	0	REGISTER			1	0	0	MODE			REGISTER		

BCHG

Bit Number Dynamic, Specified in a Register

15	14	13	12	11	10	9	8	7	6	5	4	3	2	1	0
0	0	0	0	REGISTER			1	0	1	EFFECTIVE ADDRESS					
										MODE			REGISTER		

BCLR

Bit Number Dynamic, Specified in a Register

15	14	13	12	11	10	9	8	7	6	5	4	3	2	1	0
0	0	0	0	REGISTER			1	1	0	EFFECTIVE ADDRESS					
										MODE			REGISTER		

BSET

Bit Number Dynamic, Specified in a Register

15	14	13	12	11	10	9	8	7	6	5	4	3	2	1	0
0	0	0	0	REGISTER			1	1	1	EFFECTIVE ADDRESS					
										MODE			REGISTER		

MOVEP

15	14	13	12	11	10	9	8	7	6	5	4	3	2	1	0
0	0	0	0	DATA REGISTER			OPMODE			0	0	1	ADDRESS REGISTER		
16-BIT DISPLACEMENT															

MOVEA

15	14	13	12	11	10	9	8	7	6	5	4	3	2	1	0
0	0	SIZE		DESTINATION REGISTER			0	0	1	SOURCE					
										MODE			REGISTER		

MOVE

15	14	13	12	11	10	9	8	7	6	5	4	3	2	1	0
0	0	SIZE		DESTINATION						SOURCE					
				REGISTER			MODE			MODE			REGISTER		

MOVE from SR

15	14	13	12	11	10	9	8	7	6	5	4	3	2	1	0
0	1	0	0	0	0	0	0	1	1	EFFECTIVE ADDRESS					
										MODE			REGISTER		

8

MOVE from CCR

15	14	13	12	11	10	9	8	7	6	5	4	3	2	1	0
											EFFECTIVE ADDRESS				
0	1	0	0	0	0	1	0	1	1		MODE			REGISTER	

NEGX

15	14	13	12	11	10	9	8	7	6	5	4	3	2	1	0
											EFFECTIVE ADDRESS				
0	1	0	0	0	0	0	0	SIZE			MODE			REGISTER	

CLR

15	14	13	12	11	10	9	8	7	6	5	4	3	2	1	0
											EFFECTIVE ADDRESS				
0	1	0	0	0	0	1	0	SIZE			MODE			REGISTER	

MOVE to CCR

15	14	13	12	11	10	9	8	7	6	5	4	3	2	1	0
											EFFECTIVE ADDRESS				
0	1	0	0	0	1	0	0	1	1		MODE			REGISTER	

NEG

15	14	13	12	11	10	9	8	7	6	5	4	3	2	1	0
											EFFECTIVE ADDRESS				
0	1	0	0	0	1	0	0	SIZE			MODE			REGISTER	

NOT

15	14	13	12	11	10	9	8	7	6	5	4	3	2	1	0
											EFFECTIVE ADDRESS				
0	1	0	0	0	1	1	0	SIZE			MODE			REGISTER	

MOVE to SR

15	14	13	12	11	10	9	8	7	6	5	4	3	2	1	0
											EFFECTIVE ADDRESS				
0	1	0	0	0	1	1	0	1	1		MODE			REGISTER	

EXT, EXTB

15	14	13	12	11	10	9	8	7	6	5	4	3	2	1	0
0	1	0	0	1	0	0		OPMODE		0	0	0		REGISTER	

LINK

Long

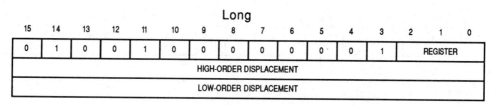

15	14	13	12	11	10	9	8	7	6	5	4	3	2	1	0
0	1	0	0	1	0	0	0	0	0	0	0	1		REGISTER	
HIGH-ORDER DISPLACEMENT															
LOW-ORDER DISPLACEMENT															

NBCD

15	14	13	12	11	10	9	8	7	6	5	4	3	2	1	0
0	1	0	0	1	0	0	0	0	0	EFFECTIVE ADDRESS					
										MODE			REGISTER		

SWAP

15	14	13	12	11	10	9	8	7	6	5	4	3	2	1	0
0	1	0	0	1	0	0	0	0	1	0	0	0		REGISTER	

BKPT

15	14	13	12	11	10	9	8	7	6	5	4	3	2	1	0
0	1	0	0	1	0	0	0	0	1	0	0	1		VECTOR	

PEA

15	14	13	12	11	10	9	8	7	6	5	4	3	2	1	0
0	1	0	0	1	0	0	0	0	1	EFFECTIVE ADDRESS					
										MODE			REGISTER		

8

BGND

15	14	13	12	11	10	9	8	7	6	5	4	3	2	1	0
0	1	0	0	1	0	1	0	1	1	1	1	1	0	1	0

ILLEGAL

15	14	13	12	11	10	9	8	7	6	5	4	3	2	1	0
0	1	0	0	1	0	1	0	1	1	1	1	1	1	0	0

TAS

15	14	13	12	11	10	9	8	7	6	5	4	3	2	1	0
										EFFECTIVE ADDRESS					
0	1	0	0	1	0	1	0	1	1	MODE			REGISTER		

TST

15	14	13	12	11	10	9	8	7	6	5	4	3	2	1	0
										EFFECTIVE ADDRESS					
0	1	0	0	1	0	1	0	SIZE		MODE			REGISTER		

MULU

Long

15	14	13	12	11	10	9	8	7	6	5	4	3	2	1	0
										EFFECTIVE ADDRESS					
0	1	0	0	1	1	0	0	0	0	MODE			REGISTER		
0	REGISTER Dl			0	SIZE	0	0	0	0	0	0	0	REGISTER Dh		

MULS

Long

15	14	13	12	11	10	9	8	7	6	5	4	3	2	1	0
										EFFECTIVE ADDRESS					
0	1	0	0	1	1	0	0	0	0	MODE			REGISTER		
0	REGISTER Dl			1	SIZE	0	0	0	0	0	0	0	REGISTER Dh		

DIVU, DIVUL

Long

15	14	13	12	11	10	9	8	7	6	5	4	3	2	1	0
										EFFECTIVE ADDRESS					
0	1	0	0	1	1	0	0	0	1	MODE			REGISTER		
0	REGISTER Dq			0	SIZE	0	0	0	0	0	0	0	REGISTER Dr		

DIVS, DIVSL

Long

15	14	13	12	11	10	9	8	7	6	5	4	3	2	1	0
0	1	0	0	1	1	0	0	0	1	EFFECTIVE ADDRESS					
										MODE			REGISTER		
0	REGISTER Dq			1	SIZE	0	0	0	0	0	0	0	REGISTER Dr		

TRAP

15	14	13	12	11	10	9	8	7	6	5	4	3	2	1	0
0	1	0	0	1	1	1	0	0	1	0	0	VECTOR			

LINK

Word

15	14	13	12	11	10	9	8	7	6	5	4	3	2	1	0
0	1	0	0	1	1	1	0	0	1	0	1	0	REGISTER		
WORD DISPLACEMENT															

UNLK

15	14	13	12	11	10	9	8	7	6	5	4	3	2	1	0
0	1	0	0	1	1	1	0	0	1	0	1	1	REGISTER		

MOVE USP

15	14	13	12	11	10	9	8	7	6	5	4	3	2	1	0
0	1	0	0	1	1	1	0	0	1	1	0	dr	REGISTER		

RESET

15	14	13	12	11	10	9	8	7	6	5	4	3	2	1	0
0	1	0	0	1	1	1	0	0	1	1	1	0	0	0	0

NOP

15	14	13	12	11	10	9	8	7	6	5	4	3	2	1	0
0	1	0	0	1	1	1	0	0	1	1	1	0	0	0	1

8

STOP

15	14	13	12	11	10	9	8	7	6	5	4	3	2	1	0
0	1	0	0	1	1	1	0	0	1	1	1	0	0	1	0
IMMEDIATE DATA															

RTE

15	14	13	12	11	10	9	8	7	6	5	4	3	2	1	0
0	1	0	0	1	1	1	0	0	1	1	1	0	0	1	1

RTD

15	14	13	12	11	10	9	8	7	6	5	4	3	2	1	0
0	1	0	0	1	1	1	0	0	1	1	1	0	1	0	0
16-BIT DISPLACEMENT															

RTS

15	14	13	12	11	10	9	8	7	6	5	4	3	2	1	0
0	1	0	0	1	1	1	0	0	1	1	1	0	1	0	1

TRAPV

15	14	13	12	11	10	9	8	7	6	5	4	3	2	1	0
0	1	0	0	1	1	1	0	0	1	1	1	0	1	1	0

RTR

15	14	13	12	11	10	9	8	7	6	5	4	3	2	1	0
0	1	0	0	1	1	1	0	0	1	1	1	0	1	1	1

MOVEC

15	14	13	12	11	10	9	8	7	6	5	4	3	2	1	0
0	1	0	0	1	1	1	0	0	1	1	1	1	0	1	dr
A/D	REGISTER		CONTROL REGISTER												

JSR

15	14	13	12	11	10	9	8	7	6	5	4	3	2	1	0
0	1	0	0	1	1	1	0	1	0	EFFECTIVE ADDRESS					

| | | | | | | | | | | MODE | | | REGISTER | | |

JMP

15	14	13	12	11	10	9	8	7	6	5	4	3	2	1	0
0	1	0	0	1	1	1	0	1	1	EFFECTIVE ADDRESS					
										MODE			REGISTER		

MOVEM

15	14	13	12	11	10	9	8	7	6	5	4	3	2	1	0
0	1	0	0	1	dr	0	0	1	SIZE	EFFECTIVE ADDRESS					
										MODE			REGISTER		
REGISTER LIST MASK															

LEA

15	14	13	12	11	10	9	8	7	6	5	4	3	2	1	0
0	1	0	0	REGISTER			1	1	1	EFFECTIVE ADDRESS					
										MODE			REGISTER		

CHK

15	14	13	12	11	10	9	8	7	6	5	4	3	2	1	0
0	1	0	0	REGISTER			SIZE		0	EFFECTIVE ADDRESS					
										MODE			REGISTER		

ADDQ

15	14	13	12	11	10	9	8	7	6	5	4	3	2	1	0
0	1	0	1	DATA			0	SIZE		EFFECTIVE ADDRESS					
										MODE			REGISTER		

SUBQ

15	14	13	12	11	10	9	8	7	6	5	4	3	2	1	0
0	1	0	1	DATA			1	SIZE		EFFECTIVE ADDRESS					
										MODE			REGISTER		

8

DBcc

15	14	13	12	11	10	9	8	7	6	5	4	3	2	1	0
0	1	0	1	CONDITION				1	1	0	0	1	REGISTER		
16-BIT DISPLACEMENT															

TRAPcc

15	14	13	12	11	10	9	8	7	6	5	4	3	2	1	0
0	1	0	1	CONDITION				1	1	1	1	1	OPMODE		
OPTIONAL WORD															
OR LONG WORD															

Scc

15	14	13	12	11	10	9	8	7	6	5	4	3	2	1	0
0	1	0	1	CONDITION				1	1	EFFECTIVE ADDRESS					
										MODE			REGISTER		

BRA

15	14	13	12	11	10	9	8	7	6	5	4	3	2	1	0
0	1	1	0	0	0	0	0	8-BIT DISPLACEMENT							
16-BIT DISPLACEMENT IF 8-BIT DISPLACEMENT = $00															
32-BIT DISPLACEMENT IF 8-BIT DISPLACEMENT = $FF															

BSR

15	14	13	12	11	10	9	8	7	6	5	4	3	2	1	0
0	1	1	0	0	0	0	1	8-BIT DISPLACEMENT							
16-BIT DISPLACEMENT IF 8-BIT DISPLACEMENT = $00															
32-BIT DISPLACEMENT IF 8-BIT DISPLACEMENT = $FF															

Bcc

15	14	13	12	11	10	9	8	7	6	5	4	3	2	1	0
0	1	1	0	CONDITION				8-BIT DISPLACEMENT							
16-BIT DISPLACEMENT IF 8-BIT DISPLACEMENT = $00															
32-BIT DISPLACEMENT IF 8-BIT DISPLACEMENT = $FF															

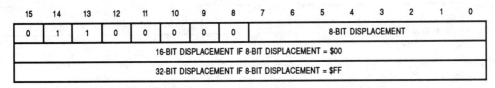

MOVEQ

15	14	13	12	11	10	9	8	7	6	5	4	3	2	1	0
0	1	1	1	REGISTER			0	DATA							

DIVU, DIVUL

Word

15	14	13	12	11	10	9	8	7	6	5	4	3	2	1	0
1	0	0	0	REGISTER			0	1	1	EFFECTIVE ADDRESS					
										MODE			REGISTER		

SBCD

15	14	13	12	11	10	9	8	7	6	5	4	3	2	1	0
1	0	0	0	REGISTER Dy/Ay			1	0	0	0	0	R/M	REGISTER Dx/Ax		

PACK

15	14	13	12	11	10	9	8	7	6	5	4	3	2	1	0
1	0	0	0	REGISTER Dy/Ay			1	0	1	0	0	R/M	REGISTER Dx/Ax		
16-BIT EXTENSION: ADJUSTMENT															

UNPK

15	14	13	12	11	10	9	8	7	6	5	4	3	2	1	0
1	0	0	0	REGISTER Dy/Ay			1	1	0	0	0	R/M	REGISTER Dx/Ax		
16-BIT EXTENSION: ADJUSTMENT															

DIVS, DIVSL

Word

15	14	13	12	11	10	9	8	7	6	5	4	3	2	1	0
1	0	0	0	REGISTER			1	1	1	EFFECTIVE ADDRESS					
										MODE			REGISTER		

OR

15	14	13	12	11	10	9	8	7	6	5	4	3	2	1	0
1	0	0	0	REGISTER			OPMODE			EFFECTIVE ADDRESS					
										MODE			REGISTER		

SUBX

15	14	13	12	11	10	9	8	7	6	5	4	3	2	1	0
1	0	0	1	REGISTER Dy/Ay			1	SIZE		0	0	R/M	REGISTER Dx/Ax		

SUB

15	14	13	12	11	10	9	8	7	6	5	4	3	2	1	0
										EFFECTIVE ADDRESS					
1	0	0	1	REGISTER			OPMODE			MODE			REGISTER		

SUBA

15	14	13	12	11	10	9	8	7	6	5	4	3	2	1	0
										EFFECTIVE ADDRESS					
1	0	0	1	REGISTER			OPMODE			MODE			REGISTER		

CMPM

15	14	13	12	11	10	9	8	7	6	5	4	3	2	1	0
1	0	1	1	REGISTER Ax			1	SIZE		0	0	1	REGISTER Ay		

CMP

15	14	13	12	11	10	9	8	7	6	5	4	3	2	1	0
										EFFECTIVE ADDRESS					
1	0	1	1	REGISTER			OPMODE			MODE			REGISTER		

CMPA

15	14	13	12	11	10	9	8	7	6	5	4	3	2	1	0
										EFFECTIVE ADDRESS					
1	0	1	1	REGISTER			OPMODE			MODE			REGISTER		

EOR

15	14	13	12	11	10	9	8	7	6	5	4	3	2	1	0
										EFFECTIVE ADDRESS					
1	0	1	1	REGISTER			OPMODE			MODE			REGISTER		

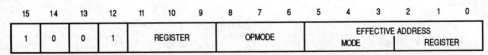

MULU

Word

15	14	13	12	11	10	9	8	7	6	5	4	3	2	1	0
1	1	0	0		REGISTER		0	1	1	EFFECTIVE ADDRESS					
										MODE			REGISTER		

ABCD

15	14	13	12	11	10	9	8	7	6	5	4	3	2	1	0
1	1	0	0		REGISTER Rx		1	0	0	0	0	R/M		REGISTER Ry	

MULS

Word

15	14	13	12	11	10	9	8	7	6	5	4	3	2	1	0
1	1	0	0		REGISTER		1	1	1	EFFECTIVE ADDRESS					
										MODE			REGISTER		

EXG

15	14	13	12	11	10	9	8	7	6	5	4	3	2	1	0
1	1	0	0		REGISTER Rx		1		OPMODE				REGISTER Ry		

AND

15	14	13	12	11	10	9	8	7	6	5	4	3	2	1	0
1	1	0	0		REGISTER			OPMODE		EFFECTIVE ADDRESS					
										MODE			REGISTER		

ADDX

15	14	13	12	11	10	9	8	7	6	5	4	3	2	1	0
1	1	0	1		REGISTER Rx		1	SIZE		0	0	R/M		REGISTER Ry	

ADDA

15	14	13	12	11	10	9	8	7	6	5	4	3	2	1	0
1	1	0	1		REGISTER			OPMODE		EFFECTIVE ADDRESS					
										MODE			REGISTER		

8

ADD

15	14	13	12	11	10	9	8	7	6	5	4	3	2	1	0
1	1	0	1	REGISTER			OPMODE			EFFECTIVE ADDRESS					
										MODE			REGISTER		

ASL, ASR

Memory Shift

15	14	13	12	11	10	9	8	7	6	5	4	3	2	1	0
1	1	1	0	0	0	0	dr	1	1	EFFECTIVE ADDRESS					
										MODE			REGISTER		

LSL, LSR

Memory Shift

15	14	13	12	11	10	9	8	7	6	5	4	3	2	1	0
1	1	1	0	0	0	1	dr	1	1	EFFECTIVE ADDRESS					
										MODE			REGISTER		

ROXL, ROXR

Memory Rotate

15	14	13	12	11	10	9	8	7	6	5	4	3	2	1	0
1	1	1	0	0	1	0	dr	1	1	EFFECTIVE ADDRESS					
										MODE			REGISTER		

ROL, ROR

Memory Rotate

15	14	13	12	11	10	9	8	7	6	5	4	3	2	1	0
1	1	1	0	0	1	1	dr	1	1	EFFECTIVE ADDRESS					
										MODE			REGISTER		

BFTST

15	14	13	12	11	10	9	8	7	6	5	4	3	2	1	0
1	1	1	0	1	0	0	0	1	1	EFFECTIVE ADDRESS					
										MODE			REGISTER		
0	0	0	0	Do	OFFSET				Dw	WIDTH					

BFEXTU

15	14	13	12	11	10	9	8	7	6	5	4	3	2	1	0
1	1	1	0	1	0	0	1	1	1	EFFECTIVE ADDRESS MODE			REGISTER		
0	REGISTER			Do	OFFSET					Dw	WIDTH				

BFCHG

15	14	13	12	11	10	9	8	7	6	5	4	3	2	1	0
1	1	1	0	1	0	1	0	1	1	EFFECTIVE ADDRESS MODE			REGISTER		
0	0	0	0	Do	OFFSET					Dw	WIDTH				

BFEXTS

15	14	13	12	11	10	9	8	7	6	5	4	3	2	1	0
1	1	1	0	1	0	1	1	1	1	EFFECTIVE ADDRESS MODE			REGISTER		
0	REGISTER			Do	OFFSET					Dw	WIDTH				

BFCLR

15	14	13	12	11	10	9	8	7	6	5	4	3	2	1	0
1	1	1	0	1	1	0	0	1	1	EFFECTIVE ADDRESS MODE			REGISTER		
0	0	0	0	Do	OFFSET					Dw	WIDTH				

BFFFO

15	14	13	12	11	10	9	8	7	6	5	4	3	2	1	0
1	1	1	0	1	1	0	1	1	1	EFFECTIVE ADDRESS MODE			REGISTER		
0	REGISTER			Do	OFFSET					Dw	WIDTH				

BFSET

15	14	13	12	11	10	9	8	7	6	5	4	3	2	1	0
1	1	1	0	1	1	1	0	1	1	EFFECTIVE ADDRESS MODE			REGISTER		
0	0	0	0	Do	OFFSET					Dw	WIDTH				

8

BFINS

15	14	13	12	11	10	9	8	7	6	5	4	3	2	1	0
1	1	1	0	1	1	1	1	1	1	EFFECTIVE ADDRESS					

15	14	13	12	11	10	9	8	7	6	5	4	3	2	1	0
1	1	1	0	1	1	1	1	1	1	EFFECTIVE ADDRESS MODE			REGISTER		
0	REGISTER			Do	OFFSET					Dw	WIDTH				

ASL, ASR

Register Shift

15	14	13	12	11	10	9	8	7	6	5	4	3	2	1	0
1	1	1	0	COUNT/ REGISTER			dr	SIZE		i/r	0	0	REGISTER		

LSL, LSR

Register Shift

15	14	13	12	11	10	9	8	7	6	5	4	3	2	1	0
1	1	1	0	COUNT/ REGISTER			dr	SIZE		i/r	0	1	REGISTER		

ROXL, ROXR

Register Rotate

15	14	13	12	11	10	9	8	7	6	5	4	3	2	1	0
1	1	1	0	COUNT/ REGISTER			dr	SIZE		i/r	1	0	REGISTER		

ROL, ROR

Register Rotate

15	14	13	12	11	10	9	8	7	6	5	4	3	2	1	0
1	1	1	0	COUNT/ REGISTER			dr	SIZE		i/r	1	1	REGISTER		

PMOVE

MC68EC030, ACx Registers

15	14	13	12	11	10	9	8	7	6	5	4	3	2	1	0
1	1	1	1	0	0	0	0	0	0	EFFECTIVE ADDRESS MODE			REGISTER		
0	0	0	P REGISTER			R/W	0	0	0	0	0	0	0	0	0

PMOVE

MC68030 only, TT Registers

15	14	13	12	11	10	9	8	7	6	5	4	3	2	1	0
1	1	1	1	0	0	0	0	0	0	EFFECTIVE ADDRESS MODE			REGISTER		
0	0	0	P REGISTER			R/W	FD	0	0	0	0	0	0	0	0

PLOAD

15	14	13	12	11	10	9	8	7	6	5	4	3	2	1	0
1	1	1	1	0	0	0	0	0	0	EFFECTIVE ADDRESS MODE			REGISTER		
0	0	1	0	0	0	R/W	0	0	0	0	FC				

PVALID

VAL Contains Access Level to Test Against

15	14	13	12	11	10	9	8	7	6	5	4	3	2	1	0
1	1	1	1	0	0	0	0	0	0	EFFECTIVE ADDRESS MODE			REGISTER		
0	0	1	0	1	0	0	0	0	0	0	0	0	0	0	0

PVALID

Main Processor Register Contains Access Level to Test Against

15	14	13	12	11	10	9	8	7	6	5	4	3	2	1	0
1	1	1	1	0	0	0	0	0	0	EFFECTIVE ADDRESS MODE			REGISTER		
0	0	1	0	1	0	0	0	0	0	0	0	0	REGISTER		

PFLUSH

MC68030 only

15	14	13	12	11	10	9	8	7	6	5	4	3	2	1	0
1	1	1	1	0	0	0	0	0	0	EFFECTIVE ADDRESS MODE			REGISTER		
0	0	1	MODE			0	0	MASK			FC				

PFLUSH
PFLUSHA
PFLUSHS

MC68851

15	14	13	12	11	10	9	8	7	6	5	4	3	2	1	0
1	1	1	1	0	0	0	0	0	0	EFFECTIVE ADDRESS					
										MODE			REGISTER		
0	0	1	MODE			0	MASK			FC					

PMOVE

MC68851, to/from TC, CRP, DRP, SRP, CAL, VAL, Scc, and AC Registers

15	14	13	12	11	10	9	8	7	6	5	4	3	2	1	0
1	1	1	1	0	0	0	0	0	0	EFFECTIVE ADDRESS					
										MODE			REGISTER		
0	1	0	P REGISTER			R/W	0	0	0	0	0	0	0	0	0

PMOVE

MC68030 only, SRP, CRP, and TC Registers

15	14	13	12	11	10	9	8	7	6	5	4	3	2	1	0
1	1	1	1	0	0	0	0	0	0	EFFECTIVE ADDRESS					
										MODE			REGISTER		
0	1	0	P REGISTER			R/W	FD	0	0	0	0	0	0	0	0

PMOVE

MC68030 only, MMUSR

15	14	13	12	11	10	9	8	7	6	5	4	3	2	1	0
1	1	1	1	0	0	0	0	0	0	EFFECTIVE ADDRESS					
										MODE			REGISTER		
0	1	1	0	0	0	R/W	0	0	0	0	0	0	0	0	0

PMOVE

MC68EC030, ACUSR

15	14	13	12	11	10	9	8	7	6	5	4	3	2	1	0
1	1	1	1	0	0	0	0	0	0	EFFECTIVE ADDRESS					
										MODE			REGISTER		
0	1	1	0	0	0	R/W	0	0	0	0	0	0	0	0	0

8

PMOVE

MC68851, to/from PSR and PCSR Registers

15	14	13	12	11	10	9	8	7	6	5	4	3	2	1	0
1	1	1	1	0	0	0	0	0	0	EFFECTIVE ADDRESS MODE			REGISTER		
0	1	1	P REGISTER			R/W	0	0	0	0	0	0	0	0	0

PMOVE

MC68851, to/from BADx and BACx Registers

15	14	13	12	11	10	9	8	7	6	5	4	3	2	1	0
1	1	1	1	0	0	0	0	0	0	EFFECTIVE ADDRESS MODE			REGISTER		
0	1	1	P REGISTER			R/W	0	0	0	0	NUM			0	0

PTEST

MC68EC030

15	14	13	12	11	10	9	8	7	6	5	4	3	2	1	0
1	1	1	1	0	0	0	0	0	0	EFFECTIVE ADDRESS MODE			REGISTER		
1	0	0	0	0	0	R/W	0	REGISTER			FC				

PTEST

MC68030 only

15	14	13	12	11	10	9	8	7	6	5	4	3	2	1	0
1	1	1	1	0	0	0	0	0	0	EFFECTIVE ADDRESS MODE			REGISTER		
1	0	0	LEVEL			R/W	A	REGISTER			FC				

PTEST

MC68851

15	14	13	12	11	10	9	8	7	6	5	4	3	2	1	0
1	1	1	1	0	0	0	0	0	0	EFFECTIVE ADDRESS MODE			REGISTER		
1	0	0	LEVEL			R/W	A REGISTER			FC					

PFLUSHR

15	14	13	12	11	10	9	8	7	6	5	4	3	2	1	0
1	1	1	1	0	0	0	0	0	0			EFFECTIVE ADDRESS			
										MODE			REGISTER		
1	0	1	0	0	0	0	0	0	0	0	0	0	0	0	0

PScc

15	14	13	12	11	10	9	8	7	6	5	4	3	2	1	0
1	1	1	1	0	0	0	0	0	1	EFFECTIVE ADDRESS					
										MODE			REGISTER		
0	0	0	0	0	0	0	0	0	0	MC68851 CONDITION					

PDBcc

15	14	13	12	11	10	9	8	7	6	5	4	3	2	1	0
1	1	1	1	0	0	0	0	0	1	0	0	1	COUNT REGISTER		
0	0	0	0	0	0	0	0	0	0	MC68851 CONDITION					
16-BIT DISPLACEMENT															

PTRAPcc

15	14	13	12	11	10	9	8	7	6	5	4	3	2	1	0
1	1	1	1	0	0	0	0	0	1	1	1	1	OPMODE		
0	0	0	0	0	0	0	0	0	0	MC68851 CONDITION					
16-BIT OPERAND OR MOST SIGNIFICANT WORD OF 32-BIT OPERAND (IF NEEDED)															
LEAST SIGNIFICANT WORD OF 32-BIT OPERAND (IF NEEDED)															

PBcc

15	14	13	12	11	10	9	8	7	6	5	4	3	2	1	0
1	1	1	1	0	0	0	0	1	SIZE	MC68851 CONDITION					
16-BIT DISPLACEMENT OR MOST SIGNIFICANT WORD OF 32-BIT DISPLACEMENT															
LEAST SIGNIFICANT WORD OF 32-BIT DISPLACEMENT (IF NEEDED)															

PSAVE

15	14	13	12	11	10	9	8	7	6	5	4	3	2	1	0
1	1	1	1	0	0	0	1	0	0	EFFECTIVE ADDRESS					
										MODE			REGISTER		

PRESTORE

15	14	13	12	11	10	9	8	7	6	5	4	3	2	1	0
											EFFECTIVE ADDRESS				
1	1	1	1	0	0	0	1	0	1		MODE			REGISTER	

PFLUSH

MC68EC040, Postincrement Source and Destination

15	14	13	12	11	10	9	8	7	6	5	4	3	2	1	0
1	1	1	1	0	1	0	1	0	0	0	OPMODE		REGISTER		

PFLUSH

MC68040/MC68LC040

15	14	13	12	11	10	9	8	7	6	5	4	3	2	1	0
1	1	1	1	0	1	0	1	0	0	0	OPMODE		REGISTER		

PTEST

MC68040/MC68LC040

15	14	13	12	11	10	9	8	7	6	5	4	3	2	1	0
1	1	1	1	0	1	0	1	0	1	R/W	0	1	REGISTER		

PTEST

MC68EC040

15	14	13	12	11	10	9	8	7	6	5	4	3	2	1	0
1	1	1	1	0	1	0	1	0	1	R/W	0	1	REGISTER		

CINV

15	14	13	12	11	10	9	8	7	6	5	4	3	2	1	0
1	1	1	1	0	1	0	0	CACHE		0	SCOPE		REGISTER		

CPUSH

15	14	13	12	11	10	9	8	7	6	5	4	3	2	1	0
1	1	1	1	0	1	0	0	CACHE		1	SCOPE		REGISTER		

8

MOVE16

Absolute Long Address Source or Destination

15	14	13	12	11	10	9	8	7	6	5	4	3	2	1	0
1	1	1	1	0	1	1	0	0	0	0	OPMODE		REGISTER Ay		
HIGH-ORDER ADDRESS															
LOW-ORDER ADDRESS															

MOVE16

Postincrement Source and Destination

15	14	13	12	11	10	9	8	7	6	5	4	3	2	1	0
1	1	1	1	0	1	1	0	0	0	1	0	0	REGISTER Ax		
1	REGISTER Ay			0	0	0	0	0	0	0	0	0	0	0	0

TBLU, TBLUN

Table Lookup and Interpolate

15	14	13	12	11	10	9	8	7	6	5	4	3	2	1	0
1	1	1	1	1	0	0	0	0	0	EFFECTIVE ADDRESS					
										MODE			REGISTER		
0	REGISTER Dx			0	R	0	1	SIZE		0	0	0	0	0	0

TBLS, TBLSN

Table Lookup and Interpolate

15	14	13	12	11	10	9	8	7	6	5	4	3	2	1	0
1	1	1	1	1	0	0	0	0	0	EFFECTIVE ADDRESS					
										MODE			REGISTER		
0	REGISTER Dx			1	R	0	1	SIZE		0	0	0	0	0	0

TBLU, TBLUN

Data Register Interpolate

15	14	13	12	11	10	9	8	7	6	5	4	3	2	1	0
1	1	1	1	1	0	0	0	0	0	0	0	0	REGISTER Dym		
0	REGISTER Dx			0	R	0	0	SIZE		0	0	0	REGISTER Dyn		

TBLS, TBLSN

Data Register Interpolate

15	14	13	12	11	10	9	8	7	6	5	4	3	2	1	0
1	1	1	1	1	0	0	0	0	0	0	0	0	REGISTER Dym		
0	REGISTER Dx			1	R	0	0	SIZE		0	0	0	REGISTER Dyn		

LPSTOP

15	14	13	12	11	10	9	8	7	6	5	4	3	2	1	0
1	1	1	1	1	0	0	0	0	0	0	0	0	0	0	0
0	0	0	0	0	0	0	1	1	1	0	0	0	0	0	0
IMMEDIATE DATA															

FMOVECR

15	14	13	12	11	10	9	8	7	6	5	4	3	2	1	0
1	1	1	1	COPROCESSOR ID			0	0	0	0	0	0	0	0	0
0	1	0	1	1	1	DESTINATION REGISTER			ROM OFFSET						

FINT

15	14	13	12	11	10	9	8	7	6	5	4	3	2	1	0
1	1	1	1	COPROCESSOR ID			0	0	0	EFFECTIVE ADDRESS MODE			REGISTER		
0	R/M	0	SOURCE SPECIFIER			DESTINATION REGISTER			0	0	0	0	0	0	1

FSINH

15	14	13	12	11	10	9	8	7	6	5	4	3	2	1	0
1	1	1	1	COPROCESSOR ID			0	0	0	EFFECTIVE ADDRESS MODE			REGISTER		
0	R/M	0	SOURCE SPECIFIER			DESTINATION REGISTER			0	0	0	0	0	1	0

FINTRZ

15	14	13	12	11	10	9	8	7	6	5	4	3	2	1	0
1	1	1	1	COPROCESSOR ID			0	0	0	EFFECTIVE ADDRESS MODE			REGISTER		
0	R/M	0	SOURCE SPECIFIER			DESTINATION REGISTER			0	0	0	0	0	1	1

8

FLOGNP1

15	14	13	12	11	10	9	8	7	6	5	4	3	2	1	0
1	1	1	1	COPROCESSOR ID			0	0	0	EFFECTIVE ADDRESS MODE			REGISTER		
0	R/M	0	SOURCE SPECIFIER			DESTINATION REGISTER			0	0	0	0	1	1	0

FETOXM1

15	14	13	12	11	10	9	8	7	6	5	4	3	2	1	0
1	1	1	1	COPROCESSOR ID			0	0	0	EFFECTIVE ADDRESS MODE			REGISTER		
0	R/M	0	SOURCE SPECIFIER			DESTINATION REGISTER			0	0	0	1	0	0	0

FTANH

15	14	13	12	11	10	9	8	7	6	5	4	3	2	1	0
1	1	1	1	COPROCESSOR ID			0	0	0	EFFECTIVE ADDRESS MODE			REGISTER		
0	R/M	0	SOURCE SPECIFIER			DESTINATION REGISTER			0	0	0	1	0	0	1

FATAN

15	14	13	12	11	10	9	8	7	6	5	4	3	2	1	0
1	1	1	1	COPROCESSOR ID			0	0	0	EFFECTIVE ADDRESS MODE			REGISTER		
0	R/M	0	SOURCE SPECIFIER			DESTINATION REGISTER			0	0	0	1	0	1	0

FASIN

15	14	13	12	11	10	9	8	7	6	5	4	3	2	1	0
1	1	1	1	COPROCESSOR ID			0	0	0	EFFECTIVE ADDRESS MODE			REGISTER		
0	R/M	0	SOURCE SPECIFIER			DESTINATION REGISTER			0	0	0	1	1	0	0

8

FATANH

15	14	13	12	11	10	9	8	7	6	5	4	3	2	1	0
1	1	1	1	COPROCESSOR ID			0	0	0	EFFECTIVE ADDRESS					
										MODE			REGISTER		
0	R/M	0	SOURCE SPECIFIER			DESTINATION REGISTER			0	0	0	1	1	0	1

FSIN

15	14	13	12	11	10	9	8	7	6	5	4	3	2	1	0
1	1	1	1	COPROCESSOR ID			0	0	0	EFFECTIVE ADDRESS					
										MODE			REGISTER		
0	R/M	0	SOURCE SPECIFIER			DESTINATION REGISTER			0	0	0	1	1	1	0

FTAN

15	14	13	12	11	10	9	8	7	6	5	4	3	2	1	0
1	1	1	1	COPROCESSOR ID			0	0	0	EFFECTIVE ADDRESS					
										MODE			REGISTER		
0	R/M	0	SOURCE SPECIFIER			DESTINATION REGISTER			0	0	0	1	1	1	1

FETOX

15	14	13	12	11	10	9	8	7	6	5	4	3	2	1	0
1	1	1	1	COPROCESSOR ID			0	0	0	EFFECTIVE ADDRESS					
										MODE			REGISTER		
0	R/M	0	SOURCE SPECIFIER			DESTINATION REGISTER			0	0	1	0	0	0	0

FTWOTOX

15	14	13	12	11	10	9	8	7	6	5	4	3	2	1	0
1	1	1	1	COPROCESSOR ID			0	0	0	EFFECTIVE ADDRESS					
										MODE			REGISTER		
0	R/M	0	SOURCE SPECIFIER			DESTINATION REGISTER			0	0	1	0	0	0	1

FTENTOX

15	14	13	12	11	10	9	8	7	6	5	4	3	2	1	0
1	1	1	1	COPROCESSOR ID			0	0	0	EFFECTIVE ADDRESS					
										MODE			REGISTER		
0	R/M	0	SOURCE SPECIFIER			DESTINATION REGISTER			0	0	1	0	0	1	0

FLOGN

15	14	13	12	11	10	9	8	7	6	5	4	3	2	1	0
1	1	1	1	COPROCESSOR ID			0	0	0	EFFECTIVE ADDRESS MODE			REGISTER		
0	R/M	0	SOURCE SPECIFIER			DESTINATION REGISTER			0	0	1	0	1	0	0

FLOG10

15	14	13	12	11	10	9	8	7	6	5	4	3	2	1	0
1	1	1	1	COPROCESSOR ID			0	0	0	EFFECTIVE ADDRESS MODE			REGISTER		
0	R/M	0	SOURCE SPECIFIER			DESTINATION REGISTER			0	0	1	0	1	0	1

FLOG2

15	14	13	12	11	10	9	8	7	6	5	4	3	2	1	0
1	1	1	1	COPROCESSOR ID			0	0	0	EFFECTIVE ADDRESS MODE			REGISTER		
0	R/M	0	SOURCE SPECIFIER			DESTINATION REGISTER			0	0	1	0	1	1	0

FCOSH

15	14	13	12	11	10	9	8	7	6	5	4	3	2	1	0
1	1	1	1	COPROCESSOR ID			0	0	0	EFFECTIVE ADDRESS MODE			REGISTER		
0	R/M	0	SOURCE SPECIFIER			DESTINATION REGISTER			0	0	1	1	0	0	1

FACOS

15	14	13	12	11	10	9	8	7	6	5	4	3	2	1	0
1	1	1	1	COPROCESSOR ID			0	0	0	EFFECTIVE ADDRESS MODE			REGISTER		
0	R/M	0	SOURCE SPECIFIER			DESTINATION REGISTER			0	0	1	1	1	0	0

FCOS

15	14	13	12	11	10	9	8	7	6	5	4	3	2	1	0
1	1	1	1	COPROCESSOR ID			0	0	0	EFFECTIVE ADDRESS MODE			REGISTER		
0	R/M	0	SOURCE SPECIFIER			DESTINATION REGISTER			0	0	1	1	1	0	1

FGETEXP

15	14	13	12	11	10	9	8	7	6	5	4	3	2	1	0
1	1	1	1	COPROCESSOR ID			0	0	0	EFFECTIVE ADDRESS — MODE			REGISTER		
0	R/M	0	SOURCE SPECIFIER			DESTINATION REGISTER			0	0	1	1	1	1	0

FGETMAN

15	14	13	12	11	10	9	8	7	6	5	4	3	2	1	0
1	1	1	1	COPROCESSOR ID			0	0	0	EFFECTIVE ADDRESS — MODE			REGISTER		
0	R/M	0	SOURCE SPECIFIER			DESTINATION REGISTER			0	0	1	1	1	1	1

FMOD

15	14	13	12	11	10	9	8	7	6	5	4	3	2	1	0
1	1	1	1	COPROCESSOR ID			0	0	0	EFFECTIVE ADDRESS — MODE			REGISTER		
0	R/M	0	SOURCE SPECIFIER			DESTINATION REGISTER			0	1	0	0	0	0	1

FSGLDIV

15	14	13	12	11	10	9	8	7	6	5	4	3	2	1	0
1	1	1	1	COPROCESSOR ID			0	0	0	EFFECTIVE ADDRESS — MODE			REGISTER		
0	R/M	0	SOURCE SPECIFIER			DESTINATION REGISTER			0	1	0	0	1	0	0

FREM

15	14	13	12	11	10	9	8	7	6	5	4	3	2	1	0
1	1	1	1	COPROCESSOR ID			0	0	0	EFFECTIVE ADDRESS — MODE			REGISTER		
0	R/M	0	SOURCE SPECIFIER			DESTINATION REGISTER			0	1	0	0	1	0	1

FSCALE

15	14	13	12	11	10	9	8	7	6	5	4	3	2	1	0
1	1	1	1	COPROCESSOR ID			0	0	0	EFFECTIVE ADDRESS — MODE			REGISTER		
0	R/M	0	SOURCE SPECIFIER			DESTINATION REGISTER			0	1	0	0	1	1	0

8

FSGLMUL

15	14	13	12	11	10	9	8	7	6	5	4	3	2	1	0
1	1	1	1	COPROCESSOR ID			0	0	0	EFFECTIVE ADDRESS MODE			REGISTER		
0	R/M	0	SOURCE SPECIFIER			DESTINATION REGISTER			0	1	0	0	1	1	1

FSINCOS

15	14	13	12	11	10	9	8	7	6	5	4	3	2	1	0
1	1	1	1	COPROCESSOR ID			0	0	0	EFFECTIVE ADDRESS MODE			REGISTER		
0	R/M	0	SOURCE SPECIFIER			DESTINATION REGISTER, FPs			0	1	1	0	DESTINATION REGISTER, FPc		

FCMP

15	14	13	12	11	10	9	8	7	6	5	4	3	2	1	0
1	1	1	1	COPROCESSOR ID			0	0	0	EFFECTIVE ADDRESS MODE			REGISTER		
0	R/M	0	SOURCE SPECIFIER			DESTINATION REGISTER			0	1	1	1	0	0	0

FTST

15	14	13	12	11	10	9	8	7	6	5	4	3	2	1	0
1	1	1	1	COPROCESSOR ID			0	0	0	EFFECTIVE ADDRESS MODE			REGISTER		
0	R/M	0	SOURCE SPECIFIER			DESTINATION REGISTER			0	1	1	1	0	1	0

FABS

15	14	13	12	11	10	9	8	7	6	5	4	3	2	1	0
1	1	1	1	COPROCESOR ID			0	0	0	EFFECTIVE ADDRESS MODE			REGISTER		
0	R/M	0	SOURCE SPECIFIER			DESTINATION REGISTER			OPMODE						

FADD

15	14	13	12	11	10	9	8	7	6	5	4	3	2	1	0
1	1	1	1	COPROCESSOR ID			0	0	0	EFFECTIVE ADDRESS MODE			REGISTER		
0	R/M	0	SOURCE SPECIFIER			DESTINATION REGISTER			OPMODE						

FDIV

15	14	13	12	11	10	9	8	7	6	5	4	3	2	1	0
1	1	1	1	COPROCESSOR ID			0	0	0	EFFECTIVE ADDRESS MODE			REGISTER		
0	R/M	0	SOURCE SPECIFIER			DESTINATION REGISTER			OPMODE						

FMOVE

Data Register, Effective Address to Register

15	14	13	12	11	10	9	8	7	6	5	4	3	2	1	0
1	1	1	1	COPROCESSOR ID			0	0	0	EFFECTIVE ADDRESS MODE			REGISTER		
0	R/M	0	SOURCE SPECIFIER			DESTINATION REGISTER			OPMODE						

FMUL

15	14	13	12	11	10	9	8	7	6	5	4	3	2	1	0
1	1	1	1	COPROCESSOR ID			0	0	0	EFFECTIVE ADDRESS MODE			REGISTER		
0	R/M	0	SOURCE SPECIFIER			DESTINATION REGISTER			OPMODE						

FNEG

15	14	13	12	11	10	9	8	7	6	5	4	3	2	1	0
1	1	1	1	COPROCESSOR ID			0	0	0	EFFECTIVE ADDRESS MODE			REGISTER		
0	R/M	0	SOURCE SPECIFIER			DESTINATION REGISTER			OPMODE						

FSQRT

15	14	13	12	11	10	9	8	7	6	5	4	3	2	1	0
1	1	1	1	COPROCESSOR ID			0	0	0	EFFECTIVE ADDRESS MODE			REGISTER		
0	R/M	0	SOURCE SPECIFIER			DESTINATION REGISTER			OPMODE						

FSUB

15	14	13	12	11	10	9	8	7	6	5	4	3	2	1	0
1	1	1	1	COPROCESSOR ID			0	0	0	EFFECTIVE ADDRESS MODE			REGISTER		
0	R/M	0	SOURCE SPECIFIER			DESTINATION REGISTER			OPMODE						

8

FMOVE

Data Register, Register to Memory

15	14	13	12	11	10	9	8	7	6	5	4	3	2	1	0
1	1	1	1	0	0	1	0	0	0	EFFECTIVE ADDRESS					
										MODE			REGISTER		
0	1	1	DESTINATION FORMAT			SOURCE REGISTER			K-FACTOR (IF REQUIRED)						

FMOVE

System Control Register

15	14	13	12	11	10	9	8	7	6	5	4	3	2	1	0
1	1	1	1	COPROCESSOR ID			0	0	0	EFFECTIVE ADDRESS					
										MODE			REGISTER		
1	0	dr	REGISTER SELECT		0	0	0	0	0	0	0	0	0	0	0

FMOVEM

Control Registers

15	14	13	12	11	10	9	8	7	6	5	4	3	2	1	0
1	1	1	1	COPROCESSOR ID			0	0	0	EFFECTIVE ADDRESS					
										MODE			REGISTER		
1	0	dr	REGISTER LIST		0	0	0	0	0	0	0	0	0	0	0

FMOVEM

Data Registers

15	14	13	12	11	10	9	8	7	6	5	4	3	2	1	0
1	1	1	1	COPROCESSOR ID			0	0	0	EFFECTIVE ADDRESS					
										MODE			REGISTER		
1	1	dr	MODE		0	0	0	REGISTER LIST							

cpGEN

15	14	13	12	11	10	9	8	7	6	5	4	3	2	1	0
1	1	1	1	COPROCESSOR ID			0	0	0	EFFECTIVE ADDRESS					
										MODE			REGISTER		
COPROCESSOR ID-DEPENDENT COMMAND WORD															
OPTIONAL EFFECTIVE ADDRESS OR COPROCESSOR ID-DEFINED EXTENSION WORDS															

FScc

15	14	13	12	11	10	9	8	7	6	5	4	3	2	1	0
1	1	1	1	COPROCESSOR ID			0	0	1	EFFECTIVE ADDRESS					
										MODE			REGISTER		
0	0	0	0	0	0	0	0	0	0	CONDITIONAL PREDICATE					

cpScc

15	14	13	12	11	10	9	8	7	6	5	4	3	2	1	0
1	1	1	1	COPROCESSOR ID			0	0	1	EFFECTIVE ADDRESS					
										MODE			REGISTER		
0	0	0	0	0	0	0	0	0	0	COPROCESSOR ID CONDITION					
OPTIONAL EFFECTIVE ADDRESS OR COPROCESSOR ID-DEFINED EXTENSION WORDS															

FBcc

15	14	13	12	11	10	9	8	7	6	5	4	3	2	1	0
1	1	1	1	COPROCESSOR ID			0	1	SIZE	CONDITIONAL PREDICATE					
16-BIT DISPLACEMENT OR MOST SIGNIFICANT WORD OF 32-BIT DISPLACEMENT															
LEAST SIGNIFICANT WORD OF 32-BIT DISPLACEMENT (IF NEEDED)															

cpBcc

15	14	13	12	11	10	9	8	7	6	5	4	3	2	1	0
1	1	1	1	COPROCESSOR ID			0	1	SIZE	COPROCESSOR ID CONDITION					
OPTIONAL COPROCESSOR ID-DEFINED EXTENSION WORDS															
WORD OR															
LONG-WORD DISPLACEMENT															

cpSAVE

15	14	13	12	11	10	9	8	7	6	5	4	3	2	1	0
1	1	1	1	COPROCESSOR ID			1	0	0	EFFECTIVE ADDRESS					
										MODE			REGISTER		

FSAVE

15	14	13	12	11	10	9	8	7	6	5	4	3	2	1	0
1	1	1	1	COPROCESSOR ID			1	0	0	EFFECTIVE ADDRESS					
										MODE			REGISTER		

8

cpRESTORE

15	14	13	12	11	10	9	8	7	6	5	4	3	2	1	0
1	1	1	1	COPROCESSOR ID			1	0	1	EFFECTIVE ADDRESS					
										MODE			REGISTER		

FRESTORE

15	14	13	12	11	10	9	8	7	6	5	4	3	2	1	0
1	1	1	1	COPROCESSOR ID			1	0	1	EFFECTIVE ADDRESS					
										MODE			REGISTER		

FDBcc

15	14	13	12	11	10	9	8	7	6	5	4	3	2	1	0
1	1	1	1	COPROCESSOR ID			0	0	1	0	0	1	COUNT REGISTER		
0	0	0	0	0	0	0	0	0	0	CONDITIONAL PREDICATE					
16-BIT DISPLACEMENT															

cpDBcc

15	14	13	12	11	10	9	8	7	6	5	4	3	2	1	0
1	1	1	1	COPROCESSOR ID			0	0	1	0	0	1	REGISTER		
0	0	0	0	0	0	0	0	0	0	COPROCESSOR ID CONDITION					
OPTIONAL COPROCESSOR ID-DEFINED EXTENSION WORDS															
16-BIT DISPLACEMENT															

FTRAPcc

15	14	13	12	11	10	9	8	7	6	5	4	3	2	1	0
1	1	1	1	COPROCESSOR ID			0	0	1	1	1	1	MODE		
0	0	0	0	0	0	0	0	0	0	CONDITIONAL PREDICATE					
16-BIT OPERAND OR MOST SIGNIFICANT WORD OF 32-BIT OPERAND (IF NEEDED)															
LEAST SIGNIFICANT WORD OR 32-BIT OPERAND (IF NEEDED)															

8

cpTRAPcc

15	14	13	12	11	10	9	8	7	6	5	4	3	2	1	0
1	1	1	1	COPROCESSOR ID			0	0	1	1	1	1	OPMODE		
0	0	0	0	0	0	0	0	0	0	COPROCESSOR ID CONDITION					
OPTIONAL COPROCESSOR ID-DEFINED EXTENSION WORDS															
OPTIONAL WORD															
OR LONG-WORD OPERAND															

FNOP

15	14	13	12	11	10	9	8	7	6	5	4	3	2	1	0
1	1	1	1	COPROCESSOR ID			0	1	0	0	0	0	0	0	0
0	0	0	0	0	0	0	0	0	0	0	0	0	0	0	0

8

8

APPENDIX A
PROCESSOR INSTRUCTION SUMMARY

This appendix provides a quick reference of the M68000 family instructions. The organization of this section is by processors and their addressing modes. All references to the MC68000, MC68020, and MC68030 include references to the corresponding embedded controllers, MC68EC000, MC68EC020, and MC68EC030. All references to the MC68040 include the MC68LC040 and MC68EC040. This referencing applies throughout this section unless otherwise specified. Table A-1 lists the M68000 family instructions by mnemonic and indicates which processors they apply to.

Table A-1. M68000 Family Instruction Set And Processor Cross-Reference

Mnemonic	68000	68008	68010	68020	68030	68040	68881/ 68882	68851	CPU32
ABCD	X	X	X	X	X	X			X
ADD	X	X	X	X	X	X			X
ADDA	X	X	X	X	X	X			X
ADDI	X	X	X	X	X	X			X
ADDQ	X	X	X	X	X	X			X
ADDX	X	X	X	X	X	X			X
AND	X	X	X	X	X	X			X
ANDI	X	X	X	X	X	X			X
ANDI to CCR	X	X	X	X	X	X			X
ANDI to SR[1]	X	X	X	X	X	X			X
ASL, ASR	X	X	X	X	X	X			X
Bcc	X	X	X	X	X	X			X
BCHG	X	X	X	X	X	X			X
BCLR	X	X	X	X	X	X			X
BFCHG				X	X	X			
BFCLR				X	X	X			
BFEXTS				X	X	X			
BFEXTU				X	X	X			
BFFFO				X	X	X			

A

Mnemonic	68000	68008	68010	68020	68030	68040	68881/ 68882	68851	CPU32
BFINS				X	X	X			
BFSET				X	X	X			
BFTST				X	X	X			
BGND									X
BKPT			X	X	X	X			X
BRA	X	X	X	X	X	X			X
BSET	X	X	X	X	X	X			X
BSR	X	X	X	X	X	X			X
BTST	X	X	X	X	X	X			X
CALLM				X					
CAS, CAS2				X	X	X			
CHK	X	X	X	X	X	X			X
CHK2				X	X	X			X
CINV[1]						X			
CLR	X	X	X	X	X	X			X
CMP	X	X	X	X	X	X			X
CMPA	X	X	X	X	X	X			X
CMPI	X	X	X	X	X	X			X
CMPM	X	X	X	X	X	X			X
CMP2				X	X	X			X
cpBcc				X	X				
cpDBcc				X	X				
cpGEN				X	X				
cpRESTORE[1]				X	X				
cpSAVE[1]				X	X				
cpScc				X	X				
cpTRAPcc				X	X				
CPUSH[1]						X			
DBcc	X	X	X	X	X	X			X
DIVS	X	X	X	X	X	X			X
DIVSL				X	X	X			X
DIVU	X	X	X	X	X	X			X
DIVUL				X	X	X			X

Mnemonic	68000	68008	68010	68020	68030	68040	68881/ 68882	68851	CPU32
EOR	X	X	X	X	X	X			X
EORI	X	X	X	X	X	X			X
EORI to CCR	X	X	X	X	X	X			X
EORI to SR[1]	X	X	X	X	X	X			X
EXG	X	X	X	X	X	X			X
EXT	X	X	X	X	X	X			X
EXTB				X	X	X			X
FABS						X^2	X		
FSABS, FDABS						X^2			
FACOS						2,3	X		
FADD						X^2	X		
FSADD, FDADD						X^2			
FASIN						2,3	X		
FATAN						2,3	X		
FATANH						2,3	X		
FBcc						X^2	X		
FCMP						X^2	X		
FCOS						2,3	X		
FCOSH						2,3	X		
FDBcc						X^2	X		
FDIV						X^2	X		
FSDIV, FDDIV						X^2			
FETOX						2,3	X		
FETOXM1						2,3	X		
FGETEXP						2,3	X		
FGETMAN						2,3	X		
FINT						2,3	X		
FINTRZ						2,3	X		
FLOG10						2,3	X		
FLOG2						2,3	X		
FLOGN						2,3	X		

A

Mnemonic	68000	68008	68010	68020	68030	68040	68881/ 68882	68851	CPU32
FLOGNP1						2,3			
FMOD						2,3	X		
FMOVE						X^2	X		
FSMOVE, FDMOVE						X^2			
FMOVECR						2,3	X		
FMOVEM						X^2	X		
FMUL						X^2	X		
FSMUL, FDMUL						X^2			
FNEG						X^2	X		
FSNEG, FDNEG						X^2			
FNOP						X^2	X		
FREM						2,3	X		
FRESTORE[1]						X^2	X		
FSAVE*						X^2	X		
FSCALE						2,3	X		
FScc						X^2	X		
FSGLDIV						2,3	X		
FSGLMUL						2,3	X		
FSIN						2,3	X		
FSINCOS						2,3	X		
FSINH						2,3	X		
FSQRT						X^2	X		
FSSQRT, FDSQRT						X^2			
FSUB						X^2	X		
FSSUB, FDSUB						X^2			
FTAN						2,3	X		
FTANH						2,3	X		
FTENTOX						2,3	X		
FTRAPcc						X^2	X		
FTST						X^2	X		

A

Mnemonic	68000	68008	68010	68020	68030	68040	68881/ 68882	68851	CPU32
FTWOTOX						2,3	X		
ILLEGAL	X	X	X	X	X	X			X
JMP	X	X	X	X	X	X			X
JSR	X	X	X	X	X	X			X
LEA	X	X	X	X	X	X			X
LINK	X	X	X	X	X	X			X
LPSTOP									X
LSL,LSR	X	X	X	X	X	X			X
MOVE	X	X	X	X	X	X			X
MOVEA	X	X	X	X	X	X			X
MOVE from CCR			X	X	X	X			X
MOVE to CCR	X	X	X	X	X	X			X
MOVE from SR[1]	4	4	X	X	X	X			X
MOVE to SR[1]	X	X	X	X	X	X			X
MOVE USP[1]	X	X	X	X	X	X			X
MOVE16						X			
MOVEC[1]			X	X	X	X			X
MOVEM	X	X	X	X	X	X			X
MOVEP	X	X	X	X	X	X			X
MOVEQ	X	X	X	X	X	X			X
MOVES[1]			X	X	X	X			X
MULS	X	X	X	X	X	X			X
MULU	X	X	X	X	X	X			X
NBCD	X	X	X	X	X	X			X
NEG	X	X	X	X	X	X			X
NEGX	X	X	X	X	X	X			X
NOP	X	X	X	X	X	X			X
NOT	X	X	X	X	X	X			X
OR	X	X	X	X	X	X			X
ORI	X	X	X	X	X	X			X
ORI to CCR	X	X	X	X	X	X			X

Mnemonic	68000	68008	68010	68020	68030	68040	68881/ 68882	68851	CPU32
ORI to SR[1]	X	X	X	X	X	X			X
PACK				X	X	X			
PBcc[1]								X	
PDBcc[1]								X	
PEA	X	X	X	X	X	X			X
PFLUSH[1]					X[5]	X		X	
PFLUSHA[1]					X[5]			X	
PFLUSHR[1]								X	
PFLUSHS[1]								X	
PLOAD[1]					X[5]			X	
PMOVE[1]					X			X	
PRESTORE[1]								X	
PSAVE[1]								X	
PScc[1]								X	
PTEST[1]					X	X		X	
PTRAPcc[1]								X	
PVALID								X	
RESET[1]	X	X	X	X	X	X			X
ROL,ROR	X	X	X	X	X	X			X
ROXL, ROXR	X	X	X	X	X	X			X
RTD				X	X	X	X		X
RTE[1]	X	X	X	X	X	X			X
RTM					X				
RTR	X	X	X	X	X	X			X
RTS	X	X	X	X	X	X			X
SBCD	X	X	X	X	X	X			X
Scc	X	X	X	X	X	X			X
STOP[1]	X	X	X	X	X	X			X
SUB	X	X	X	X	X	X			X
SUBA	X	X	X	X	X	X			X
SUBI	X	X	X	X	X	X			X
SUBQ	X	X	X	X	X	X			X
SUBX	X	X	X	X	X	X			X

Table A-1. M68000 Family Instruction Set And Processor Cross-Reference (Concluded)

Mnemonic	68000	68008	68010	68020	68030	68040	68881/ 68882	68851	CPU32
SWAP	X	X	X	X	X	X			X
TAS	X	X	X	X	X	X			X
TBLS, TBLSN									X
TBLU, TBLUN									X
TRAP	X	X	X	X	X	X			X
TRAPcc				X	X	X			X
TRAPV	X	X	X	X	X	X			X
TST	X	X	X	X	X	X			X
UNLK	X	X	X	X	X	X			X
UNPK				X	X	X			

NOTES:
1. Privileged (Supervisor) Instruction
2. Not applicable to MC68EC040 and MC68LC040.
3. These instructions are software supported on the MC68040.
4. This instruction is not privileged for the MC68000 and MC68008.
5. Not applicable to MC68EC030.

A

Table A-2 lists the M68000 family instructions by mnemonics, followed by the descriptive name.

Table A-2. M68000 Family Instruction Set

Mnemonic	Description
ABCD	Add Decimal with Extend
ADD	Add
ADDA	Address
ADDI	Add Immediate
ADDQ	Add Quick
ADDX	Add with Extend
AND	Logical AND
ANDI	Logical AND Immediate
ANDI to CCR	AND Immediate to Condition Code Register
ANDI to SR	AND Immediate to Status Register
ASL, ASR	Arithmetic Shift Left and Right
Bcc	Branch Conditionally
BCHG	Test Bit and Change
BCLR	Test Bit and Clear
BFCHG	Test Bit Field and Change
BFCLR	Test Bit Field and Clear
BFEXTS	Signed Bit Field Extract
BFEXTU	Unsigned Bit Field Extract
BFFFO	Bit Field Find First One
BFINS	Bit Field Insert
BFSET	Test Bit Field and Set
BFTST	Test Bit Field
BGND	Enter Background Mode
BKPT	Breakpoint
BRA	Branch
BSET	Test Bit and Set
BSR	Branch to Subroutine
BTST	Test Bit
CALLM	CALL Module
CAS	Compare and Swap Operands
CAS2	Compare and Swap Dual Operands
CHK	Check Register Against Bound
CHK2	Check Register Against Upper and Lower Bounds
CINV	Invalidate Cache Entries
CLR	Clear
CMP	Compare
CMPA	Compare Address
CMPI	Compare Immediate
CMPM	Compare Memory to Memory
CMP2	Compare Register Against Upper and Lower Bounds
cpBcc	Branch on Coprocessor Condition
cpDBcc	Test Coprocessor Condition Decrement and Branch
cpGEN	Coprocessor General Function
cpRESTORE	Coprocessor Restore Function

A

Mnemonic	Description
cpSAVE	Coprocessor Save Function
cpScc	Set on Coprocessor Condition
cpTRAPcc	Trap on Coprocessor Condition
CPUSH	Push then Invalidate Cache Entries
DBcc	Test Condition, Decrement and Branch
DIVS, DIVSL	Signed Divide
DIVU, DIVUL	Unsigned Divide
EOR	Logical Exclusive-OR
EORI	Logical Exclusive-OR Immediate
EORI to CCR	Exclusive-OR Immediate to Condition Code Register
EORI to SR	Exclusive-OR Immediate to Status Register
EXG	Exchange Registers
EXT, EXTB	Sign Extend
FABS	Floating-Point Absolute Value
FSFABS, FDFABS	Floating-Point Absolute Value (Single/Double Precision)
FACOS	Floating-Point Arc Cosine
FADD	Floating-Point Add
FSADD, FDADD	Floating-Point Add (Single/Double Precision)
FASIN	Floating-Point Arc Sine
FATAN	Floating-Point Arc Tangent
FATANH	Floating-Point Hyperbolic Arc Tangent
FBcc	Floating-Point Branch
FCMP	Floating-Point Compare
FCOS	Floating-Point Cosine
FCOSH	Floating-Point Hyperbolic Cosine
FDBcc	Floating-Point Decrement and Branch
FDIV	Floating-Point Divide
FSDIV, FDDIV	Floating-Point Divide (Single/Double Precision)
FETOX	Floating-Point e^x
FETOXM1	Floating-Point $e^x - 1$
FGETEXP	Floating-Point Get Exponent
FGETMAN	Floating-Point Get Mantissa
FINT	Floating-Point Integer Part
FINTRZ	Floating-Point Integer Part, Round-to-Zero
FLOG10	Floating-Point Log_{10}
FLOG2	Floating-Point Log_2
FLOGN	Floating-Point Log_e
FLOGNP1	Floating-Point $\text{Log}_e (x + 1)$
FMOD	Floating-Point Modulo Remainder
FMOVE	Move Floating-Point Register
FSMOVE,FDMOVE	Move Floating-Point Register (Single/Double Precision)
FMOVECR	Move Constant ROM
FMOVEM	Move Multiple Floating-Point Registers
FMUL	Floating-Point Multiply
FSMUL,FDMUL	Floating-Point Multiply (Single/Double Precision)
FNEG	Floating-Point Negate
FSNEG,FDNEG	Floating-Point Negate (Single/Double Precision)
FNOP	Floating-Point No Operation

A

Mnemonic	Description
FREM	IEEE Remainder
FRESTORE	Restore Floating-Point Internal State
FSAVE	Save Floating-Point Internal State
FSCALE	Floating-Point Scale Exponent
FScc	Floating-Point Set According to Condition
FSGLDIV	Single-Precision Divide
FSGLMUL	Single-Precision Multiply
FSIN	Sine
FSINCOS	Simultaneous Sine and Cosine
FSINH	Hyperbolic Sine
FSQRT	Floating-Point Square Root
FSSQRT,FDSQRT	Floating-Point Square Root (Single/Double Precision)
FSUB	Floating-Point Subtract
FSSUB,FDSUB	Floating-Point Subtract (Single/Double Precision)
FTAN	Tangent
FTANH	Hyperbolic Tangent
FTENTOX	Floating-Point 10^X
FTRAPcc	Floating-Point Trap On Condition
FTST	Floating-Point Test
FTWOTOX	Floating-Point 2^X
ILLEGAL	Take Illegal Instruction Trap
JMP	Jump
JSR	Jump to Subroutine
LEA	Load Effective Address
LINK	Link and Allocate
LPSTOP	Low-Power Stop
LSL, LSR	Logical Shift Left and Right
MOVE	Move
MOVEA	Move Address
MOVE from CCR	Move from Condition Code Register
MOVE from SR	Move from Status Register
MOVE to CCR	Move to Condition Code Register
MOVE to SR	Move to Status Register
MOVE USP	Move User Stack Pointer
MOVE16	16-Byte Block Move
MOVEC	Move Control Register
MOVEM	Move Multiple Registers
MOVEP	Move Peripheral
MOVEQ	Move Quick
MOVES	Move Alternate Address Space
MULS	Signed Multiply
MULU	Unsigned Multiply
NBCD	Negate Decimal with Extend
NEG	Negate
NEGX	Negate with Extend
NOP	No Operation
NOT	Logical Complement

A

Table A-2. M68000 Family Instruction Set (Concluded)

Mnemonic	Description
OR	Logical Inclusive-OR
ORI	Logical Inclusive-OR Immediate
ORI to CCR	Inclusive-OR Immediate to Condition Code Register
ORI to SR	Inclusive-OR Immediate to Status Register
PACK	Pack BCD
PBcc	Branch on PMMU Condition
PDBcc	Test, Decrement, and Branch on PMMU Condition
PEA	Push Effective Address
PFLUSH	Flush Entry(ies) in the ATCs
PFLUSHA	Flush Entry(ies) in the ATCs
PFLUSHR	Flush Entry(ies) in the ATCs and RPT Entries
PFLUSHS	Flush Entry(ies) in the ATCs
PLOAD	Load an Entry into the ATC
PMOVE	Move PMMU Register
PRESTORE	PMMU Restore Function
PSAVE	PMMU Save Function
PScc	Set on PMMU Condition
PTEST	Test a Logical Address
PTRAPcc	Trap on PMMU Condition
PVALID	Validate a Pointer
RESET	Reset External Devices
ROL, ROR	Rotate Left and Right
ROXL, ROXR	Rotate with Extend Left and Right
RTD	Return and Deallocate
RTE	Return from Exception
RTM	Return from Module
RTR	Return and Restore
RTS	Return from Subroutine
SBCD	Subtract Decimal with Extend
Scc	Set Conditionally
STOP	Stop
SUB	Subtract
SUBA	Subtract Address
SUBI	Subtract Immediate
SUBQ	Subtract Quick
SUBX	Subtract with Extend
SWAP	Swap Register Words
TAS	Test Operand and Set
TBLS, TBLSN	Signed Table Lookup with Interpolate
TBLU, TBLUN	Unsigned Table Lookup with Interpolate
TRAP	Trap
TRAPcc	Trap Conditionally
TRAPV	Trap on Overflow
TST	Test Operand
UNLK	Unlink
UNPK	Unpack BCD

A

A.1 MC68000, MC68008, MC68010 PROCESSORS

The following paragraphs provide information on the MC68000, MC68008, and MC68010 instruction set and addressing modes.

A.1.1 M68000, MC68008, and MC68010 Instruction Set

Table A-3 lists the instructions used with the MC68000 and MC68008 processors, and Table A-4 lists the instructions used with MC68010.

Table A-3. MC68000 and MC68008 Instruction Set

Mnemonic	Description
ABCD	Add Decimal with Extend
ADD	Add
ADDA	Add Address
ADDI	Add Immediate
ADDQ	Add Quick
ADDX	Add with Extend
AND	Logical AND
ANDI	Logical AND Immediate
ANDI to CCR	AND Immediate to Condition Code Register
ANDI to SR	AND Immediate to Status Register
ASL, ASR	Arithmetic Shift Left and Right
Bcc	Branch Conditionally
BCHG	Test Bit and Change
BCLR	Test Bit and Clear
BRA	Branch
BSET	Test Bit and Set
BSR	Branch to Subroutine
BTST	Test Bit
CHK	Check Register Against Bound
CLR	Clear
CMP	Compare
CMPA	Compare Address
CMPI	Compare Immediate
CMPM	Compare Memory to Memory
DBcc	Test Condition, Decrement, and Branch
DIVS	Signed Divide
DIVU	Unsigned Divide
EOR	Logical Exclusive-OR
EORI	Logical Exclusive-OR Immediate
EORI to CCR	Exclusive-OR Immediate to Condition Code Register
EORI to SR	Exclusive-OR Immediate to Status Register
EXG	Exchange Registers
EXT	Sign Extend
ILLEGAL	Take Illegal Instruction Trap
JMP	Jump
JSR	Jump to Subroutine

A

Mnemonic	Description
LEA	Load Effective Address
LINK	Link and Allocate
LSL, LSR	Logical Shift Left and Right
MOVE	Move
MOVEA	Move Address
MOVE to CCR	Move to Condition Code Register
MOVE from SR	Move from Status Register
MOVE to SR	Move to Status Register
MOVE USP	Move User Stack Pointer
MOVEM	Move Multiple Registers
MOVEP	Move Peripheral
MOVEQ	Move Quick
MULS	Signed Multiply
MULU	Unsigned Multiply
NBCD	Negate Decimal with Extend
NEG	Negate
NEGX	Negate with Extend
NOP	No Operation
NOT	Logical Complement
OR	Logical Inclusive-OR
ORI	Logical Inclusive-OR Immediate
ORI to CCR	Inclusive-OR Immediate to Condition Code Register
ORI to SR	Inclusive-OR Immediate to Status Register
PEA	Push Effective Address
RESET	Reset External Devices
ROL, ROR	Rotate Left and Right
ROXL, ROXR	Rotate with Extend Left and Right
RTE	Return from Exception
RTR	Return and Restore
RTS	Return from Subroutine
SBCD	Subtract Decimal with Extend
Scc	Set Conditionally
STOP	Stop
SUB	Subtract
SUBA	Subtract Address
SUBI	Subtract Immediate
SUBQ	Subtract Quick
SUBX	Subtract with Extend
SWAP	Swap Register Words
TAS	Test Operand and Set
TRAP	Trap
TRAPV	Trap on Overflow
TST	Test Operand
UNLK	Unlink

A

Table A-4. MC68010 Instruction Set

Mnemonic	Description
ABCD	Add Decimal with Extend
ADD	Add
ADDA	Add Address
ADDI	Add Immediate
ADDQ	Add Quick
ADDX	Add with Extend
AND	Logical AND
ANDI	Logical AND Immediate
ANDI to CCR	AND Immediate to Condition Code Register
ANDI to SR	AND Immediate to Status Register
ASL, ASR	Arithmetic Shift Left and Right
Bcc	Branch Conditionally
BCHG	Test Bit and Change
BCLR	Test Bit and Clear
BKPT	Breakpoint
BRA	Branch
BSET	Test Bit and Set
BSR	Branch to Subroutine
BTST	Test Bit
CHK	Check Register Against Bound
CLR	Clear
CMP	Compare
CMPA	Compare Address
CMPI	Compare Immediate
CMPM	Compare Memory to Memory
DBcc	Test Condition, Decrement and Branch
DIVS	Signed Divide
DIVU	Unsigned Divide
EOR	Logical Exclusive-OR
EORI	Logical Exclusive-OR Immediate
EORI to CCR	Exclusive-OR Immediate to Condition Code Register
EORI to SR	Exclusive-OR Immediate to Status Register
EXG	Exchange Registers
EXT	Sign Extend
ILLEGAL	Take Illegal Instruction Trap
JMP	Jump
JSR	Jump to Subroutine

A

Mnemonic	Description
LEA	Load Effective Address
LINK	Link and Allocate
LSL, LSR	Logical Shift Left and Right
MOVE	Move
MOVEA	Move Address
MOVE from CCR	Move from Condition Code Register
MOVE from SR	Move from Status Register
MOVE to CCR	Move to Condition Code Register
MOVE to SR	Move to Status Register
MOVE USP	Move User Stack Pointer
MOVEC	Move Control Register
MOVEM	Move Multiple Registers
MOVEP	Move Peripheral
MOVEQ	Move Quick
MOVES	Move Address Space
MULS	Signed Multiply
MULU	Unsigned Multiply
NBCD	Negate Decimal with Extend
NEG	Negate
NEGX	Negate with Extend
NOP	No Operation
NOT	Logical Complement
OR	Logical Inclusive-OR
ORI	Logical Inclusive-OR Immediate
ORI to CCR	Inclusive-OR Immediate to Condition Code Register
ORI to SR	Inclusive-OR Immediate to Status Register
PEA	Push Effective Address
RESET	Reset External Devices
ROL, ROR	Rotate Left and Right
ROXL, ROXR	Rotate with Extend Left and Right
RTD	Return and Deallocate
RTE	Return from Exception
RTR	Return and Restore
RTS	Return from Subroutine
SBCD	Subtract Decimal with Extend
Scc	Set Conditionally
STOP	Stop
SUB	Subtract
SUBA	Subtract Address
SUBI	Subtract Immediate
SUBQ	Subtract Quick
SUBX	Subtract with Extend
SWAP	Swap Register Words
TAS	Test Operand and Set
TRAP	Trap
TRAPV	Trap on Overflow
TST	Test Operand
UNLK	Unlink

A

A.1.2 MC68000, MC68008, and MC68010 Addressing Modes

The MC68000, MC68008, and MC68010 support 14 addressing modes as shown in Table A-5.

**Table A-5. MC68000, MC68008, and MC68010
Data Addressing Modes**

Mode	Generation
Register Direct Addressing	
Data Register Direct	\<ea\> = Dn
Address Register Direct	\<ea\> = An
Absolute Data Addressing	
Absolute Short	\<ea\> = (Next Word)
Absolute Long	\<ea\> = (Next Two Words)
Program Counter Relative Addressing	
Relative with Offset	$\<ea\> = (PC) + d_{16}$
Relative with Index and Offset	$\<ea\> = (PC) + d_8$
Register Indirect Addressing	
Register Indirect	\<ea\> = (An)
Postincrement Register Indirect	\<ea\> = (An), An ♦ An + N
Predecrement Register Indirect	An ♦ An–N, \<ea\> = (An)
Register Indirect with Offset	$\<ea\> = (An) + d_{16}$
Indexed Register Indirect with Offset	$\<ea\> = (An) + (Xn) + d_8$
Immediate Data Addressing	
Immediate	DATA = Next Word(s)
Quick Immediate	Inherent Data
Implied Addressing	\<ea\> = SR, USP, SSP,
Implied Register	PC, VBR, SFC, DFC

NOTE: N = 1 for byte, 2 for word, and 4 for long word. If An is the stack pointer and the operand size is byte, N = 2 to keep the stack pointer on a word boundary.

A

A.2 MC68020 PROCESSORS

The following paragraphs provide information on the MC68020 instruction set and addressing modes.

A.2.1 MC68020 Instruction Set

Table A-6 lists the instructions used with the MC68020 processors.

Table A-6. MC68020 Instruction Set Summary

Mnemonic	Description
ABCD	Add Decimal with Extend
ADD	Add
ADDA	Add Address
ADDI	Add Immediate
ADDQ	Add Quick
ADDX	Add with Extend
AND	Logical AND
ANDI	Logical AND Immediate
ANDI to CCR	AND Immediate to Condition Code Register
ANDI to SR	AND Immediate to Status Register
ASL, ASR	Arithmetic Shift Left and Right
Bcc	Branch Conditionally
BCHG	Test Bit and Change
BCLR	Test Bit and Clear
BFCHG	Test Bit Field and Change
BFCLR	Test Bit Field and Clear
BFEXTS	Signed Bit Field Extract
BFEXTU	Unsigned Bit Field Extract
BFFFO	Bit Field Find First One
BFINS	Bit Field Insert
BFSET	Test Bit Field and Set
BFTST	Test Bit Field
BKPT	Breakpoint
BRA	Branch
BSET	Test Bit and Set
BSR	Branch to Subroutine
BTST	Test Bit
CALLM	CALL Module
CAS	Compare and Swap Operands
CAS2	Compare and Swap Dual Operands
CHK	Check Register Against Bound
CHK2	Check Register Against Upper and Lower Bounds
CLR	Clear
CMP	Compare
CMP2	Compare Register Against Upper and Lower Bounds
CMPA	Compare Address
CMPI	Compare Immediate

A

Table A-6. MC68020 Instruction Set Summary (Continued)

Mnemonic	Description
CMPM	Compare Memory to Memory
cpBcc	Branch to Coprocessor Condition
cpDBcc	Test Coprocessor Condition, Decrement and Branch
cpGEN	Coprocessor General Function
cpRESTORE	Coprocessor Restore Function
cpSAVE	Coprocessor Save Function
cpScc	Set on Coprocessor Condition
cpTRACPcc	Trap on Coprocessor Condition
DBcc	Test Condition, Decrement, and Branch
DIVS, DIVSL	Signed Divide
DIVU, DIVUL	Unsigned Divide
EOR	Logical Exclusive-OR
EORI	Logical Exclusive-OR Immediate
EORI to CCR	Exclusive-OR Immediate to Condition Code Register
EORI to SR	Exclusive-OR Immediate to Status Register
EXG	Exchange Registers
EXT, EXTB	Sign Extend
ILLEGAL	Take Illegal Instruction Trap
JMP	Jump
JSR	Jump to Subroutine
LEA	Load Effective Address
LINK	Link and Allocate
LSL, LSR	Logical Shift Left and Right
MOVE	Move
MOVEA	Move Address
MOVE from CCR	Move from Condition Code Register
MOVE from SR	Move from Status Register
MOVE to CCR	Move to Condition Code Register
MOVE to SR	Move to Status Register
MOVE USP	Move User Stack Pointer
MOVEC	Move Control Register
MOVEM	Move Multiple Registers
MOVEP	Move Peripheral
MOVEQ	Move Quick
MOVES	Move Alternate Address Space
MULS	Signed Multiply
MULU	Unsigned Multiply
NBCD	Negate Decimal with Extend
NEG	Negate
NEGX	Negate with Extend
NOP	No Operation
NOT	Logical Complement

A

Table A-6. MC68020 Instruction Set Summary
(Concluded)

Mnemonic	Description
OR	Logical Inclusive-OR
ORI	Logical Inclusive-OR Immediate
ORI to CCR	Inclusive-OR Immediate to Condition Code Register
ORI to SR	Inclusive-OR Immediate to Status Register
PACK	Pack BCD
PEA	Push Effective Address
RESET	Reset External Devices
ROL, ROR	Rotate Left and Right
ROXL, ROXR	Rotate with Extend Left and Right
RTD	Return and Deallocate
RTE	Return from Exception
RTM	Return from Module
RTR	Return and Restore
RTS	Return from Subroutine
SBCD	Subtract Decimal with Extend
Scc	Set Conditionally
STOP	Stop
SUB	Subtract
SUBA	Subtract Address
SUBI	Subtract Immediate
SUBQ	Subtract Quick
SUBX	Subtract with Extend
SWAP	Swap Register Words
TAS	Test Operand and Set
TRAP	Trap
TRAPcc	Trap Conditionally
TRAPV	Trap on Overflow
TST	Test Operand
UNLK	Unlink
UNPK	Unpack BCD

A

A.2.2 MC68020 Addressing Modes

The MC68020 supports 18 addressing modes as shown in Table A-7.

Table A-7. MC68020 Data Addressing Modes

Addressing Modes	Syntax
Register Direct	
Address Register Direct	Dn
Address Register Direct	An
Register Indirect	
Address Register Indirect	(An)
Address Register Indirect with Postincrement	(An)+
Address Register Indirect with Predecrement	−(An)
Address Register Indirect with Displacement	(d_{16},An)
Register Indirect with Index	
Address Register Indirect with Index (8-Bit Displacement)	(d_8,An,Xn)
Address Register Indirect with Index (Base Displacement)	(bd,An,Xn)
Memory Indirect	
Memory Indirect Postindexed	([bd,An],Xn,od)
Memory Indirect Preindexed	([bd,An,Xn],od)
Program Counter Indirect with Displacement	(d_{16},PC)
Program Counter Indirect with Index	
PC Indirect with Index (8-Bit Displacement)	(d_8,PC,Xn)
PC Indirect with Index (Base Displacement)	(bd,PC,Xn)
Program Counter Memory Indirect	
PC Memory Indirect Postindexed	([bd,PC],Xn,od)
PC Memory Indirect Preindexed	([bd,PC,Xn],od)
Absolute	
Absolute Short	(xxx).W
Absolute Long	(xxx).L
Immediate	#<data>

A

A.3 MC68030 PROCESSORS

The following paragraphs provide information on the MC68030 instruction set and addressing modes.

A.3.1 MC68030 Instruction Set

Table A-8 lists the instructions used with the MC68030 processors.

Table A-8. MC68030 Instruction Set Summary

Mnemonic	Description
ABCD	Add Decimal with Extend
ADD	Add
ADDA	Add Address
ADDI	Add Immediate
ADDQ	Add Quick
ADDX	Add with Extend
AND	Logical AND
ANDI	Logical AND Immediate
ANDI to CCR	AND Immediate to Condition Code Register
ANDI to SR	AND Immediate to Status Register
ASL, ASR	Arithmetic Shift Left and Right
Bcc	Branch Conditionally
BCHG	Test Bit and Change
BCLR	Test Bit and Clear
BFCHG	Test Bit Field and Change
BFCLR	Test Bit Field and Clear
BFEXTS	Signed Bit Field Extract
BFEXTU	Unsigned Bit Field Extract
BFFFO	Bit Field Find First One
BFINS	Bit Field Insert
BFSET	Test Bit Field and Set
BFTST	Test Bit Field
BKPT	Breakpoint
BRA	Branch
BSET	Test Bit and Set
BSR	Branch to Subroutine
BTST	Test Bit
CAS	Compare and Swap Operands
CAS2	Compare and Swap Dual Operands
CHK	Check Register Against Bound
CHK2	Check Register Against Upper and Lower Bounds
CLR	Clear
CMP	Compare
CMPA	Compare Address
CMPI	Compare Immediate
CMPM	Compare Memory to Memory

A

Table A-8. MC68030 Instruction Set Summary
(Continued)

Mnemonic	Description
CMP2	Compare Register Against Upper and Lower Bounds
cpBcc	Branch on Coprocessor Condition
cpDBcc	Test Coprocessor Condition, Decrement and Branch
cpGEN	Coprocessor General Function
cpRESTORE	Coprocessor Restore Function
cpSAVE	Coprocessor Save Function
cpScc	Set on Coprocessor Condition
cpTRAPcc	Trap on Coprocessor Condition
DBcc	Test Condition, Decrement and Branch
DIVS, DIVSL	Signed Divide
DIVU, DIVUL	Unsigned Divide
EOR	Logical Exclusive-OR
EORI	Logical Exclusive-OR Immediate
EORI to CCR	Exclusive-OR Immediate to Condition Code Register
EORI to SR	Exclusive-OR Immediate to Status Register
EXG	Exchange Registers
EXT, EXTB	Sign Extend
ILLEGAL	Take Illegal Instruction Trap
JMP	Jump
JSR	Jump to Subroutine
LEA	Load Effective Address
LINK	Link and Allocate
LSL, LSR	Logical Shift Left and Right
MOVE	Move
MOVEA	Move Address
MOVE from CCR	Move from Condition Code Register
MOVE to CCR	Move to Condition Code Register
MOVE from SR	Move from Status Register
MOVE to SR	Move to Status Register
MOVE USP	Move User Stack Pointer
MOVEC	Move Control Register
MOVEM	Move Multiple Registers
MOVEP	Move Peripheral
MOVEQ	Move Quick
MOVES	Move Alternate Address Space
MULS	Signed Multiply
MULU	Unsigned Multiply
NBCD	Negate Decimal with Extend
NEG	Negate
NEGX	Negate with Extend
NOP	No Operation
NOT	Logical Complement

A

Table A-8. MC68030 Instruction Set Summary
(Concluded)

Mnemonic	Description
NBCD	Negate Decimal with Extend
NEG	Negate
NEGX	Negate with Extend
NOP	No Operation
NOT	Logical Complement
OR	Logical Inclusive-OR
ORI	Logical Inclusive-OR Immediate
ORI to CCR	Inclusive-OR Immediate to Condition Code Register
ORI to SR	Inclusive-OR Immediate to Status Register
PACK	Pack BCD
PEA	Push Effective Address
PFLUSH*	Invalidate Entries in the ATC
PFLUSHA*	Invalidate all Entries in the ATC
PLOAD*	Load an Entry into the ATC
PMOVE	Move PMMU Register
PTEST	Get Information about Logical Address
RESET	Reset External Devices
ROL, ROR	Rotate Left and Right
ROXL, ROXR	Rotate with Extend Left and Right
RTD	Return and Deallocate
RTE	Return from Exception
RTR	Return and Restore
RTS	Return from Subroutine
SBCD	Subtract Decimal with Extend
Scc	Set Conditionally
STOP	Stop
SUB	Subtract
SUBA	Subtract Address
SUBI	Subtract Immediate
SUBQ	Subtract Quick
SUBX	Subtract with Extend
SWAP	Swap Register Words
TAS	Test Operand and Set
TRAP	Trap
TRAPcc	Trap Conditionally
TRAPV	Trap on Overflow
TST	Test Operand
UNLK	Unlink
UNPK	Unpack BCD

* Not applicable to the MC68EC030.

A

A.3.2 MC68030 Addressing Modes

The MC68030 supports 18 addressing modes as shown in Table A-9.

Table A-9. MC68030 Data Addressing Modes

Addressing Modes	Syntax
Register Direct	
Data Register Direct	Dn
Address Register Direct	An
Register Indirect	
Address Register Indirect	(An)
Address Register Indirect with Postincrement	(An)+
Address Register Indirect with Predecrement	–(An)
Address Register Indirect with Displacement	(d_{16},An)
Register Indirect with Index	
Address Register Indirect with Index (8-Bit Displacement)	(d_8,An,Xn)
Address Register Indirect with Index (Base Displacement)	(bd,An,Xn)
Memory Indirect	
Memory Indirect Postindexed	([bd,An],Xn,od)
Memory Indirect Preindexed	([bd,An,Xn],od)
Program Counter Indirect with Displacement	(d_{16},PC)
Program Counter Indirect with Index	
PC Indirect with Index (8-Bit Displacement)	(d_8,PC,Xn)
PC Indirect with Index (Base Displacement)	(bd,PC,Xn)
Program Counter Memory Indirect	
PC Memory Indirect Postindexed	([bd,PC],Xn,od)
PC Memory Indirect Preindexed	([bd,PC,Xn],od)
Absolute	
Absolute Short	(xxx).W
Absolute Long	(xxx).L
Immediate	#<data>

A

A.4 MC68040 PROCESSORS

The following paragraphs provide information on the MC68040 instruction set and addressing modes.

A.4.1 MC68040 Instruction Set

Table A-10 lists the instructions used with the MC68040 processor.

Table A-10. MC68040 Instruction Set

Mnemonic	Description
ABCD	Add Decimal with Extend
ADD	Add
ADDA	Add Address
ADDI	Add Immediate
ADDQ	Add Quick
ADDX	Add with Extend
AND	Logical AND
ANDI	Logical AND Immediate
ANDI to CCR	AND Immediate to Condition Code Register
ANDI to SR	AND Immediate to Status Register
ASL, ASR	Arithmetic Shift Left and Right
Bcc	Branch Conditionally
BCHG	Test Bit and Change
BCLR	Test Bit and Clear
BFCHG	Test Bit Field and Change
BFCLR	Test Bit Field and Clear
BFEXTS	Signed Bit Field Extract
BFEXTU	Unsigned Bit Field Extract
BFFFO	Bit Field Find First One
BFINS	Bit Field Insert
BFSET	Test Bit Field and Set
BFTST	Test Bit Field
BKPT	Breakpoint
BRA	Branch
BSET	Test Bit and Set
BSR	Branch to Subroutine
BTST	Test Bit
CAS	Compare and Swap Operands
CAS2	Compare and Swap Dual Operands
CHK	Check Register Against Bound
CHK2	Check Register Against Upper and Lower Bounds
CINV	Invalidate Cache Entries
CLR	Clear
CMP	Compare
CMPA	Compare Address

A

Table A-10. MC68040 Instruction Set (Continued)

Mnemonic	Description
CMPI	Compare Immediate
CMPM	Compare Memory to Memory
CMP2	Compare Register Against Upper and Lower Bounds
CPUSH	Push then Invalidate Cache Entries
DBcc	Test Condition, Decrement and Branch
DIVS, DIVSL	Signed Divide
DIVU, DIVUL	Unsigned Divide
EOR	Logical Exclusive-OR
EORI	Logical Exclusive-OR Immediate
EORI to CCR	Exclusive-OR Immediate to Condition Code Register
EORI to SR	Exclusive-OR Immediate to Status Register
EXG	Exchange Registers
EXT, EXTB	Sign Extend
FABS[1]	Floating-Point Absolute Value
FSABS, FDABS[1]	Floating-Point Absolute Value (Single/Double Precision)
FACOS[1,2]	Floating-Point Arc Cosine
FADD[1]	Floating-Point Add
FSADD, FDADD[1]	Floating-Point Add (Single/Double Precision)
FASIN[1,2]	Floating-Point Arc Sine
FATAN[1,2]	Floating-Point Arc Tangent
FATANH[1,2]	Floating-Point Hyperbolic Arc Tangent
FBcc[1]	Floating-Point Branch
FCMP[1]	Floating-Point Compare
FCOS[1,2]	Floating-Point Cosine
FCOSH[1,2]	Floating-Point Hyperbolic Cosine
FDBcc[1]	Floating-Point Decrement and Branch
FDIV[1]	Floating-Point Divide
FSDIV, FDDIV[1]	Floating-Point Divide (Single/Double Precision)
FETOX[1,2]	Floating-Point e^x
FETOXM1[1,2]	Floating-Point $e^x - 1$
FGETEXP[1,2]	Floating-Point Get Exponent
FGETMAN[1,2]	Floating-Point Get Mantissa
FINT[1,2]	Floating-Point Integer Part
FINTRZ[1,2]	Floating-Point Integer Part, Round-to-Zero
FLOG10[1,2]	Floating-Point Log_{10}
FLOG2[1,2]	Floating-Point Log_2
FLOGN[1,2]	Floating-Point Log_e
FLOGNP1[1,2]	Floating-Point Log_e $(x + 1)$
FMOD[1,2]	Floating-Point Modulo Remainder
FMOVE[1]	Move Floating-Point Register
FSMOVE, FDMOVE[1]	Move Floating-Point Register (Single/Double Precision)
FMOVECR[1]	Move Constant ROM
FMOVEM[1]	Move Multiple Floating-Point Registers
FMUL[1]	Floating-Point Multiply
FSMUL, FDMUL[1]	Floating-Point Multiply (Single/Double Precision)

A

Mnemonic	Description
FNEG[1]	Floating-Point Negate
FSNEG, FDNEG[1]	Floating-Point Negate (Single/Double Precision)
FNOP[1]	Floating-Point No Operation
FREM[1,2]	IEEE Remainder
FRESTORE[1]	Restore Floating-Point Internal State
FSAVE[1]	Save Floating-Point Internal State
FSCALE[1,2]	Floating-Point Scale Exponent
FScc[1]	Floating-Point Set According to Condition
FSGLDIV[1,2]	Single-Precision Divide
FSGLMUL[1,2]	Single-Precision Multiply
FSIN[1,2]	Sine
FSINCOS[1,2]	Simultaneous Sine and Cosine
FSINH[1,2]	Hyperbolic Sine
FSQRT[1]	Floating-Point Square Root
FSSQRT, FDSQRT[1]	Floating-Point Square Root (Single/Double Precision)
FSUB[1]	Floating-Point Subtract
FSSUB, FDSUB[1]	Floating-Point Subtract (Single/Double Precision)
FTAN[1,2]	Tangent
FTANH[1,2]	Hyperbolic Tangent
FTENTOX[1,2]	Floating-Point 10^x
FTRAPcc[1,2]	Floating-Point Trap On Condition
FTST[1]	Floating-Point Test
FTWOTOX[1,2]	Floating-Point 2^x
ILLEGAL	Take Illegal Instruction Trap
JMP	Jump
JSR	Jump to Subroutine
LEA	Load Effective Address
LINK	Link and Allocate
LSL, LSR	Logical Shift Left and Right
MOVE	Move
MOVEA	Move Address
MOVE from CCR	Move from Condition Code Register
MOVE to CCR	Move to Condition Code Register
MOVE from SR	Move from Status Register
MOVE to SR	Move to Status Register
MOVE USP	Move User Stack Pointer
MOVEC	Move Control Register
MOVEM	Move Multiple Registers
MOVEP	Move Peripheral
MOVEQ	Move Quick
MOVES	Move Alternate Address Space
MOVE16	16-Byte Block Move
MULS	Signed Multiply
MULU	Unsigned Multiply

A

Table A-10. MC68040 Instruction Set (Concluded)

Mnemonic	Description
NBCD	Negate Decimal with Extend
NEG	Negate
NEGX	Negate with Extend
NOP	No Operation
NOT	Logical Complement
OR	Logical Inclusive-OR
ORI	Logical Inclusive-OR Immediate
ORI to CCR	Inclusive-OR Immediate to Condition Code Register
ORI to SR	Inclusive-OR Immediate to Status Register
PACK	Pack BCD
PEA	Push Effective Address
PFLUSH	Flush Entry(ies) in the ATCs
PFLUSHA	Flush all Entry(ies) in the ATCs
PTEST	Test a Logical Address
RESET	Reset External Devices
ROL, ROR	Rotate Left and Right
ROXL, ROXR	Rotate with Extend Left and Right
RTD	Return and Deallocate
RTE	Return from Exception
RTR	Return and Restore
RTS	Return from Subroutine
SBCD	Subtract Decimal with Extend
Scc	Set Conditionally
STOP	Stop
SUB	Subtract
SUBA	Subtract Address
SUBI	Subtract Immediate
SUBQ	Subtract Quick
SUBX	Subtract with Extend
SWAP	Swap Register Words
TAS	Test Operand and Set
TRAP	Trap
TRAPcc	Trap Conditionally
TRAPV	Trap on Overflow
TST	Test Operand
UNLK	Unlink
UNPK	Unpack BCD

NOTES:
1. Not applicable to the MC68EC040 and MC68LC040.
2. These instructions are software supported.

A

A.4.2 MC68040 Addressing Modes

The MC68040 supports 18 addressing modes as shown in Table A-11.

Table A-11. MC68040 Data Addressing Modes

Addressing Modes	Syntax

Register Direct
    Data Register Direct
    Address Register Direct
	
	Dn
	An

Register Indirect
    Address Register Indirect
    Address Register Indirect with Postincrement
    Address Register Indirect with Predecrement
    Address Register Indirect with Displacement
	
	(An)
	(An)+
	–(An)
	(d_{16},An)

Register Indirect with Index
    Address Register Indirect with Index (8-Bit Displacement)
    Address Register Indirect with Index (Base Displacement)
	
	(d_8,An,Xn)
	(bd,An,Xn)

Memory Indirect
    Memory Indirect Postindexed
    Memory Indirect Preindexed
	
	([bd,An],Xn,od)
	([bd,An,Xn],od)

Program Counter Indirect with Displacement	(d_{16},PC)

Program Counter Indirect with Index
    PC Indirect with Index (8-Bit Displacement)
    PC Indirect with Index (Base Displacement)
	
	(d_8,PC,Xn)
	(bd,PC,Xn)

Program Counter Memory Indirect
    PC Memory Indirect Postindexed
    PC Memory Indirect Preindexed
	
	([bd,PC],Xn,od)
	([bd,PC,Xn],od)

Absolute
    Absolute Short
    Absolute Long
	
	xxx.W
	xxx.L

Immediate	#<data>

A

A.5 MC68881/MC68882 COPROCESSORS

The following paragraphs provide information on the MC68881/MC68882 instruction set and addressing modes.

A.5.1 MC68881/MC68882 Instruction Set

Table A-12 lists the instructions used with the MC68881/MC68882 coprocessors.

Table A-12. MC68881/MC68882 Instruction Set

Mnemonic	Description
FABS	Floating-Point Absolute Value
FACOS	Floating-Point Arc Cosine
FADD	Floating-Point Add
FASIN	Floating-Point Arc Sine
FATAN	Floating-Point Arc Tangent
FATANH	Floating-Point Hyperbolic Arc Tangent
FBcc	Floating-Point Branch
FCMP	Floating-Point Compare
FCOS	Floating-Point Cosine
FCOSH	Floating-Point Hyperbolic Cosine
FDBcc	Floating-Point Decrement and Branch
FDIV	Floating-Point Divide
FETOX	Floating-Point e^x
FETOXM1	Floating-Point $e^x - 1$
FGETEXP	Floating-Point Get Exponent
FGETMAN	Floating-Point Get Mantissa
FINT	Floating-Point Integer Part
FINTRZ	Floating-Point Integer Part, Round-to-Zero
FLOG10	Floating-Point Log_{10}
FLOG2	Floating-Point Log_2
FLOGN	Floating-Point Log_e
FLOGNP1	Floating-Point $\text{Log}_e (x + 1)$
FMOD	Floating-Point Modulo Remainder
FMOVE	Move Floating-Point Register
FMOVECR	Move Constant ROM
FMOVEM	Move Multiple Floating-Point Registers
FMUL	Floating-Point Multiply
FNEG	Floating-Point Negate
FNOP	Floating-Point No Operation
FREM	IEEE Remainder
FRESTORE	Restore Floating-Point Internal State
FSAVE	Save Floating-Point Internal State
FSCALE	Floating-Point Scale Exponent
FScc	Floating-Point Set According to Condition
FSGLDIV	Single-Precision Divide
FSGLMUL	Single-Precision Multiply
FSIN	Sine
FSINCOS	Simultaneous Sine and Cosine
FSINH	Hyperbolic Sine

Table A-12. MC68881/MC68882 Instruction Set (Continued)

Mnemonic	Description
FSQRT	Floating-Point Square Root
FSUB	Floating-Point Subtract
FTAN	Tangent
FTANH	Hyperbolic Tangent
FTENTOX	Floating-Point 10^X
FTRAPcc	Floating-Point Trap On Condition
FTST	Floating-Point Test
FTWOTOX	Floating-Point 2^X

A.5.2 MC68881/MC68882 Addressing Modes

The MC68881/MC68882 does not perform address calculations. When the floating-point coprocessor instructs the processor to transfer an operand via the coprocessor interface, the processor performs the addressing mode calculation requested in the instruction.

A.6 MC68851 COPROCESSORS

The following paragraphs provide information on the MC68851 instruction set and addressing modes.

A.6.1 MC68851 Instruction Set

Table A-13 lists the instructions used with the MC68851 coprocessor.

Table A-13. MC68851 Instruction Set

Mnemonic	Description
PBcc	Branch on PMMU Condition
PDBcc	Test, Decrement, and Branch on PMMU Condition
PFLUSH	Flush Entry(ies) in the ATCs
PFLUSHA	Flush Entry(ies) in the ATCs
PFLUSHR	Flush Entry(ies) in the ATCs and RPT Entries
PFLUSHS	Flush Entry(ies) in the ATCs
PLOAD	Load an Entry into the ATC
PMOVE	Move PMMU Register
PRESTORE	PMMU Restore Function
PSAVE	PMMU Save Function
PScc	Set on PMMU Condition
PTEST	Test a Logical Address
PTRAPcc	Trap on PMMU Condition
PVALID	Validate a Pointer

A.6.2 MC68851 Addressing Modes

The MC68851 supports the same addressing modes as the MC68020 (see Table A-7).

A

APPENDIX B
EXCEPTION PROCESSING REFERENCE

This appendix provides a quick reference for system programmers who are already familiar with the stack frames. For more detail, please refer to the appropriate user's manual.

B.1 EXCEPTION VECTOR ASSIGNMENTS FOR THE M68000 FAMILY

Table B-1 lists all vector assignments up to and including the MC68040 and its derivatives. Many of these vector assignments are processor specific. For instance, vector 13, the coprocessor protocol violation vector, only applies to the MC68020, MC68EC020, MC68030, and MC68EC030. Refer to the appropriate user's manual to determine which exception type is applicable to a specific processor.

B

Table B-1. Exception Vector Assignments for the M68000 Family

Vector Number(s)	Vector Offset (Hex)	Assignment
0	000	Reset Initial Interrupt Stack Pointer
1	004	Reset Initial Program Counter
2	008	Access Fault
3	00C	Address Error
4	010	Illegal Instruction
5	014	Integer Divide by Zero
6	018	CHK, CHK2 Instruction
7	01C	FTRAPcc, TRAPcc, TRAPV Instructions
8	020	Privilege Violation
9	024	Trace
10	028	Line 1010 Emulator (Unimplemented A-Line Opcode)
11	02C	Line 1111 Emulator (Unimplemented F-Line Opcode)
12	030	(Unassigned, Reserved)
13	034	Coprocessor Protocol Violation
14	038	Format Error
15	03C	Uninitialized Interrupt
16–23	040–05C	(Unassigned, Reserved)
24	060	Spurious Interrupt
25	064	Level 1 Interrupt Autovector
26	068	Level 2 Interrupt Autovector
27	06C	Level 3 Interrupt Autovector
28	070	Level 4 Interrupt Autovector
29	074	Level 5 Interrupt Autovector
30	078	Level 6 Interrupt Autovector
31	07C	Level 7 Interrupt Autovector
32–47	080–0BC	TRAP #0 – 15 Instruction Vectors
48	0C0	FP Branch or Set on Unordered Condition
49	0C4	FP Inexact Result
50	0C8	FP Divide by Zero
51	0CC	FP Underflow
52	0D0	FP Operand Error
53	0D4	FP Overflow
54	0D8	FP Signaling NAN
55	0DC	FP Unimplemented Data Type (Defined for MC68040)
56	0E0	MMU Configuration Error
57	0E4	MMU Illegal Operation Error
58	0E8	MMU Access Level Violation Error
59–63	0EC–0FC	(Unassigned, Reserved)
64–255	100–3FC	User Defined Vectors (192)

B.2 EXCEPTION STACK FRAMES

Figures B-1 through B-15 illustrate all exception stack frames for the M68000 family.

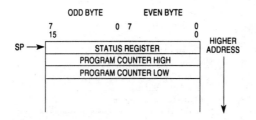

**Figure B-1. MC68000 Group 1 and 2
Exception Stack Frame**

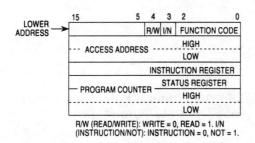

R/W (READ/WRITE): WRITE = 0, READ = 1. I/N
(INSTRUCTION/NOT): INSTRUCTION = 0, NOT = 1.

**Figure B-2. MC68000 Bus or Address Error
Exception Stack Frame**

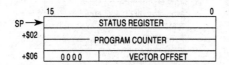

Figure B-3. Four-Word Stack Frame, Format $0

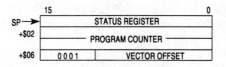

**Figure B-4. Throwaway Four-Word
Stack Frame, Format $1**

B

```
              15                        0
SP ──▶ │      STATUS REGISTER       │
+$02   │──   PROGRAM COUNTER   ──  │
+$06   │ 0 0 1 0 │   VECTOR OFFSET  │
+$08   │──       ADDRESS       ──  │
```

Figure B-5. Six-Word Stack Frame, Format $2

```
              15                        0
SP ──▶ │      STATUS REGISTER       │
+$02   │──   PROGRAM COUNTER   ──  │
+$06   │ 0 0 1 0 │   VECTOR OFFSET  │
+$08   │──   EFFECTIVE ADDRESS  ──  │
```

**Figure B-6. MC68040 Floating-Point Post-Instruction
Stack Frame, Format $3**

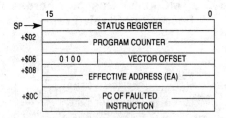

```
              15                        0
SP ──▶ │      STATUS REGISTER       │
+$02   │──   PROGRAM COUNTER   ──  │
+$06   │ 0 1 0 0 │   VECTOR OFFSET  │
+$08   │── EFFECTIVE ADDRESS (EA) ──│
+$0C   │──     PC OF FAULTED     ──│
       │         INSTRUCTION        │
```

**Figure B-7. MC68EC040 and MC68LC040
Floating-Point Unimplemented Stack Frame,
Format $4**

```
            15                                0
SP ──►    ┌──────────────────────────────────────┐
          │          STATUS REGISTER              │
+$02      ├──────── PROGRAM COUNTER ──────────────┤
          │                                        │
+$06      │ 0 1 1 1  │      VECTOR OFFSET          │
+$08      ├──────── EFFECTIVE ADDRESS (EA) ────────┤
+$0A      │                                        │
+$0C      │        SPECIAL STATUS WORD             │
+$0E      │  $00     │  WRITEBACK 3 STATUS (WB3S)   │
+$10      │  $00     │  WRITEBACK 2 STATUS (WB2S)   │
+$12      │  $00     │  WRITEBACK 1 STATUS (WB1S)   │
+$14      ├──────── FAULT ADDRESS (FA) ────────────┤
          │                                        │
+$18      ├──── WRITEBACK 3 ADDRESS (WB3A) ────────┤
          │                                        │
+$1C      ├──── WRITEBACK 3 DATA (WB3D) ───────────┤
          │                                        │
+$20      ├──── WRITEBACK 2 ADDRESS (WB2A) ────────┤
          │                                        │
+$24      ├──── WRITEBACK 2 DATA (WB2D) ───────────┤
          │                                        │
+$28      ├──── WRITEBACK 1 ADDRESS (WB1A) ────────┤
          │                                        │
+$2C      ├─WRITEBACK 1 DATA/PUSH DATA LW0 (WB1D/PD0)┤
          │                                        │
+$30      ├──── PUSH DATA LW 1 (PD1) ──────────────┤
          │                                        │
+$34      ├──── PUSH DATA LW 2 (PD2) ──────────────┤
          │                                        │
+$38      └──── PUSH DATA LW 3 (PD3) ──────────────┘
```

**Figure B-8. MC68040 Access Error
Stack Frame, Format $7**

```
            15                                0
SP ──►    ┌──────────────────────────────────────┐
          │          STATUS REGISTER              │
+$02      │        PROGRAM COUNTER HIGH           │
          │        PROGRAM COUNTER LOW            │
+$06      │ 1  0  0  0 │     VECTOR OFFSET        │
+$08      │        SPECIAL STATUS WORD            │
          │        FAULT ADDRESS HIGH             │
+$0C      │        FAULT ADDRESS LOW              │
          │        UNUSED, RESERVED               │
+$10      │        DATA OUTPUT BUFFER             │
          │        UNUSED, RESERVED               │
+$14      │        DATA INPUT BUFFER              │
+$16      │        UNUSED, RESERVED               │
+$18      │     INSTRUCTION OUTPUT BUFFER         │
$1A       │           IVERSIONI                   │
+$50      │           INUMBERI                    │
          ├ ─ ─ ─ ─ ─ ─ ─ ─ ─ ─ ─ ─ ─ ─ ─ ─ ─ ─ ┤
          │   INTERNAL INFORMATION, 16 WORDS      │
          └──────────────────────────────────────┘
```

NOTE: The stack pointer decrements by 29 words, although only 26 words of information actually write to memory. Motorola reserves the three additional words for future use.

**Figure B-9. MC68010 Bus and Address Error
Stack Frame, Format $8**

B

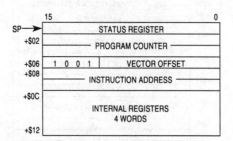

Figure B-10. MC68020 and MC68030 Coprocessor
Mid-Instruction Stack Frame, Format $9

	15				0
SP →	STATUS REGISTER				
+$02	PROGRAM COUNTER				
+$06	1	0	1	0	VECTOR OFFSET
+$08	INTERNAL REGISTER				
+$0A	SPECIAL STATUS REGISTER				
+$0C	INSTRUCTION PIPE STAGE C				
+$0E	INSTRUCTION PIPE STATE B				
+$10	DATA CYCLE FAULT ADDRESS				
+$12					
+$14	INTERNAL REGISTER				
+$16	INTERNAL REGISTER				
+$18	DATA OUTPUT BUFFER				
+$1A					
+$1C	INTERNAL REGISTER				
+$1E	INTERNAL REGISTER				

Figure B-11. MC68020 and MC68030
Short Bus Cycle Stack Frame, Format $A

B

```
          15                                    0
SP →   ┌──────────────────────────────────────┐
       │           STATUS REGISTER            │
+$02   ├────────── PROGRAM COUNTER ───────────┤
       │                                      │
+$06   │ 1  0  1  1 │      VECTOR OFFSET      │
+$08   ├──────────────────────────────────────┤
       │          INTERNAL REGISTER           │
+$0A   │       SPECIAL STATUS REGISTER        │
+$0C   │       INSTRUCTION PIPE STAGE C       │
+$0E   │       INSTRUCTION PIPE STAGE B       │
+$10   ├────── DATA CYCLE FAULT ADDRESS ──────┤
+$12   │                                      │
+$14   │          INTERNAL REGISTER           │
+$16   │          INTERNAL REGISTER           │
+$18   ├──────── DATA  OUTPUT BUFFER ─────────┤
+$1A   │                                      │
+$1C   │                                      │
+$1E   │                                      │
       │       INTERNAL REGISTERS, 4 WORDS    │
+$22   │                                      │
+$24   ├──────── STAGE B ADDRESS ─────────────┤
       │                                      │
+$28   │       INTERNAL REGISTERS, 2 WORDS    │
+$2A   │                                      │
+$2C   ├──────── DATA INPUT BUFFER ───────────┤
       │                                      │
+$30   │                                      │
       │       INTERNAL REGISTERS, 3 WORDS    │
+$36   │                                      │
+$38   │ VERSION # │   INTERNAL INFORMATION   │
       │                                      │
       │       INTERNAL REGISTERS 18 WORDS    │
+$5A   └──────────────────────────────────────┘
```

**Figure B-12. MC68020 and MC68030
Long Bus Cycle Stack Frame, Format $B**

```
          15                                    0
SP →   ┌──────────────────────────────────────┐
       │           STATUS REGISTER            │
+$02   │       RETURN PROGRAM COUNTER HIGH    │
       │       RETURN PROGRAM COUNTER LOW     │
+$06   │ 1  1  0  0 │      VECTOR OFFSET      │
+$08   │         FAULTED ADDRESS HIGH         │
       │         FAULTED ADDRESS LOW          │
+$0C   │             DBUF HIGH                │
       │             DBUF LOW                 │
+$10   │  CURRENT INSTRUCTION PROG. COUNTER HIGH │
       │  CURRENT INSTRUCTION PROG. COUNTER LOW  │
+$14   │     INTERNAL TRANSFER COUNT REGISTER │
+$16   │ 0  0 │     SPECIAL STATUS WORD       │
       └──────────────────────────────────────┘
```

**Figure B-13. CPU32 Bus Error for
Prefetches and Operands Stack Frame, Format $C**

B

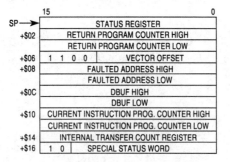

15				0
SP→	STATUS REGISTER			
+$02	RETURN PROGRAM COUNTER HIGH			
	RETURN PROGRAM COUNTER LOW			
+$06	1 1 0 0	VECTOR OFFSET		
+$08	FAULTED ADDRESS HIGH			
	FAULTED ADDRESS LOW			
+$0C	DBUF HIGH			
	DBUF LOW			
+$10	CURRENT INSTRUCTION PROG. COUNTER HIGH			
	CURRENT INSTRUCTION PROG. COUNTER LOW			
+$14	INTERNAL TRANSFER COUNT REGISTER			
+$16	0 1	SPECIAL STATUS WORD		

Figure B-14. CPU32 Bus Error on MOVEM Operand Stack Frame, Format $C

15				0
SP→	STATUS REGISTER			
+$02	RETURN PROGRAM COUNTER HIGH			
	RETURN PROGRAM COUNTER LOW			
+$06	1 1 0 0	VECTOR OFFSET		
+$08	FAULTED ADDRESS HIGH			
	FAULTED ADDRESS LOW			
+$0C	DBUF HIGH			
	DBUF LOW			
+$10	CURRENT INSTRUCTION PROG. COUNTER HIGH			
	CURRENT INSTRUCTION PROG. COUNTER LOW			
+$14	INTERNAL TRANSFER COUNT REGISTER			
+$16	1 0	SPECIAL STATUS WORD		

Figure B-15. CPU32 Four- and Six-Word Bus Error Stack Frame, Format $C

B.3 FLOATING-POINT STACK FRAMES

Figures B-16 through B-23 illustrate floating-point stack frames for the MC68881/MC68882 and the MC68040.

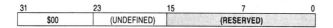

**Figure B-16. MC68881/MC68882 and
MC68040 Null Stack Frame**

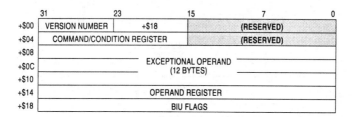

Figure B-17. MC68881 Idle Stack Frame

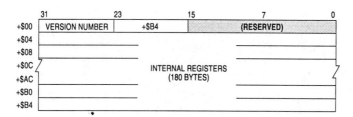

Figure B-18. MC68881 Busy Stack Frame

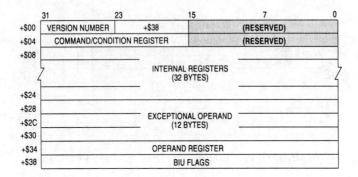

Figure B-19. MC68882 Idle Stack Frame

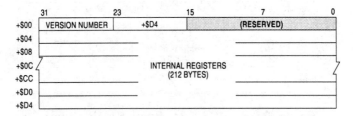

Figure B-20. MC68882 Busy Stack Frame

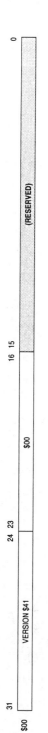

Figure B-21. MC68040 Idle Stack Frame

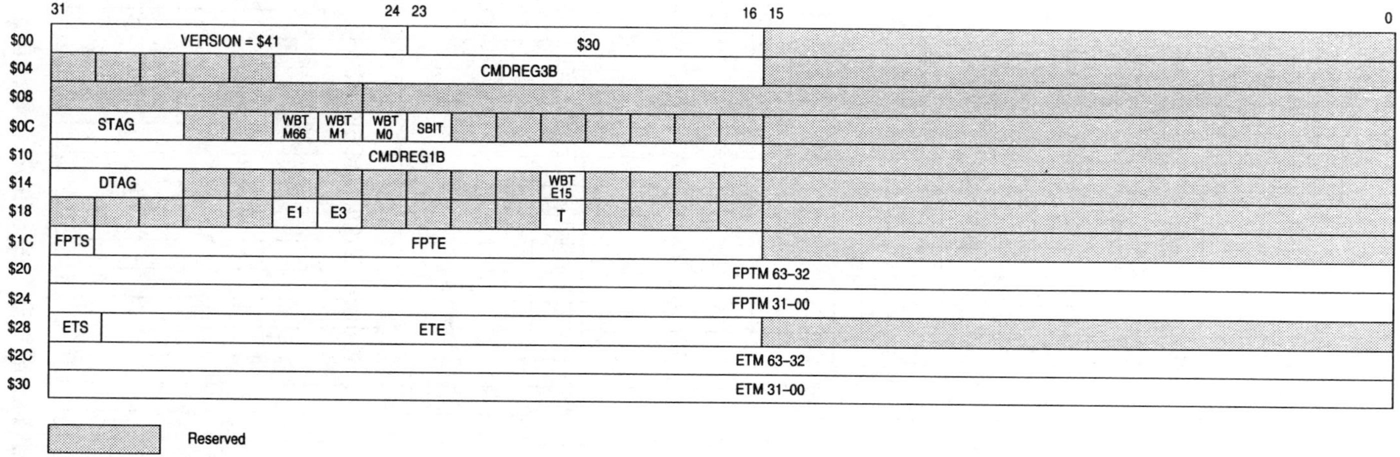

Figure B-22. MC68040 Unimplimented Instruction Stack Frame

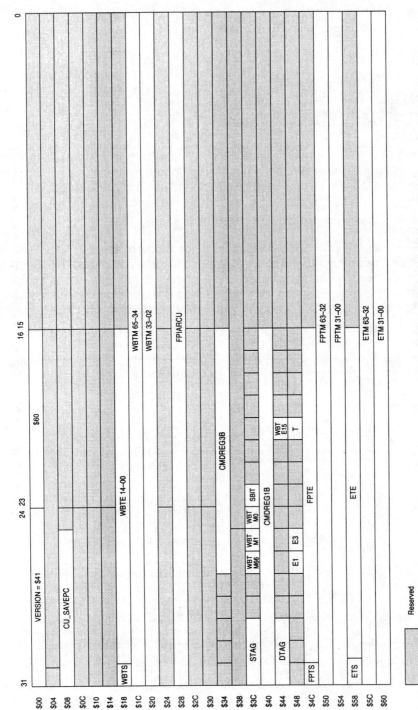

Figure B-23. MC68040 Busy Stack Frame

APPENDIX C
S-RECORD OUTPUT FORMAT

The S-record format for output modules is for encoding programs or data files in a printable format for transportation between computer systems. The transportation process can be visually monitored, and the S-records can be easily edited.

C.1 S-RECORD CONTENT

Visually, S-records are essentially character strings made of several fields that identify the record type, record length, memory address, code/data, and checksum. Each byte of binary data encodes as a two-character hexadecimal number: the first character represents the high-order four bits, and the second character represents the low-order four bits of the byte. Figure C-1 illustrates the five fields that comprise an S-record. Table C-1 lists the composition of each S-record field.

TYPE	RECORD LEGNTH	ADDRESS	CODE/DATA	CHECKSUM

Figure C-1. Five Fields of an S-Record

Table C-1. Field Composition of an S-Record

Field	Printable Characters	Contents
Type	2	S-record type—S0, S1, etc.
Record Length	2	The count of the character pairs in the record, excluding the type and record length.
Address	4, 6, or 8	The 2-, 3-, or 4-byte address at which the data field is to be loaded into memory.
Code/Data	0–2n	From 0 to n bytes of executable code, memory loadable data, or descriptive information. For compatibility with teletypewriters, some programs may limit the number of bytes to as few as 28 (56 printable characters in the S-record).
Checksum	2	The least significant byte of the one's complement of the sum of the values represented by the pairs of characters making up the record length, address, and the code/data fields.

When downloading S-records, each must be terminated with a CR. Additionally, an S-record may have an initial field that fits other data such as line numbers generated by some time-sharing systems. The record length (byte count) and checksum fields ensure transmission accuracy.

C.2 S-RECORD TYPES

There are eight types of S-records to accommodate the encoding, transportation, and decoding functions. The various Motorola record transportation control programs (e.g. upload, download, etc.), cross assemblers, linkers, and other file creating or debugging programs, only utilize S-records serving the program's purpose. For more information on support of specific S-records, refer to the user's manual for that program.

An S-record format module may contain S-records of the following types:

S0— The header record for each block of S-records. The code/data field may contain any descriptive information identifying the following block of S-records. Under VERSAdos, the resident linker's IDENT command can be used to designate module name, version number, revision number, and description information that will make up the header record. The address field is normally zeros.

S1— A record containing code/data and the 2-byte address at which the code/data is to reside.

S2— A record containing code/data and the 3-byte address at which the code/data is to reside.

S3— A record containing code/data and the 4-byte address at which the code/data is to reside.

S5— A record containing the number of S1, S2, and S3 records transmitted in a particular block. This count appears in the address field. There is no code/data field.

S7— A termination record for a block of S3 records. The address field may optionally contain the 4-byte address of the instruction to which control is to be passed. There is no code/data field.

S8— A termination record for a block of S2 records. The address field may optionally contain the 3-byte address of the instruction to which control is to be passed. There is no code/data field.

S9— A termination record for a block of S1 records. The address field may optionally contain the 2-byte address of the instruction to which control is to be passed. Under VERSAdos, the resident linker's ENTRY command can be used to specify this address. If this address is not specified, the first entry point specification encountered in the object module input will be used. There is no code/data field.

Each block of S-records uses only one termination record. S7 and S8 records are only active when control is to be passed to a 3- or 4-byte address; otherwise, an S9 is used for termination. Normally, there is only one header record, although it is possible for multiple header records to occur.

C.3 S-RECORD CREATION

Dump utilities, debuggers, a VERSAdos resident linkage editor, or cross assemblers and linkers produce S-record format programs. On VERSAdos systems, the build load module (MBLM) utility allows an executable load module to be built from S-records. It has a counterpart utility in BUILDS that allows an S-record file to be created from a load module.

Programs are available for downloading or uploading a file in S-record format from a host system to an 8- or 16-bit microprocessor-based system. A typical S-record-format module is printed or displayed as follows:

```
S00600004844521B
S1130000285F245F2212226A000424290008237C2A
S11300100002000800082629001853812341001813
S113002041E900084E42234300182342000824A952
S107003000144ED492
S9030000FC
```

The module has an S0 record, four S1 records, and an S9 record. The following character pairs comprise the S-record-format module.

S0 Record:

    S0—S-record type S0, indicating that it is a header record.
    06—Hexadecimal 06 (decimal 6), indicating that six character pairs (or ASCII bytes) follow.
    0000—A 4-character, 2-byte address field; zeros in this example.
    48—ASCII H
    44—ASCII D
    52—ASCII R
    1B—The checksum.

First S1 Record:

    S1—S-record type S1, indicating that it is a code/data record to be loaded/verified at a 2-byte address.
    13—Hexadecimal 13 (decimal 19), indicating that 19 character pairs, representing 19 bytes of binary data, follow.
    0000—A 4-character, 2-byte address field (hexadecimal address 0000) indicating where the data that follows is to be loaded.

The next 16 character pairs of the first S1 record are the ASCII bytes of the actual program code/data. In this assembly language example, the program's hexadecimal opcodes are sequentially written in the code/data fields of the S1 records.

Opcode	Instruction	
285F	MOVE.L	(A7) +, A4
245F	MOVE.L	(A7) +, A2
2212	MOVE.L	(A2), D1
226A0004	MOVE.L	4(A2), A1
24290008	MOVE.L	FUNCTION(A1), D2
237C	MOVE.L	#FORCEFUNC, FUNCTION(A1)

The rest of this code continues in the remaining S1 record's code/data fields and stores in memory location 0010, etc.

2A—The checksum of the first S1 record.

The second and third S1 records also contain hexadecimal 13 (decimal 19) character pairs and end with checksums 13 and 52, respectively. The fourth S1 record contains 07 character pairs and has a checksum of 92.

S9 Record:

S9—S-record type S9, indicating that it is a termination record.

03—Hexadecimal 03, indicating that three character pairs (3 bytes) follow.

0000—The address field, zeros.

FC—The checksum of the S9 record.

Each printable character in an S-record encodes in hexadecimal (ASCII in this example) representation of the binary bits that transmit. Figure C-2 illustrates the sending of the first S1 record. Table C-2 lists the ASCII code for S-records.

TYPE		RECORD LENGTH		ADDRESS				CODE/DATA					CHECKSUM	
S	1	1	3	0	0	0	0	2	8	5	F	••••	2	A
5	3	3	1	3	1	3	3	3	0	3	0	3	0	3	0	3	2	3	8	3	5	4	6	••••	3	2	4	1
0101 0011	0011 0001	0011 0001	0011 0011	0011 0000	0011 0000	0011 0000	0011 0000	0011 0010	0011 1000	0011 0101	0100 0110	••••	0011 0010	0100 0001

Figure C-2. Transmission of an S1 Record

Table C-2. ASCII Code

Least Significant Digit	Most Significant Digit							
	0	1	2	3	4	5	6	7
0	NUL	DLE	SP	0	@	P	`	p
1	SOH	DC1	!	1	A	Q	a	q
2	STX	DC2	"	2	B	R	b	r
3	ETX	DC3	#	3	C	S	c	s
4	EOT	DC4	$	4	D	T	d	t
5	ENQ	NAK	%	5	E	U	e	u
6	ACK	SYN	&	6	F	V	f	v
7	BEL	ETB	'	7	G	W	g	w
8	BS	CAN	(	8	H	X	h	x
9	HT	EM	)	9	I	Y	i	y
A	LF	SUB	*	:	J	Z	j	z
B	VT	ESC	+	;	K	[	k	{
C	FF	FS	,	<	L	\	l	¦
D	CR	GS	–	=	M	]	m	}
E	SO	RS	.	>	N	^	n	~
F	SI	US	/	?	O	_	o	DEL

1ATX24684-4 PRINTED IN USA 4/92 GTE SUPPLIER 14225 25,000 MPU YGABAA